38

bb

UCLA Symposia on Molecular and Cellular Biology, New Series

Series Editor, C. Fred Fox

Please contact the publisher for information about previous titles in this series.

Molecular Biology of Stress

Molecular Biology of Stress

Proceedings of a Director's Sponsors-UCLA Symposium
Held at Keystone, Colorado
April 10–17, 1988

Editors

Shlomo Breznitz
Department of Psychology
University of Haifa
Haifa, Israel

Oren Zinder
Department of Clinical Biochemistry
Rambam Medical Center
Haifa, Israel

Alan R. Liss, Inc. • New York

Address all Inquiries to the Publisher
Alan R. Liss, Inc., 41 East 11th Street, New York, NY 10003

Library of Congress Cataloging-in-Publication Data

Molecular biology of stress : proceedings of a director's sponsors
-UCLA symposia held at Keystone, Colorado, April 10–17, 1988 /
editors, Shlomo Breznitz, Oren Zinder.
    p. cm.—(UCLA symposia on molecular and cellular biology ;
new ser., v. 97)
    Proceedings of the UCLA Symposium on Molecular Biology of
Stress.
    Includes bibliographies and index.
    ISBN 0-8451-2696-2
    1. Stress (Physiology)—Congresses.
2. Psychoneuroimmunoendocrinology—Congresses. 3. Molecular
biology—Congresses. 4. Neuropeptides—Physiological effect
Congresses. I. Breznitz, Shlomo. II. Zinder, O.
III. University of California, Los Angeles. IV. UCLA Symposium on Molecular Biology of Stress (1988 : Keystone, Colo.) V.
Series.
QP82.2.S8M64   1989   88-37910
612—dc19   CIP

Contents

Contributors

Hussein Amer, Department of Clinical Biochemistry, Rambam Medical Center and The Faculty of Medicine, The Technion, Haifa, Israel 31096 **[167]**

Ada Armfield, Division of Clinical Immunopathology, Department of Pathology, University of Pittsburgh, Pittsburgh, PA 15217-3417 **[205]**

Greti Aguilera, Endocrinology and Reproduction Research Branch, National Institute of Child Health and Development, National Institutes of Health, Bethesda, MD 20892 **[3]**

J.F. Bach, INSERM U 25-CNRS LA 122, Hôpital Necker, 75015 Paris, France **[225]**

George Battaglia, Neuroscience Branch, National Institute of Drug Abuse, Baltimore, MD 21224 **[19]**

Peter Bergsten, Laboratory of Cell Biology and Genetics, Digestive Diseases Branch, National Institutes of Health, Bethesda, MD 20892 **[191]**

Craig W. Berridge, Department of Neuroscience, University of Florida, Gainsville, FL 32610 **[57]**

John F. Bishop, Experimental Therapeutics Branch, National Institute of Neurological and Communicative Disorders and Stroke, Bethesda, MD 20892 **[107]**

Garth Bissette, Departments of Psychiatry and Pharmacology, Duke University Medical Center, Durham, NC 27710 **[67]**

Pamela E. Bond, Departments of Psychiatry and Pharmacology, Duke University Medical Center, Durham, NC 27710 **[67]**

Shlomo Breznitz, Ray D. Wolfe Centre for Study of Psychological Stress, University of Haifa, Haifa, Israel **[xvii, 253]**

Stephen J. Bunn, Department of Biochemistry, University of Melbourne, Parkville, Victoria 3052, Australia; present address: Neuroscience Group, Faculty of Medicine, University of Newcastle, NSW, Australia **[179]**

Elizabeth Burnell, Department of Pediatrics, Harbor-UCLA Medical Center, UCLA School of Medicine, Torrance, CA 90509 **[143]**

Pamela D. Butler, Departments of Psychiatry and Pharmacology, Duke University Medical Center, Durham, NC 27710 **[67]**

Judy L. Cameron, Departments of Psychiatry and Behavioral Neuroscience, University of Pittsburgh School of Medicine, Pittsburgh, PA 15213 **[97]**

The numbers in brackets are the opening page numbers of the contributors' articles.

Kevin J. Catt, Endocrinology and Reproduction Research Branch, National Institute of Child Health and Human Development, National Institutes of Health, Bethesda, MD 20892 **[3]**

Lucienne Chatenoud, INSERM U 25-CNRS LA 122, Hôpital Necker, 75015 Paris, France **[225]**

Robert T. Chatterton, Jr., Department of Obstetrics and Gynecology, Northwestern University Medical School, Chicago, IL 60611 **[265]**

Joan E. Cunnick, Division of Clinical Immunopathology, Department of Pathology, University of Pittsburgh, Pittsburgh, PA 15217-3417 **[205]**

Joseph D. DeCristofaro, Departments of Pediatrics and Neurobiology and Behavior, School of Medicine, State University of New York at Stony Brook, Stony Brook, NY 11794-8111 **[153]**

Frank A. DeLeon-Jones, Department of Research and Development, Westside VA Hospital, Chicago, IL 60612 **[265]**

Paul H. Desan, Department of Neurology, Stanford University School of Medicine, Stanford, CA 94305 **[285]**

Errol B. De Souza, Neuroscience Branch, National Institute of Drug Abuse, Baltimore, MD 21224 **[19]**

Kuldeep Dhariwal, Laboratory of Cell Biology and Genetics, Digestive Diseases Branch, National Institutes of Health, Bethesda, MD 20892 **[191]**

James O. Douglass, Vollum Institute for Advanced Biomedical Research, The Oregon Health Sciences University, Portland, OR 97201 **[49]**

Adrian J. Dunn, Department of Neuroscience, University of Florida, Gainsville, FL 32610 **[57]**

Michael Eckardt, Laboratory of Clinical Studies, DICBR, NIAAA, Bethesda, MD 20892 **[277]**

Graeme Eisenhofer, National Institutes of Health, National Institute of Neurological and Communicative Disorders and Stroke, Bethesda, MD 20892 **[123]**

Joanne T. Emerman, Department of Anatomy, Faculty of Medicine, The University of British Columbia, Vancouver, B.C. V6T 1W5, Canada **[295]**

John M. Farah, Jr., Central Nervous System Diseases Research, G.D. Searle and Company, St. Louis, MS 63198 **[107]**

Linda T. Fatkin, Behavioral Research Division, U.S. Army Human Engineering Laboratory, Aberdeen Proving Ground, MD 21005-5001 **[265]**

John D. Fernstrom, Departments of Psychiatry and Behavioral Neuroscience, University of Pittsburgh School of Medicine, Pittsburgh, PA 15213 **[97]**

M. Garbarg, INSERM U 109, Centre Paul Broca, 75014 Paris, France **[225]**

Thomas Garrick, Department of Psychiatry and Biobehavioral Sciences, University of California, Los Angeles, CA 90024, and Center for Ulcer Research and Education, West Los Angeles Veterans Administration Medical Center, Los Angeles, CA 90073 **[241]**

David Gershon, Department of Biology, Technion-Israel Institute of Technology, Haifa, Israel 32000 **[233]**

Allan L. Goldstein, Department of Biochemistry, The George Washington University School of Medicine and Health Sciences, Washington, DC 20037 [107]

David Goldstein, National Institutes of Health, National Institute of Neurological and Communicative Disorders and Stroke, Bethesda, MD 20892 [123]

Avital Greenberg, Department of Clinical Biochemistry, The Rambam Medical Center and The Faculty of Medicine, The Technion, Haifa, Israel 31096 [167]

Nicholas R. Hall, Department of Biochemistry, The George Washington University School of Medicine and Health Sciences, Washington, DC 20037; present address: Departments of Psychiatry and Immunology, University of South Florida, Tampa, FL 33613 [107]

William Hartzell, Laboratory of Cell Biology and Genetics, Digestive Diseases Branch, National Institutes of Health, Bethesda, MD 20892 [191]

James P. Harwood, Endocrinology and Reproduction Research Branch, National Institute of Child Health and Human Development, National Institutes of Health, Bethesda, MD 20892 [3]

Richard L. Hauger, Department of Psychiatry, San Diego VA Medical Center and University of California San Diego, La Jolla, CA 92161 [3]

D.W. Hendrix, Department of Pharmacology, Oral Roberts University School of Medicine, Tulsa, OK 74137 [87]

Yael Hiram, Faculty of Chemical Engineering, The Technion, Israel Institute of Technology, Haifa, Israel 31096 [167]

Gerald A. Hudgens, Behavioral Research Division, U.S. Army Engineering Laboratory, Aberdeen Proving Ground, MD 21005-5001 [265]

Thomas R. Insel, Laboratory of Clinical Science, National Institute of Mental Health, Bethesda, MD 20892 [19]

Priscilla Kehoe, Department of Psychology, Trinity College, Hartford, CT 06106 [307]

Louis G. Keith, Department of Obstetrics and Gynecology, Northwestern University Medical School, Chicago, IL 60611 [265]

Zeinab Khalil, Department of Biochemistry, University of Melbourne, Parkville, Victoria 3052, Australia; present address: Department of Gerontology, University of Melbourne, Mount Royal, Parkville, Victoria, Australia [179]

James M. King, Behavioral Research Division, U.S. Army Human Engineering Laboratory, Aberdeen Proving Ground, MD 21005-5001 [265]

Irwin J. Kopin, National Institutes of Health, National Institute of Neurological and Communicative Disorders and Stroke, Bethesda, MD 20892 [123]

Roland P.S. Kwok, Departments of Psychiatry and Behavioral Neuroscience, University of Pittsburgh School of Medicine, Pittsburgh, PA 15213 [97]

Edmund F. La Gamma, Departments of Pediatrics and Neurobiology and Behavior, School of Medicine, State University of New York at Stony Brook, Stony Brook, NY 11794-8111 **[153]**

Mark Levine, Laboratory of Cell Biology and Genetics, Digestive Diseases Branch, National Institutes of Health, Bethesda, MD 20892 **[191]**

Richard Lister, Laboratory of Clinical Studies, DICBR, NIAAA, Bethesda, MD 20892 **[277]**

Bruce G. Livett, Department of Biochemistry, University of Melbourne, Parkville, Victoria 3052, Australia **[179]**

Marge Lorang, Department of Psychiatry, San Diego VA Medical Center and University of California San Diego, La Jolla, CA 92161 **[3]**

Donald T. Lysle, Division of Clinical Immunopathology, Department of Pathology, University of Pittsburgh, Pittsburgh, PA 15217-3417 **[205]**

Nancy S. Magnuson, Department of Microbiology, Washington State University, Pullman, WA 99164 **[215]**

Steven F. Maier, Department of Psychology, University of Colorado, Boulder, CO 80309 **[285]**

Philip D. Marley, Department of Biochemistry, University of Melbourne, Parkville, Victoria 3052, Australia **[179]**

Alma M. Martinez, Department of Pediatrics, Harbor-UCLA Medical Center, UCLA School of Medicine, Torrance, CA 90509 **[143]**

Jeffrey F. McKelvy, Department of Neurobiology and Behavior, SUNY at Stony Brook, Stony Brook, NY 11794-5230; present address: Abbott Laboratories, Abbott Park, IL 60064 **[49]**

Patricia McLaughlin, Department of Anatomy, Pennsylvania State University College of Medicine, M.S. Hershey Medical Center, Hershey, PA 17033 **[77]**

Jacquelyn Michel, Central Nervous System Diseases Research, G.D. Serle and Company, St. Louis, MO 63198 **[107]**

Monica Millan, Endocrinology and Reproduction Research Branch, National Institute of Child Health and Human Development, National Institutes of Health, Bethesda, MD 20892 **[3]**

Charles B. Nemeroff, Departments of Psychiatry and Pharmacology, Duke University Medical Center, Durham, NC 27710 **[67]**

Avi Nir, Faculty of Chemical Engineering, The Technion, Israel Institute of Technology, Haifa, Israel 31096 **[167]**

Thomas L. O'Donohue, Central Nervous System Diseases Research, G.D. Serle and Company, St. Louis, MO 63198 **[107]**

Michael J. Owens, Departments of Psychiatry and Pharmacology, Duke University Medical Center, Durham, NC 27710 **[67]**

James F. Padbury, Department of Pediatrics, Harbor-UCLA Medical Center, UCLA School of Medicine, Torrance, CA 90509 **[143]**

Bruce S. Rabin, Division of Clinical Immunopathology, Department of Pathology, University of Pittsburgh, Pittsburgh, PA 15217-3417 **[205]**

Robert W. Rebar, Department of Obstetrics and Gynecology, Northwestern University Medical School, Chicago, Il 60611 **[265]**

Raymond Reeves, Department of Genetics and Cell Biology, Washington State University, Pullman, WA 99164 **[215]**

Abraham Z. Reznick, Department of Morphological Sciences, The Rappaport Institute for Research in the Medical Sciences and Faculty of Medicine, Technion, Haifa, Israel 31096 **[233]**

H.M. Rhee, Department of Pharmacology, Oral Roberts University School of Medicine, Tulsa, OK 74137 **[87]**

Catherine Rivier, The Clayton Foundation Laboratories for Peptide Biology, The Salk Institute, La Jolla, CA 92037 **[31]**

J.C. Schwartz, INSERM U 109, Centre Paul Broca, 75014 Paris, France **[225]**

Frederic J. Seidler, Department of Pharmacology, Duke University Medical Center, Durham, NC 27710 **[133]**

Michael Silbermann, Department of Morphological Sciences, The Rappaport Institute for Research in the Medical Sciences and Faculty of Medicine, Technion, Haifa, Israel 31096 **[233]**

Lee H. Silbert, Department of Psychology, University of Colorado, Boulder, CO 80309 **[285]**

Sue E. Slager, Department of Obstetrics and Gynecology, Northwestern University Medical School, Chicago, IL 60611 **[265]**

Theodore A. Slotkin, Department of Pharmacology, Duke University Medical Center, Durham, NC 27710 **[133]**

Barbara A. Sorg, Department of Genetics and Cell Biology, Washington State University, Pullman, WA 99164; present address: Department of Psychology, Washington State University, Pullman, WA 99164 **[215]**

E. Steinhagen–Thiessen, Medical Clinic, University of Hamburg Medical School, Hamburg, West Germany; present address: Medical Clinic, Max Berger Hospital, Berlin, West Germany **[233]**

Robert L. Stephens, Department of Psychiatry and Biobehavioral Sciences, University of California, Los Angeles, CA 90024, and Center for Ulcer Research and Education, West Los Angeles Veterans Administration Medical Center, Los Angeles, CA 90073 **[241]**

Yvette Taché, Center for Ulcer Research and Education, West Los Angeles Veterans Administration Medical Center, Los Angeles, CA 90073 **[241]**

Siang L. Thio, Department of Pediatrics, Harbor-UCLA Medical Center, UCLA School of Medicine, Torrance, CA 90509 **[143]**

Robert C. Thompson, Vollum Institute for Advanced Biomedical Research, The Oregon Health Sciences University, Portland, OR 97201 **[49]**

James Torre, Jr., Behavioral Research Division, U.S. Army Human Engineering Laboratory, Aberdeen Proving Ground, MD 21005-5001 **[265]**

Rosalie M. Uht, Department of Neurobiology and Behavior, SUNY at Stony Brook, Stony Brook, NY 11794-5230 **[49]**

Françoise Villemain, INSERM U 25-CNRS LA 122, Hôpital Necker, 75015 Paris, France **[225]**

David C-C. Wan, Department of Biochemistry, University of Melbourne, Parkville, Victoria 3052, Australia **[179]**

Philip Washko, Laboratory of Cell Biology and Genetics, Digestive Diseases Branch, National Institutes of Health, Bethesda, MD 20892 **[191]**

Joanne Weinberg, Department of Anatomy, Faculty of Medicine, The University of British Columbia, Vancouver, B.C., V6T 1W5, Canada **[295]**

Herbert Weiner, Department of Psychiatry and Biobehavioral Sciences, University of California, Los Angeles, CA 90024 **[241]**

Herbert Weingartner, Department of Psychology, The George Washington University, Washington, DC 20052, and Laboratory of Clinical Studies, DICBR, NIAAA, Bethesda, MD 20892 **[277]**

Whitney W. Woodmansee, Department of Psychology, University of Colorado, Boulder, CO 80309 **[285]**

Ian S. Zagon, Department of Anatomy, Pennsylvania State University College of Medicine, M.S. Hershey Medical Center, Hershey, PA 17033 **[77]**

Xin-fu Zhou, Department of Biochemistry, University of Melbourne, Parkville, Victoria 3052, Australia **[179]**

Oren Zinder, Department of Clinical Biochemistry, Rambam Medical Center and The Faculty of Medicine, The Technion, Haifa, Israel 31096 **[xvii,167]**

Preface

The UCLA Symposium on **Molecular Biology of Stress** was held at Keystone Colorado, April 10–17, 1988. The conference was attended by scientists from a number of disciplines, all touching upon the mechanisms that underlie stress and the molecular consequences of the stress response. The purpose of the symposium was to emphasize the multifactorial nature of the stress entity and to enable researchers in the various fields to find points of contact in their studies so that a more comprehensive pattern of the stress response might be elucidated.

Studies of the location of neuroactive peptides in the brain and the pathways of their movement under various stimuli have been greatly enhanced by use of immunofluorescent staining techniques. The ability to introduce neuroactive substances into the brains of rats via an indwelling catheter inserted into the lateral ventricle in freely-moving animals has enabled researchers to study more closely the biological series of events that follow stress induction. Such investigations also permit manipulation of the influence of the neuroactive compounds by the introduction of antagonists or chemical compounds that have competing biological effects. Among these neuroactive peptides are vasopressin, oxytocin, enkephalins, endorphins, neuropeptide Y, substance P, and catecholamines (epinephrine, norepinephrine, and dopamine), all of whose effects, mechanisms, and location of action have been the subject of intense investigations. The interactions between these substances in the brain as part of the stress response were the subject of a number of highly original and provocative studies presented at this meeting. There was a striking convergence of a number of presentations on corticotropin-releasing factor (CRF) as a major factor in stress, since it has been shown to be involved in both physiological and psychological responses to stress stimuli.

Another exciting aspect of stress research that was highlighted involves the developmental aspects of the biology of stress. With the ability to monitor mRNA for protein synthesis of numerous compounds and to carry out gene analysis, it has become possible to describe molecular events that occur in response to stress stimulation. This should further our knowledge of receptor development in the brain. In addition, by monitoring receptor activity following stressful stimuli, it should become possible to identify the pathways of various neuroactive peptides.

One of the most intriguing aspects of stress research today is the profound effect of both physical and psychological stress on the immune system. Chronic exposure to stress impairs the immune response of the organism, resulting in high susceptibility to various diseases, including cancer. The possibility that this effect may be connected to the appearance of heat-shock proteins in a variety of cells opens a whole new aspect of the study of stress, which up to now had been examined mainly in connection with metabolic, cardiovascular, and psychological responses.

The probing and stimulating discussions following each session—and between the sessions—were especially interesting since the participants came from a variety of disciplines each with his, or her expertise. Many new avenues of research were discussed that will almost certainly enhance our practical knowledge of stress.

We sincerely thank all the participants for their excellent presentations, posters, and comments, which were contributing factors in the success of the conference. We also gratefully acknowledge the 1988 UCLA Symposia Director's Sponsors—Cetus Corporation, ICI Pharmaceuticals Group, Monsanto, Schering Corporation, and the Upjohn Company—for their support of this symposium, and we especially thank Robin Yeaton, Jackie Wester, and the enthusiastic UCLA Symposia staff for their cheerful and efficient assistance in running this conference.

Shlomo Breznitz
Oren Zinder

I. NEUROPEPTIDES AND THE STRESS RESPONSE

Molecular Biology of Stress, pages 3–17
© 1989 Alan R. Liss, Inc.

RECEPTORS FOR CORTICOTROPIN RELEASING FACTOR IN THE PITUITARY AND BRAIN: REGULATORY EFFECTS OF GLUCOCORTICOIDS, CRF, AND STRESS

Richard L. Hauger,[1,3] Monica Millan,[2] James P. Harwood,[2] Marge Lorang,[1] Kevin J. Catt,[2] and Greti Aguilera[2]

ABSTRACT   High affinity corticotropin releasing factor (CRF) receptors which mediate CRF action are present in the central and peripheral nervous systems and the pituitary. In the anterior pituitary, but not the intermediate lobe or brain, CRF receptors undergo downregulation and desensitization following adrenalectomy. Corticosteroids also decrease anterior pituitary CRF receptors in parallel with the reduction in ACTH secretion in the absence of any changes in CRF binding in the CNS. Acute restraint causes a 10-fold rise in plasma ACTH, but no change occurs in pituitary CRF receptors. Following chronic immobilization stress plasma ACTH levels increase only 2-fold, whereas CRF receptors in the anterior pituitary are reduced by 40%. Despite the decrease in pituitary CRF receptors, the corticotroph responsiveness is maintained suggesting the presence of spare CRF receptors and the participation of other ACTH secretagogues. Similar to the effects of adrenalectomy and glucocorticoids, chronic stress does not produce any changes in CRF binding in the CNS further supporting the differential regulation of CRF receptors in the pituitary and brain.

---

[1] San Diego VA Medical Center and UCSD Department of Psychiatry, La Jolla, California 92161
[2] ERRB, NICHD, National Institutes of Health, Bethesda, Maryland 20892
[3] RLH is a recipient of a Pfizer Scholars Award, and Research Associate and Merit Review Awards from the Veterans Administration.

The wide distribution of CRF receptors is consistent with the multiple roles of CRF in mediating endocrine, autonomic and behavioral responses to stress.

INTRODUCTION

The earliest biological response to stress is an "alarm" reaction that results in an immediate and large activation of the HPA axis (1-3). Although acute stress rapidly elicits the secretion of high levels of ACTH and glucorticoids in rats, Hans Selye described, in his classic monograph, a biphasic response to stress characterized by the initial alarming effect of acute stress followed by "adaptation" during chronic stress (1). In contrast to the sustained activation of the HPA axis following adrenalectomy, animals that sustain continuous or prolonged intermittent exposure to stressful stimuli lose the behavioral arousal and the activation of pituitary-adrenal secretion characteristic of acute stress (1-3). This state of biological "adaptation" to the increased physical or psychological demands provoked by stress in Selye's stage of "resistance" is believed to be coordinated through the CNS and results in behavioral, autonomic and endocrine responses that allow animals and humans to adapt to or overcome the stress.

The attenuation of the pituitary-adrenal response in chronic stress may involve a number of homeostatic mechanisms including increased glucocorticoid feedback, decreased hypothalamic secretion of corticotropin releasing factor(s), exhaustion of the secretory capacity of the corticotroph, and a decrease in pituitary receptors for ACTH regulators. Despite this apparent diminution of the ACTH response following prolonged exposure to stress, some studies have described a hyper-responsiveness of the HPA axis to a novel, superimposed stress after sustained exposure to a preceding stressful stimulus (2,3). This paradoxical finding suggests that chronic stress may reduce the sensitivity of the brain-pituitary unit to glucocorticoid negative feedback. Alternatively, sensitization of the hypothalamic-pituitary unit to a second stressor may involve stimulation of different neural pathways that converge in the PVN and that ultimately result in the release of CRF and other ACTH secretagogues (2-4).

Since the characterization of corticotropin releasing factor (CRF) in 1981, evidence has accumulated to indicate

that the hypothalamic peptide plays an important role in the
regulation of ACTH secretion as well as in mediating complex
neuroendocrine, visceral, and behavioral responses to stress
(5-8). The CRF peptide is a potent stimulus of ACTH and β-
endorphin secretion from the anterior pituitary and also of
the POMC derived peptides α-MSH, β-endorphin and
corticotropin-like intermediate lobe peptide (CLIP) from the
intermediate lobe of the pituitary. In addition to its
actions in the pituitary gland, CRF has been also implicated
in the non-endocrine responses to stress. In this regard,
immunoreactive CRF has been shown to be present in several
extrahypothalamic sites in the brain, and intraventricular
injection of the peptide causes changes in behavior and
endocrine function that mimic stress-induced responses (5).
Since the regulatory actions of peptide hormones are always
mediated through specific cell-surface receptors, the
identification, characterization and distribution of
specific receptors for CRF is crucial for the understanding
of the physiological role of the peptide in the response and
adaptation to stress.

CHARACTERISTICS OF CRF RECEPTORS

Pituitary CRF Receptors. Receptors for CRF have been
identified and characterized in the pituitary gland from rat
and a number of primates (9-12). In all species,
autoradiographic analysis of the binding of radiolabeled CRF
have shown the receptors to be localized in the anterior and
intermediate lobes, with no staining in the neural lobe.
The binding affinity of individual CRF analogs for the
pituitary sites closely parallels the potencies of these
peptides as stimuli of ACTH secretion. The maximal ACTH
response to CRF occurs with about 50% receptor occupancy,
indicating the presence of spare receptors. Such excess of
CRF receptors in the corticotroph could be relevant to the
effects of adrenalectomy, in which high rates of ACTH
secretion are maintained in the presence of marked down-
regulation of CRF receptors. The concentrations of CRF
reported in portal blood (7) are in the range of the
pituitary CRF receptor affinity (K_d of 1 nM), supporting the
view that the binding sites detected by radioligand assay
represent the functional receptors through which CRF
regulates ACTH secretion.
In the pituitary, CRF receptors are coupled to
adenylate cyclase and occupancy of the CRF receptor site
leads to consequent increases in intracellular cyclic AMP

levels and activation of cyclic AMP-dependent protein kinase
(6,8). Furthermore, the binding of CRF to pituitary
membranes is markedly influenced by guanyl nucleotides.
Such guanyl nucleotide action is characteristic of receptors
that are coupled to adenylate cyclase by a guanyl nucleotide
regulatory protein, as is likely to be the case for the CRF
receptor (6,8,10,13). In addition, CRF action in the
pituitary gland also involves calcium/arachidonic acid
dependent mechanisms (14,15).

An important aspect of the action of CRF in the
pituitary is the potentiation of CRF stimulation of ACTH
secretion by other stimulators, such as vasopressin (VP),
angiotensin II (AII) and norepinephrine (NE), each of which
alone has only a weak effect (6,8). In contrast to the
predominant cyclic AMP-dependent actions of CRF, the other
stimulants do not increase cyclic AMP production and
probably exert their action through calcium/ phospholipid
dependent mechanisms and activation of protein kinase C
(16). The potentiating effect of VP on CRF-stimulated ACTH
production involves enhancement of CRF-stimulated cyclic AMP
levels, which probably results from phosphorylation of an
inhibitory GTP binding subunit of adenylate cyclase via
activation of protein kinase C.

Brain CRF Receptors. In addition to the presence of
CRF receptors in the anterior and intermediate lobes of the
pituitary, CRF receptor sites have been identified in the
central nervous system, the peripheral sympathetic nervous
system, the adrenal medulla (where CRF stimulates the
release of met-enkephalin and catecholamines from chromaffin
cells), and the kidney (6,8,17,18). As in the pituitary
gland, CRF receptors in the cerebral cortex and amygdala are
linked to adenylate cyclase and cAMP production (19-21).
Autoradiographic mapping in rat and monkey brains has
established a predominant localization of CRF receptors in
two functionally distinct systems, the neocortex and the
limbic system (19,20,22). In rat brain, the receptors are
highly concentrated throughout the cerebral cortex, with
relatively higher densities in the anterior cingulate
cortex, frontoparietal (somato-sensory area) and temporal
cortex (auditory area). The highest concentration is found
in layer IV of the cerebral cortex, followed by layers I to
III. Two cortical structures related to the limbic system,
the subiculum and the hippocampus, also contain moderate
receptor densities. The function of CRF receptors in the
cerebral cortex is unknown at present. Although CRF content
in cortical areas is not detectable and only a few CRF-

immunoreactive interneurons without any terminals can be
identified in the cerebral cortex (23,24), the coupling of
the CRF receptor with adenylate cyclase-linked messenger
systems may be greatest in parts of the cortical mantle
(21). Furthermore, changes in CRF receptor concentrations
in the cerebral cortex have been measured in post-mortem
brain samples from victims of Alzheimer's disease and
suicide (25,26).

In the monkey, CRF receptor distribution in the brain
cortex and limbic system-related structures resembles that
observed in the rat brain. Whereas in the rat and marmoset
the receptors are evenly distributed throughout the cortex,
in the cynomolgus monkey there are marked differences
between the cortical areas. The highest binding is in the
prefrontal, orbital, and insular cortices, regions of
relatively late phylogenetic acquisition that are well
developed only in primates and particularly man (27). These
areas receive abundant innervation from the dorsomedial
nucleus of the thalamus, which relays impulses from several
autonomic centers (27). This area of the thalamus, which
plays an important role in emotional responses, also
contains abundant CRF receptors.

CRF receptors can also be found in other stress-
sensitive brain centers. The locus coeruleus and connected
structures contain immunoreactive CRF and CRF receptors.
Since local neuronal activation has been observed after
microinjection of CRF in the locus coeruleus of the rat
(28), CRF receptors in this brain center may have an
integrative role in autonomic responses to stress.

A high density of CRF receptors is also observed in the
amygdala. This important component of the limbic system has
both efferent and afferent connections with the cortical
areas that contain the highest CRF receptor concentrations,
namely, the frontal, orbital, cingulate, temporal, and
insular cortices. The amygdaloid nuclei also receive
projections from the locus coeruleus, hypothalamus, and
dorsomedial thalamic nucleus and have efferent projections
to the dorsomedial thalamic nucleus, nucleus stria
terminalis, preoptic area, septal regions, and arculate
nucleus. All of these areas connected to the amygdala were
found to contain CRF receptors. It should be noted that the
connections of the amygdala to the septal and preoptic area
are unique for the higher mammals (29), a feature that
correlates with the presence of CRF receptors in these
regions in the monkey but not in the rat (6,8,20).
Electrical stimulation of the amygdala in experimental

animals has been shown to cause arousal, attention, fear and rage reactions associated with sympathetic activation (30). These reactions are similar to those observed during stress and after central administration of CRF (5). Since CRF and its receptors are present in the amygdala, it is likely that the peptide is important in the generation of some of these responses.

In the primate, there is a high CRF receptor concentration throughout the limbic lobe, a structure composed of the cingulate and para-hippocampal cortex, and the hippocampus. The limbic lobe is connected with the hypothalamus, other limbic structures and the neocortex (31). The limbic system has a primary role in the control of behavior, emotion, and autonomic and endocrine functions, and a number of these limbic system-mediated responses can be mimicked by CRF injection into the brain of the rat, dog and monkey (5,32,33). Another interesting aspect of CRF receptor distribution in the CNS is the coexistence of CRF and POMC-derived peptides in many structures that contain CRF receptors, such as the nucleus accumbens, stria terminalis, preoptic area and arcuate nucleus, amygdala, geniculate bodies, locus coeruleus, and parabrachial nucleus (34). The similar anatomical distribution of CRF and its receptors and of opiocortin peptides suggests that, as in the pituitary gland, both systems are functionally related in the brain and that this relationship may have an important regulatory role in stress adaptation.

CRF RECEPTOR REGULATION

Effects of Adrenalectomy, Glucocorticoids, CRF, and Vasopressin

Anterior Pituitary CRF Receptors. Pituitary CRF receptors are dependent on physiological variations in the hypothalamic-pituitary-adrenal (HPA) axis. Following adrenalectomy, despite progressively increasing plasma ACTH levels, pituitary CRF binding is significantly reduced by 24 hrs, followed by a sustained 80% decrease in receptor concentration after 48 hrs. The reduction in binding is due to a decrease in receptor concentration with no change in binding activity (35).

The reduction of CRF receptors after adrenalectomy is accompanied by a 60% decrease in CRF-stimulated adenylate cyclase activity at 24 hr, with no further change at later times. The decreases in CRF receptors and adenylate cyclase

activity following adrenalectomy are prevented by
dexamethasone treatment. Consistent with the decreased
capacity of CRF to activate adenylate cyclase in membranes,
CRF-stimulated cyclic AMP production is significantly
reduced in cultured pituitary cells from adrenalectomized
rats. However, in contrast to the decrease in CRF receptors
and cyclic AMP production, CRF-stimulated ACTH release in
cultured pituitary cells is increased, with no change in
sensitivity to CRF. Since the corticotroph response to CRF
is increased during adrenalectomy despite reduced CRF
receptors and a desensitization of adenylate cyclase to CRF,
elevated ACTH secretion can be maintained by occupancy of a
few receptors and the generation of only small quantities of
cyclic AMP. It is likely that synergistic interactions
between CRF and other ACTH secretagogues contribute to the
sustained increase in ACTH secretion that follows
adrenalectomy (35).

Glucocorticoids also regulate CRF receptor
concentration in the pituitary in vitro and in vivo. In
isolated pituitary cells, incubation with corticosterone
results in CRF receptor loss measured using biotinylated or
fluorescein labeled CRF (36,37). In vivo, corticosterone
(0.5 to 150 mg/day) or dexamethasone (500 to 2500 ug/day)
administration for 1 to 4 days in adult male rats causes a
dose-dependent decrease in the number of CRF receptors in
the anterior pituitary, in parallel with the reduction in
ACTH secretion (35,38). Low doses of corticosterone, which
produce only transient increases in plasma steroid levels,
caused significant reductions in both plasma ACTH and
pituitary CRF receptors. The latter effect of low doses of
the naturally occurring glucocorticoid suggests that
receptor down-regulation in the anterior pituitary may be of
physiological importance, and could participate in the
inhibitory action of glucocorticoids on ACTH release.
However, glucocorticoids inhibit not only CRF-stimulated
ACTH release, but the response to other hormones such as VP,
norepinephrine and angiotensin II, as well as to post-
receptor stimulators such as 8-Br-cyclic AMP and phorbol
esters (39). Therefore, the decrease in cell-surface CRF
receptors can only partially account for the inhibitory
effects of glucocorticoids on ACTH release.

Glucocorticoids have been shown to act directly on the
corticotroph to inhibit POMC gene transcription and protein
synthesis. Consequently, the decrease in CRF receptors may
reflect a general inhibitory effect of glucocorticoids upon
the corticotroph and result from the reduced synthesis of

cellular proteins including the CRF receptor. The direct down-regulatory effect of glucocorticoids on pituitary CRF receptors differs from the effects of glucocorticoid replacement in adrenalectomized rats. In the latter situation, glucocorticoids are likely to block ligand-induced CRF receptor down-regulation by suppressing the increased release of CRF, VP, and possibly other hypothalamic releasing factors into the portal circulation secondary to adrenalectomy (35). This hypothesis has been supported by recent studies in which lesions of the medial basal hypothalamus completely prevented the effect of adrenalectomy on anterior pituitary CRF receptors (41).

Increased exposure of target tissues to peptide hormones is commonly associated with down-regulation and desensitization of the homologous receptors (40). Subcutaneous or intravenous CRF infusion for 48 hours in normal rats produces a prolonged activation of ACTH secretion and a maximal decrease of 45% CRF receptor concentration in the anterior pituitary at the highest dose (100 ng/min) (41). Since adrenalectomy, which raises CRF levels in portal blood, results in a two-fold greater increase in ACTH levels and an 80% reduction in CRF receptors, increases in CRF alone are only partially responsible for the effect of adrenalectomy on pituitary CRF receptor concentration. The effect of central administration of CRF has recently been examined. A single intracisternal injection of CRF can initially reduce CRF binding to anterior pituitary membranes, but the number of pituitary CRF receptors can be replenished to normal levels 24 hours after 4 days of chronic CRF injections (42).

The secretion of VP into the portal circulation is increased after adrenalectomy, and recent studies have shown that in addition to potentiating CRF-stimulated ACTH secretion, VP also influences the regulation of CRF receptors in the anterior pituitary (8). In di/di Brattleboro rats which lack endogenous brain VP, adrenalectomy only causes a slight decrease in CRF receptors compared with the 80% loss in Sprague Dawley or Long Evans rats, but the latter could be reproduced by infusion of VP during the postadrenalectomy period (8). Also in Sprague-Dawley rats, in contrast to the minor receptor loss obtained with CRF infusion alone, the simultaneous infusion of CRF and VP mimicked the effect of adrenalectomy on pituitary CRF receptors (8).

Pituitary CRF Receptors in the Intermediate Lobe. Although the optical density of CRF receptor autoradiography

decreases by 80% in the anterior pituitary of
adrenalectomized rats, the intermediate lobe, which normally
is less sensitive to negative corticosteroid feedback and
lacks glucocorticoid receptors, had no change in receptor
density after adrenalectomy (19). Corticosterone
administrations, however, can increase autoradiographic CRF
labeling in the intermediate lobe (38). Therefore,
glucocorticoids act indirectly to increase CRF receptors in
the intermediate lobe by influencing higher centers in the
brain.

   Brain CRF Receptors. In contrast to the marked effects
of adrenalectomy and glucocorticoid administration on CRF
binding in the anterior pituitary, CRF receptors in several
areas of the brain including the cortex, lateral septum,
amygdala, hippocampus, olfactory bulb and bed nucleus of the
stria terminalis, CRF receptors remain unchanged following
exposure to high steroid levels or after adrenalectomy, as
shown by quantitative autoradiography and by receptor assays
in membrane preparations (19). These findings are
consistent with the absence of changes in CRF-
immunoreactivity in these brain areas following
adrenalectomy (24,43) and suggest that extrahypothalamus CRF
levels are not regulated by glucocorticoid feedback. The
mechanisms by which pituitary and brain CRF receptors are
differentially regulated have not been elucidated, but it is
likely that the interaction of CRF with its brain receptor
is different from the processing of the hormone receptor
complex by endocytosis and receptor desensitization that
occurs in the pituitary gland.

   In recent studies, the regulatory effect of central CRF
administration on brain CRF receptors has been examined. A
persistent loss of CRF receptor sites in the amydala was
present 24 hours after 4 days of daily CRF injections (42).
Since pituitary CRF receptor concentrations were restored to
normal levels following similar recovery periods from
multiple CRF injections into the brain, pituitary and brain
CRF receptors also appear to be differentially regulated by
CRF itself.

Effects of Chronic Stress

   Pituitary CRF Receptors. After short-term immobilization,
plasma ACTH and corticosterone levels are markedly increased
(by at least 20- and 10-fold, respectively), but pituitary
CRF receptors are unchanged (2,3,44). Prolonged
immobilization stress for more than 12 hr results in

reduction of CRF receptor number in the anterior pituitary
(44). Likewise, chronic intermittent restraint stress (2.5
hr/day for 4 to 10 days) decreases CRF binding to the
anterior pituitary (45). Several factors may contribute to
the pituitary CRF receptor downregulation during stress such
as increased secretion of hypothalamic CRF and VP, and
elevated plasma glucocorticoid levels. A significant
reduction in CRF content has been observed in the median
eminence during chronic immobilization (44) which may be
related to increased CRF release into the portal circulation
in response to restraint stress. In this regard,
hypophysial portal concentrations of immunoreactive CRF have
been found to be increased after hypovolemic, hypotensive
hemorrhage (7). Additionally, plasma corticosterone remains
elevated during chronic immobilization, possibly due to
increased sensitivity of the adrenal during stress, and
these high levels of circulating glucocorticoids may also
influence pituitary CRF receptor concentrations.

The decrease in pituitary CRF receptors is accompanied
by decreased CRF stimulated cyclic AMP and ACTH release in
cultured pituitary cells from 48 hr restrained rats (44).
However, concomitant incubation of the cells with CRF and VP
restores cyclic AMP and ACTH responses to levels observed in
control cells, suggesting that the simultaneous release of
both regulators from the hypothalamus determines the ACTH
response. In contrast with the desensitization of the cells
to CRF in vitro, ACTH responses to CRF injection in vivo are
increased following 48 hr immobilization probable due to
interaction of CRF with other endogenous regulators(44). On
the other hand, after 6 days daily 3 hr foot shock stress,
plasma ACTH responses to CRF are decreased suggesting the
involvement of different neural pathways and releasing
factors in different types of stress (46). ACTH responses
to novel stimuli are usually enhanced during chronic stress
          consistent with the concept that the responsiveness
of the corticotroph is preserved despite the pituitary CRF
receptor desensitization due to the coordinated action of
CRF and other regulators (3,4,44).

Pituitary CRF Receptors in the Intermediate Lobe. CRF
receptors in the intermediate lobe were unchanged after
acute restraint or chronic continuous or intermittent
immobilization stress (45).

Brain CRF Receptors. In contrast with the down-
regulation of CRF receptors in the anterior pituitary after
prolonged immobilization, CRF receptors in the CNS remain
unchanged during chronic stress (44).

DISCUSSION

Consistent with the recognized actions of CRF, receptor sites for CRF have been identified in the anterior and intermediate lobes of the pituitary, and in the nervous system at sites related to the stress response. In the anterior pituitary the affinity of CRF analogues for the CRF receptor parallel the ACTH secretory activity of the peptides. In pituitary and brain membrane fractions the binding is enhanced by divalent cations and is inhibited by guanylnucleotides, which is consistent with this receptor being coupled to adenylate cyclase. Furthermore, CRF increases cAMP accumulation in pituitary cells, stimulates adenylate cyclase activity, and activates cAMP-dependent protein kinase at concentrations in the range of its ACTH stimulating activity. With regard to the CNS actions of CRF, the distribution of CRF receptors in cortical and limbic areas of the brain correlate with the immunohistochemical localization of imunoreactive CRF pathways and the effects of centrally administrered CRF on behavioral and autonomic responses.

CRF receptors in the pituitary but not in the brain, undergo regulatory changes following alterations in the HPA axis. Following adrenalectomy and chronic stress, the increased ACTH secretion is accompanied by a loss of pituitary CRF receptors a result of the coordinated actions of CRF and vasopressin in the corticotroph. During glucocorticoid administration, CRF receptors decrease in parallel with inhibition of ACTH secretion suggesting that CRF receptor down-regulation may contribute to the negative feedback effects of adrenal steroids. The central infusion of CRF also appears to exert a discordant regulatory effect on its receptor sites in the CNS and pituitary. The reasons for the differential regulation of pituitary and brain CRF receptors (figure 1) are not fully understood. However, it appears at the present time that the interaction of CRF with its brain receptor involves mechanisms different from the processing of the hormone-receptor complex by endocytosis and receptor desensitization which occur in the pituitary. The widespread distribution of CRF binding sites in the pituitary, cortical and limbic areas of the brain and peripheral nervous system emphasize the importance of CRF as a mediator of the endocrine as well as the behavioral and autonomic responses to stress.

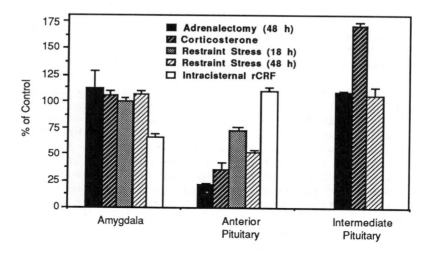

FIGURE 1. Regulation of CRF receptors in the pituitary
and amygdala by glucocorticoids, CRF, and immobilization
stress.

ACKNOWLEDGEMENTS

We wish to thank Maria Bongiovanni for her gracious
preparation of the manuscript.

REFERENCES

1. Selye H (1976). "Stress in Health and Disease."
    Boston: Butterworth.
2. Yates FE, Maran JW (1974). "Handbook of Physiology."
    Washington, D.C.: American Physiological Society,
    p 367.
3. Keller-Wood ME, Dallman MF (1984). Corticosteroid
    inhibition of ACTH secretion. Endocr Rev 5:1-24.
4. Gann DS, Bereiter DA, Carlson DE, Thrivikraman KV
    (1985). Neural interaction in control of
    adrenocorticotropin. Fed Proc 44:161.
5. Vale W, Rivier C, Brown MR, Spiess J, Koob G, Swanson
    L, Bilezikjian L, Bloom F, Rivier J (1983). Chemical
    and biological characterization of corticotropin

releasing factor. Recent Prog Horm Res 39:245-270.

6. Aguilera G, Wynn PC, Harwood JP, Hauger RL, Millan MA,
    Grewe C, Catt KJ (1986). Receptor-mediated actions of
    corticotropin-releasing factor in pituitary gland and
    nervous system. Neuroendocrinology 43:79-88.

7. Rivier CL, Plotsky PM (1986). Mediation by
    corticotropin releasing factor (CRF) of adenohypo-
    hysial hormone secretion. Annu Rev Physiol 48:475-494.

8. Aguilera G, Millan MA, Hauger RL, Catt KJ (1987).
    Corticotropin-releasing factor receptors: Distribution
    and regulation in brain, pituitary, and peripheral
    tissues. Ann NY Acad Sci 512:48-66.

9. Wynn PC, Aguilera G, Morell J, Catt KJ (1983).
    Properties and regulation of high-affinity receptors
    for corticotropin-releasing factor. Biochem Biophys Res
    Comm 110:602.

10. Holmes MC, Antoni FA, Szentendrei T (1984). Pituitary
    receptors for corticotropin-releasing factor: no effect
    of vasopressin on binding or activation of adenylate
    cyclase. Neuroendocrinology 39:162-169.

11. DeSouza EB, Perrin MH, Rivier JE, Vale WW, Kuhar MJ
    (1984). Corticotropin-releasing factor receptors in
    rat pituitary gland: autoradiographic localization.
    Brain Res 296:202-207.

12. Millan MA, Abou-Samra AB, Wynn PC, Catt KJ, Aguilera G
    (1987). Receptors and actions of corticotropin-
    releasing hormone in the primate pituitary gland. J
    Clin Endocrinol Metab 64:1036-1041.

13. Perin MH, Haas Y, Rivier JE, Vale WW (1986).
    Corticotropin-releasing factor binding to the anterior
    pituitary receptor is modulated by divalent cations and
    guanyl nucleotides. Endocrinology 118:1171.

14. Abou-Samra A-B, Catt KJ, Aguilera G (1986). Role of
    arachidonic acid in the regulation of adreno-
    corticotropin release from rat anterior pituitary cell
    cultures. Endocrinology 119:1427.

15. Abou-Samra A-B, Catt KJ, Aguilera G (1987). Calcium-
    dependent control of corticotropin release in rat
    anterior pituitary cell cultures. Endocrinology
    121:965.

16. Abou-Samra A-B, Catt KJ, Aguilera G (1986). Involvement
    of protein kinase C in the regulation of adreno-
    corticotropin release from rat anterior pituitary
    cells. Endocrinology 118:212.

17. Udelsman R, Harwood JP, Millan MA, Chrousos GP,
    Goldstein DS, Zimlichman R, Catt KJ, Aguilera G (1986).

29.   Nauta WJH (1986).   Fibre degeneration following lesions of the amygdaloid complex in the monkey. J Anat 95:515–531.

30.   Kaada BR (1972).   Stimulation and ablation of the amygdaloid complex with reference to functional representations. In Eleftheriou BE (ed): "The Neurobiology of the Amygdala," New York: Plenum press, p 205–281.

31.   MacLean PD (1952).   Some psyhiatric implications of physiological studies on frontotemporal portions of limbic system. Electroencephalogr Clin Neurophysiol 4:407–418.

32.   Kalin NH (1985).   Behavioral effects of ovine corticotropin-releasing factor administered to rhesus monkeys. Fed Proc 44:249–253.

33.   Britton KR, Lee G, Dana R, Risch SC, Koob GF (1986). Activating and `anxiogenic´ effects of corticotropin releasing factor are not inhibited by blockade of the pituitary-adrenal system with dexamethasone. Life Sci 39:1281–1286.

34.   Knigge KM, Joseph SA (1984).   Anatomy of the opioid-systems of the brain. Can J Neurol Sci 11:14–23.

35.   Wynn PC, Harwood JP, Catt KJ, Aguilera G (1985). Regulation of corticotropin-releasing factor (CRF) receptors in the rat pituitary gland: Effects of adrenalectomy on CRF receptors and corticotroph responses. Endocrinology 116:1653–1659.

36.   Childs GV, Morell JL, Niendorf A, Aguilera G (1986). Cytochemical studies of corticotropin-releasing factor (CRF) receptors in anterior lobe corticotropes: binding, glucocorticoid regulation, and endocytosis of [Biotinyl-Ser^1]CRF. Endocrinology 119:2129–2142.

37.   Schwartz J, Billestrup N, Perrin M, Rivier J, Vale W (1986).   Identification of corticotropin-releasing factor (CRF) target cells and effects of dexamethasone on binding in anterior pituitary using a fluorescent analog of CRF. Endocrinology 119:2376–2382.

38.   Hauger RL, Millan MA, Catt KJ, Aguilera G (1987a). Differential regulation of brain and pituitary corticotropin-releasing factor receptors by corticosterone. Endocrinology 120:1527–1533.

39.   Abou-Samra A-B, Catt KJ, Aguilera G (1986).   Biphasic inhibition of adrenocorticotropin release by corticosterone in cultured anterior pituitary cells. Endocrinology 119:972.

40.   Catt KJ, Harwood JP, Aguilera G, Dufau ML (1979).

Hormonal regulation of peptide receptors and target cell responses. Nature 280:109-116.

41. Wynn PC, Harwood JP, Catt KJ, Aguilera G (1988). Corticotropin-releasing factor (CRF) induces desensitization of the rat pituitary CRF receptor-adenylate cyclase complex. Endocrinology 122:351-358.

42. Hauger RL, Lorang M (1988). Persistent loss of CRF receptors in the amygdala following restoration of anterior pituitary CRF receptor sites after repeated, but not continuous, central administration of CRF. Endocrinology 122:228A.

43. Swanson LW (1986). Organization of mammalian neuroendocrine system. In "Handbook of Physiology, Section 1: The Nervous System" Bethesda, Maryland: American Physiological Society, pp 317-363.

44. Hauger RL, Millan MA, Lorang M, Harwood JP, Aguilera G (1988). Corticotropin-releasing factor receptors and pituitary adrenal responses during immobilization stress. Endocrinology 123:396-405.

45. Hauger RL, Lorang M, Aguilera G (1987b). Differential regulation of anterior pituitary and brain CRF receptors by chronic stress. Clin Res 35:396A.

46. Rivier C, Vale W (1987). Diminished responsiveness of the hypothalamic-pituitary adrenal axis of the rat during exposure to prolonged stress: a pituitary-mediated mechanism. Endocrinology 121:1320.

Molecular Biology of Stress, pages 19–30
Published 1989 Alan R. Liss, Inc.

BRAIN CORTICOTROPIN RELEASING FACTOR AND DEVELOPMENT

Thomas R. Insel,[1] George Battaglia,[2]
Errol B. De Souza[2]

[1]Laboratory of Clinical Science
National Institute of Mental Health
Bethesda, MD 20892

[2]Neuroscience Branch
National Institute of Drug Abuse
Baltimore, MD 21224

ABSTRACT   Studies of the ontogeny of CRF pathways in
rat brain demonstrate development of receptors by
fetal day 17. Receptors increase to 318% of adult
levels by postnatal day 8. Studies of linkage to
second messenger (cAMP) suggest that these receptors
are functional early in postnatal life. The
distribution of CRF receptors at this time is
strikingly different from the adult pattern. In
addition, the behavioral effects of exogenous
administration of CRF to week-old rat pups is
different from the patterns of activation noted with
adults. Central but not peripheral administration of
CRF decreases the number of distress calls emitted in
response to social isolation. The long-term
consequences of repeated administration of CRF to rat
pups include effects on the rate of development and
patterns of behavioral responsiveness in adulthood.

INTRODUCTION

Research on corticotropin releasing hormone (CRF)
during development has been mostly focussed on the
pituitary.[1,2] It has been known for more than two decades
that glucocorticoid release in rat pups is relatively
unresponsive to stress (from day 2 until day 12).[3] Studies

of the development of the hypothalamic-pituitary-adrenal
(HPA) axis have described increased pituitary sensitivity to
glucocorticoid feedback[2] during this period. In addition,
there is a transient overshoot of CRF receptors in the
anterior pituitary during the first postnatal week[1] and an
early appearance of CRF in the hypothalamus.[4] By contrast,
almost nothing is known about the extra-hypothalamic
development of CRF, although these pathways appear to
profoundly influence behavior and autonomic function. In
this chapter, we will review the development of CRF
receptors in the rat brain, then we will describe some
unique behavioral effects of CRF in development, and finally
we will present some preliminary results regarding possible
organizational effects of CRF during development.

CRF RECEPTORS IN THE DEVELOPING RAT BRAIN

      CRF receptors have been characterized and mapped in
the adult brains of several species. These receptors
generally, though not exclusively, use adenylate cyclase as
a second messenger. They are not in perfect register with
CRF terminals, suggesting to some[5] that CRF may affect its
extra-hypothalamic receptors in a non-synaptic "action at a
distance" fashion. If this hypothesis were true, then the
receptor map of where CRF acts may be functionally more
important than the immunohistochemical map of where CRF is
released. For this reason, and because of the variability
in CRF immunohistochemical maps, we chose to study the
ontogeny of CRF receptors rather than CRF immunoreactivity
in development.[6]

      Receptor binding in brain homogenates. Initially, CRF
receptor binding was assessed using ^{125}I-Tyr°-ovine CRF in
whole rat brain homogenates as described elsewhere.[6]

      With this method, specific CRF binding can be detected
as early as day 17 of gestation (E17), that is, 5 days prior
to birth (Fig. 1). Receptor number increases steadily, with
a peak at postnatal day 8 (P8) when the total number of
receptors is 318% of adult values. The number then
decreases, reaching final adult values by P28. This
overshoot of receptor number is not due to a transient

decrease in protein in brain homogenates as the protein
concentration increases steadily until P 21 (Fig. 1).

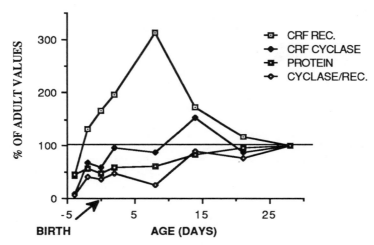

FIGURE 1   Binding of ^{125}I-tyr°-0-CRF to whole rat
brain homogenates is expressed as percent of Day 28 value.
Each point represents the mean of three brains at each age.
The same brain homogenates were used for measurement of
adenylate cyclase.   The ontogeny of CRF receptor linkage to
cyclase was calculated by dividing amount of cyclase
generated by CRF at each age by number of receptors at this
age.   Further details available in Reference 6 from which
this figure is adapted.

Receptor binding in brain sections.   To localize CRF
receptors through ontogeny, we used *in vitro* receptor
autoradiography.   This technique, which uses the same ligand
and buffers as in the homogenate study, employs 16 µ thick
cryostat cut sections of unfixed brain.   Binding was carried
out at room temperature, using approximately 0.1 nM of ^{125}I-
Tyr°-ovine-CRF.   In addition to providing light microscopic
resolution, this technique uses an iodinated ligand which
should not be affected by changes in white matter and brain
water content that alter the quenching of radioisotopes such
as ^{3}H during development.

By autoradiography, CRF receptors were found to develop along the same time course as described for homogenate binding. Receptors appear initially in the striatum, where they show the highest density from E 17 until P 8, after which they decrease markedly in density. The large overshoot noted with homogenate binding is due to both this striatal component and to an extremely dense distribution across several layers of neocortex. CRF receptors in amygdala and claustrum and the adult laminar distribution in cortex can be seen by P 14.

The transient proliferation of receptors in striatum is probably not just a reflection of subsequent decreased neuronal density, as the characteristic patchy distribution noted with other receptors that become diffused during development is not apparent with CRF in adulthood. In addition, these striatal CRF receptors are probably not on migrating neural elements as cortical neurons are formed earlier and migrate from a more medial, periventricular zone. It is more likely that the transient CRF receptors in striatum are labeling a neural or synaptic population that is eliminated between P 8 and P 21. It is also possible that these receptors are expressed only transiently in cells that survive.

Receptor linkage to adenylate cyclase. When do CRF receptors become functional? Linkage to cyclase was measured by adding 1 mM ATP/^{32}P-ATP to at 37° with or without 1 µM rat/human CRF. The reaction was stopped after 10 minutes by adding 100 µl of 50 mM Tris HCl, 45 mM ATP, and 2% sodium dodecyl sulfate. The separation of ^{32}P-cAMP for ^{32}P-ATP was accomplished by sequential elution over Dowex and alumina columns and the amount of ^{32}P cAMP was measured.

CRF can stimulate adenylate cyclase in brain homogenates by E 19 and adult levels of cyclase are generated by P 2 (Figure 1), suggesting that this receptor system becomes functional very early in brain. However, if one takes into account the large number of CRF receptors present during these first 14 days, the efficiency of this system seems less precocious. Expressed as cyclase generated per receptor, the adult value is not approached until P 14 (Fig. 1). In other words, although the CRF receptor appears fully linked to adenylate cyclase by P 2, relatively few of the receptors show this linkage at this age. Indeed, the striatum with its abundance of receptors until P 8 does not appear to generate cyclase in response to CRF.[6] Using linkage to cyclase as our criterion, CRF receptors in striatum do not appear to be functional. Of course, these transient receptors may be linked to another second messenger or ion channel or provide a trophic or cell surface marker role in development. Additional studies will be needed to test this hypothesis.

BEHAVIORAL EFFECTS OF CRF IN DEVELOPMENT

The fetus may be exposed to very high levels of CRF, as studies with several species have demonstrated high circulating levels of CRF during pregnancy.[7,8] How much of this peptide can cross the fetal blood-brain barrier is not known. Our own studies in the rat using simultaneous intra-carotid injections of ^{125}I-CRF, ^{14}C-inulin, and ^{3}H-water demonstrate significant transport of CRF across the blood-brain barrier as late as P 24. This selective permeability to CRF is similar to what has previously been reported with insulin[9] and may involve a similar carrier mechanism.

Response to single dose administration of CRF.

Does CRF have behavioral effects in the developing rat? Many of the behaviors affected by CRF in adulthood, such as rearing and exploration are not within the repertoire of pup behavior and thus are not reasonable measures with which to assess CRF's effects in development. When rat pups are stressed, they emit ultrasonic vocalizations (USV). These vocalizations, also known as distress calls, are usually in the 30-40 kHz range and are extremely potent stimuli for maternal retrieval. Drugs such as diazepam which decrease anxiety will decrease USV; drugs such as pentylenetetrazol which increase anxiety increase USV; and strains of rats bred for "nervousness" emit more USV when isolated for brief periods.[10] As central administration of CRF to adult rats has been associated with "anxiety-like" behaviors, we hypothesized that CRF would increase rat pup USV.

Our protocol involved a baseline session of 2 minutes of isolation for 5- or 6-day-old rat pups. Pups were matched for baseline recording rate and then administered 1 μl volumes of either saline or ovine-CRF by direct intracerebroventricular (ICV) injection. Thirty minutes later, pups were isolated again for 2 minutes, and USV and locomotor behavior were measured. Each injection volume included 10% india ink. Immediately following the second isolation test, each pup brain was examined to ensure that the injection filled the ventricle. Only pups with injections showing ventricular filling were used for data analysis.

Contrary to expectations, CRF decreased rather than increased USV in a dose-dependent fashion (Fig. 2).

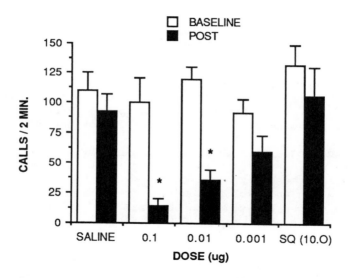

Figure 2   Ultrasonic vocalization in 5-6-day-old rat pups isolated at room temperature for 2 minutes pre and 30 minutes post ICV or peripheral injection of o-CRF. Data represent means from between 6 and 12 pups at each dose and are analyzed by repeated measure ANOVA. * signifies change from pre to post significantly different ($p < .05$) from corresponding change with ICV saline administration.

Doses as low as 0.01 µg CRF (roughly 1 µg/kg) had
significant effects. This decrease in USV was not secondary
to decreased arousal as central administration of CRF did
not significantly affect locomotor behavior nor did it alter
either rectal or skin temperature. Peripheral
(subcutaneous) administration of CRF did not affect USV
(Fig. 2).

Generally, pups emit fewer calls with each passing
minute of separation. If CRF induced an isolation-like
syndrome, as previously described in rhesus monkeys,[14] then
the peak interval of calling may have occurred during the
30-minute interval between injection and isolation. A
longitudinal study of the CRF effect excluded this
possibility as pups showed decreased distress calling within
10 minutes of CRF administration and the effect persisted
for 90 minutes. Thus, it appears that CRF has central
effects in 5-6-day-old rat pups related to distress
behavior, and specifically is associated with decreased
distress calling.

Effects of repeated CRF administration.

Recent studies have demonstrated long-term effects
following neonatal peptide treatments.[12] The notion that
early administration of a neuropeptide could have long-term
effects on behavior and even morphology may be particularly
relevant to clinical psychiatry. Depression, which has been
associated with early loss, is also associated with
resistance to dexamethasone suppression and hypersecretion
of CRF. If early stress permanently alters the sensitivity
of CRF receptors, via "organizing" effects at some sensitive
period of development, then stressors in adulthood might be
expected to elicit altered activity of the HPA axis and
potentially abnormal behavior related to extrahypothalamic
pathways of CRF.

To test this hypothesis, we administered CRF (10 µg or
1 µg) daily (days P 1 - P7) to rat pups by subcutaneous
injection (100 µl) at the nape of the neck. Controls were
littermates who received saline or, in some cases, were
untreated. Pups were then observed for differences in
growth and development (P 1 - P 21), and differences in
behavioral responses to stress (adulthood).

   1.   Growth and development. The most striking effect
of repeated CRF administration was in growth and
development.   Eye opening, which normally occurs on day P
14- 15 in the rat pup, occurred between P 12 and P 14 in
pups given 10.0 µg of CRF daily (Fig. 3).

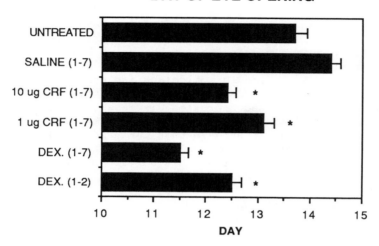

DAY OF EYE OPENING

Figure 3   Day of eye opening is accelerated by daily
peripheral administration of either CRF (1 µg or 10 µg) or
dexamethasone (1 µg) given from P 1 - P 7 or dexamethasone
(1 µg) given on postnatal days 1 and 2 only.   Data represent
means (± SEM) of at least 17 pups for each treatment.   *
indicates significant (*p* < .05) differences from saline
treatment by Student's t test.   Saline treatment does not
differ from uninjected controls.

A similar effect has been described by Zadina and Kastin.[13]
Glucocorticoids alone, even given only on days P 1 and P 2
also shorten the latency to eye opening (Fig. 3)--providing
a potential mechanism for the CRF effect.

   CRF (10 µg) did not affect weight gain, although the
pups receiving 1.0 µg of dexamethasone and the two litters
receiving the low dose of CRF (1 µg) showed retarded
growth.

3. _Long-Term Consequences_. Long-term consequences of neonatal CRF administration were studied in several ways. In an open field arena, adults treated with CRF (10 µg) as pups showed increased exploration compared to saline or dexamethasone treated controls. This effect was evident under both red light (low stress) and white light (high stress) conditions (Fig. 4).

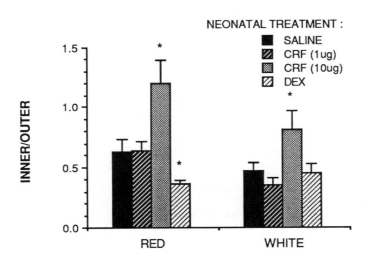

Figure 4 Exploratory behavior in adults with neonatal daily treatments of CRF (10 µg or 1 µg), dexamethasone (1 µg), or saline. Values represent crossovers into inner squares divided by crossovers into outer squares during a 2-minute open field test. Open field testing was done under low stress (red light) and high stress (white light) conditions. * indicates significant (p < .05) difference from saline by Student's t test.

As dexamethasone appears to show opposite effects to CRF, it may appear that the peptide effects are not mediated by secondary glucocorticoid release. Nevertheless, it is possible that corticosterone, the native glucocorticoid, would have effects quite distinct from dexamethasone, and thus mediate these apparent long-term consequences of CRF on exploratory behavior.

Taken together, it appears that CRF administered to pups has acute effects on growth and development, which may be related to increases in glucocorticoids, and long-term effects on exploratory behavior. Contrary to our initial hypothesis, animals receiving CRF showed more exploratory behavior in an open field arena (i.e. appeared less rather than more stress sensitive). In related studies, we have shown that animals treated postnatally with CRF subsequently exhibit blunted corticosterone responses to either stress or exogenous CRF. Our experimental results do not clearly model a developmental hypothesis of HPA axis abnormalities in clinical depression. On the other hand, these results are generally consistent with an earlier literature[14,15] documenting long-term effects of handling rat pups. Stress during infancy has long been thought to immunize the rat pup, so that during adulthood, stressors elicit less behavioral and physiologic responses. It is still far from clear however that CRF given either peripherally or centrally to rat pups is the neuroendocrine equivalent of stress.

SUMMARY

These studies have examined three aspects of the ontogeny of brain CRF pathways. CRF receptors were found to develop by E 17 and to show developmentally restricted expression early in postnatal life. Exogenous CRF administration was associated with decreased USV production. This pharmacologic effect was elicited by central but not peripheral administration of the peptide. Finally, repeated administration of CRF through the first postnatal week was shown to confer effects on growth and development (probably via increased corticosterone) and long-term effects on exploratory behavior. The extent to which peripheral administration of CRF results in increased brain levels of the peptide remains unclear although preliminary data suggest that in the rat a carrier mechanism for transporting this peptide across the blood brain barrier exists until P 24. An even more critical question is the extent to which environmental stressors increase CRF production during development. As data accumulate documenting alterations in brain CRF content or receptors in several human disease states, the study of the development of CRF pathways and the process by which their sensitivity becomes regulated during development takes on increasing importance.

REFERENCES

1. Walker C-D, Perrin M, Vale W, Rivier C (1986). Ontogeny of the stress response in the rat: Role of the pituitary and the hypothalamus. Endocrinology 118:1445.
2. Walker C-D, Sapolsky RM, Meaney MJ, Vale WW, Rivier C (1986). Increased pituitary sensitivity to glucocorticoid feedback during the stress nonresponsive period in the neonatal rat. Endocrinology 119:1816.
3. Sapolsky RM, Meaney MJ (1986). Maturation of the adrenocortical stress response: Neuroendocrine control mechanisms and the stress hyporesponsive period. Brain Res Rev 11:65.
4. Bugnon C, Fellmann D, Gouget A, Cardot J (1982). Ontogeny of the corticoliberin neuroglandular system in rat brain. Nature 298:159.
5. Herkenham M (1987). Mismatches between neurotransmitter and receptor localizations in brain: Observations and implications. Neuroscience 23:1.
6. Insel TR, Battaglia G, Fairbanks DW, De Souza EB (in press). The ontogeny of brain receptors for corticotropin-releasing factor and the development of their functional association with adenylate cyclase. J Neuroscience.
7. Sasaki A, Shinkawa O, Margioris AN, Liotta A, Sato S, Murakami O, Meigan G, Shimizu Y, Hanew K, Yoshinaga K (1987). Immunoreactive CRF in human plasma during pregnancy, labor and delivery. J Clin Endocrinol Metab 64:224.
8. Goland RS, Starle SL, Brown LS, Frantz AG (1986). High levels of CRF immunoreactive in maternal and fetal plasma during pregnancy. J Clin Endocrinol Metab 63:1199.
9. Duffy KR, Pardridge WM (1987). Blood-brain barrier transcytosis of insulin in developing rabbits. Brain Res 420:32.
10. Insel TR, Hill JL, Mayor RB (1986). Rat pup ultrasonic isolation calls: Possible mediation by the benzodiazepine receptor complex. Pharmacol Biochem Behav 24:1263.

11. Kalin NH, Shelton SE, Kraemer GW, McKinney WE (1983).
    Corticotropin-releasing factor administered
    intraventricularly to rhesus monkeys. Peptides 4:217
12. Handelmann GE, Selsky JH, Helke CJ (1984). Substance P
    administration to neonatal rats increases adult
    sensitivity to substance P. J Physiol Rev 33:297.
13. Zadina JE, Kastin AJ (1986). Neonatal peptides affect
    developing rats: ß-Endorphin alters nociception and
    opiate receptors, corticotropin-releasing factor alters
    corticosterone. Dev Brain Res 29:21.
14. Levine S, Mullins RF, Jr (1966). Hormonal influence on
    brain organization in infant rats. Science 152:1585.
15. Denenberg VH (1969). The effects of early experience.
    In Hafez ESE (eds): "The Behavior of Domestic
    Animals," Baltimore: Williams and Wilkins, p 95.

Molecular Biology of Stress, pages 31–47
© 1989 Alan R. Liss, Inc.

INVOLVEMENT OF ENDOGENOUS CORTICOTROPIN-RELEASING FACTOR (CRF) IN MODULATING ACTH AND LH SECRETION FUNCTION DURING EXPOSURE TO STRESS, ALCOHOL OR COCAINE IN THE RAT

Catherine   Rivier

The   Clayton   Foundation   Laboratories
for   Peptide   Biology
The   Salk   Institute
10010   North   Torrey   Pines   Road
La Jolla, CA   92037

Research   supported   by   NIH   grants   AA06420   and
AM26741.   Research   conducted   in   part   by   the
Clayton   Foundation   for   Research,   California
Division.   C. Rivier   is   a   Clayton   Foundation
investigator.

Exposure to stress has profound effects on a number of endocrine functions, including increased secretion of ACTH and corticosteroids, and decreased gonadotropin and androgen release. A large body of clinical and experimental evidence had suggested that the hypothalamus played a major role in integrating many of the endocrine, autonomic and behavioral responses to stress, and in 1948 Harris postulated that the hypothalamus released a substance into the hypophysial portal blood which stimulated ACTH production (1). The isolation and characterization in 1981 of corticotropin-releasing factor (CRF) (2-5), a 41-amino acid peptide present in hypothalamic, brain and peripheral tissues [review in (6-9)] which specifically releases ACTH (10), led to numerous studies aimed at investigating a possible role of this factor in mediating some effects of stress. While we now know that CRF acts in concert with other secretagogues in modulating a variety of stress responses [reviews in (11-14)], this chapter will be restricted to the discussion of the physiological role played by CRF and vasopressin in modulating stress-induced ACTH release, stress-mediated inhibition of reproductive functions, and the secretion of ACTH induced by drugs such as alcohol and cocaine.

Modulation of ACTH Secretion During Stress

As illustrated in Fig. 1, a large variety of stresses stimulate ACTH secretion. Because there is evidence that different stresses activate different pathways within the brain [review in (15-17)], and because the regulation of ACTH release is multifactorial [including secretagogues such as corticotropin-releasing-factor (CRF), vasopressin, catecholamines (18-21), among others] our laboratory and others have attempted to delineate the respective role of these factors, as well as their possible interactions, in modulating the increased ACTH secretion due to well-defined stresses.

Following the isolation and characterization of CRF (3-5), we (22-24) and others (25-30) demonstrated the importance of endogenous CRF in mediating ACTH release under basal and specific stressful circumstances. These studies were followed by the demonstration that stresses such as hemorrhage caused increases in the hypophysial-portal plasma concentration of CRF (31), thereby providing strong support that CRF participated in the mediation of the ACTH secretory responses to at least some stressful stimuli. However, the above-quoted studies also indicated that vasopressin, catecholamines and possibly oxytocin not only were released by some stresses, but also played a role in the increased ACTH secretion measured during these stresses (13,32-36).

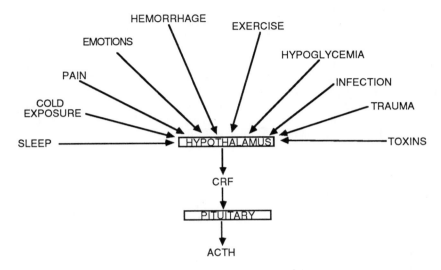

Fig. 1:   ACTH secretion is stimulated by a large variety of stresses.

Because vasopressin has long been heralded as a putative physiological regulator of ACTH release [review in (14,37)], we studied the interaction between vasopressin and CRF in studies aimed at better delineating the specific role of both factors. We first observed that while the peripheral injection of arginine vasopressin (AVP) to non-anesthesized intact adult rats caused dose-dependent increases in plasma ACTH concentrations, the pharmacological blockade of endogenous CRF release by anesthesia markedly blunted the ACTH response to AVP (21,35,38). This suggested a possible interaction between endogenous CRF and AVP, which as subsequently shown by us (20,21,23) and others (39-41), depends at least in part on the activation of V1-type of vasopressin receptors. However, the ultimate demonstration of the physiological role of this interaction, derived from studies showing that the immunoneutralization of endogenous CRF in intact rats markedly interfered with AVP-induced ACTH secretion (21,35), and led to the conclusion that CRF exerted both an obligatory and permissive role in permitting the expression of vasopressin on the corticotrophs.

A number of studies by Plotsky, et al. have also suggested that the hypophysiotropic coding of ACTH secretion was stimulus-specific, but that the presence of CRF was obligatory for eliciting an ACTH response (11-13). We therefore studied the effect of specifically blocking either V1-type vasopressin receptors, or CRF receptors, on the stimulation of ACTH release by various stresses. The vasopressin antagonist used was [1-deaminopenicilamine-2-(O-methyl)tyrosine] arginine-vasopressin (42), and the CRF antagonist, α-helCRF$^{9-41}$ (23). The increases in plasma ACTH levels measured after 10 min of restraint, were not altered by V1-receptors blockade but significantly (P ≤ 0.01) reduced when the rats were restrained for 20 min (Fig. 2). At both time points, injection of the CRF

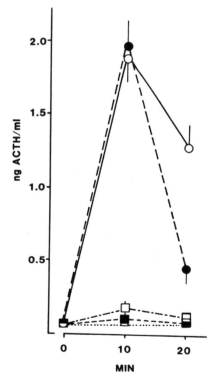

Fig. 2: Interaction between the V1-receptor antagonist [1-deaminopenicilamine-2-(O-methyl)tyrosine]arginine-vasopressin and the CRF antagonist α-helCRF$^{9-41}$ on ACTH secretion induced by restraint in adult male rats. (O, restraint alone; ●, V1-antagonist; ❑ CRF antagonist; ■, V1- and CRF antagonist.) Each point represents the mean ± SEM of 5 rats.

antagonist markedly (P ≤ 0.01), but not totally, abolished the ACTH response to stress. Return to base-line levels, however, was only achieved by the concomitant administration of the AVP and the CRF antagonist. These results supported the hypothesis that endogenous CRF represents an important modulator of the ACTH secretion in response to stress. They also suggested that the role of other factors--vasopressin in this particular example--might be time-dependent in the case of restraint stress, as we had previously demonstrated for ether stress (23), and may be a function of the development of other superimposed stimuli such as hypoxia.

The relative role of vasopressin and CRF was further examined during stimuli such as electroshocks, ether vapors and transfer. As illustrated by Fig. 3, a 10 min period of

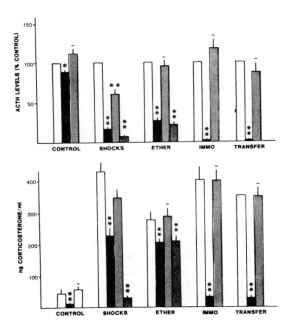

Fig. 3: Interaction between a V1-receptor antagonist (see Legend to Fig. 2) and a CRF-antiserum on ACTH secretion stimulated by a 10 min exposure to mild electroshocks (shocks) (1.5 mA; 1 sec; 2/min), ether vapors, immobilization (IMMO) or transfer to another cage. Each bar represents the mean ± SEM of 5 rats; -, P > 0.05 from control; *, P ≤ 0.05; **, P ≤ 0.01.

transfer between cages (a stress considered purely phychological) elicited an increase in ACTH secretion which was mainly dependent upon CRF release. By contrast, exposure to ether vapors or electrical shocks caused elevations in plasma ACTH levels which could only be blunted by both the CRF antagonist and the vasopressin antagonist. This suggested the involvement of CRF as well as vasopressin pathways in mediating this response. We therefore conclude that, in accordance with studies of the organization of the neural circuitry which underlies the integration of the stress response (15,16), our results demonstrate that the regulation of the ACTH response to stress depends upon the integration of various neurosecretory pathways which include CRF and vasopressin.

Modulation of LH Secretion During Stress

The deleterious effect of stress on reproductive functions is well established [for review, see references in (43)], but the mechanisms through which stress interferes with LH and testosterone secretion have long remained elusive. Because stress releases CRF (31), endogenous opiates (44), as well as ACTH and corticosteroids (23), we investigated the possible role of these hormones in stress-induced inhibition of LH secretion.

We first observed (45) that the subcutaneous administration of CRF to intact male rats for 7 days caused a marked decline in plasma testosterone levels, a result which could be duplicated by the injection of ACTH. Interestingly, adrenalectomy interfered with the inhibitory effects of both CRF and ACTH (45), suggesting the importance of adrenal steroids as modulators of the decline in androgen production. We further demonstrated the ability of corticosteroids to mediate gonadotropin secretion by showing that in acute experiments, the injection of dexamethasone or progesterone interfered with GnRH-induced LH secretion (Fig. 4). This suggested that corticoids can indeed act at the pituitary level to alter gonadotropin release. However, we observed that removal of the adrenal did not significantly interfere with the effect of acute stress on circulating LH values (43). This led to the hypothesis that at least under acute circumstances, adrenal steroids do not represent essential mediators of the stress-induced inhibition of LH secretion. Consequently because as mentioned earlier, stress releases CRF (31), we then investigated the possibility that this increased CRF might also represent a mechanism through which stress lowered plasma LH levels. We observed that the central (i.e., into the lateral ventricle of the brain), but not the peripheral, (i.e., into the jugular vein) injection of CRF markedly inhibited LH secretion (46). We therefore examined a possible role of increased endogenous CRF secretion in modulating the effect of stress by injecting a CRF antagonist (24) prior to submitting the rats to electroshocks. We observed that while the peripheral administration of this antagonist did not alter LH secretion in shocked animals, the central injection of the peptide restored the normal pulsatile pattern of LH release despite the presence of the shocks (43). These results provided evidence that endogenous CRF represents an important mediator of the stress-induced inhibition of LH secretion.

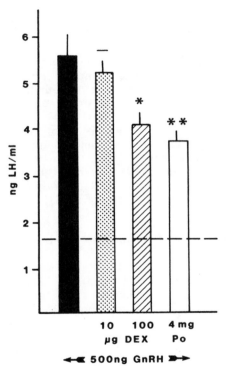

Fig. 4: Interaction between gonadotropin-releasing hormone (GnRH) and dexamethasone (DEX) or progesterone (Po) on LH secretion by intact adult male rats. The steroids were administered sc 4 h prior to the experiment. Blood samples were obtained 10 min following injection of GnRH. --, control levels. Each bar represents the mean $\pm$ SEM of 5 rats. -, P > 0.05 from GnRH alone; *, P $\leq$ 0.05; **, P $\leq$ 0.01.

Opiates, which are also released during stress (44), are well-known to alter gonadotropin secretion (47-54). We had observed that blockade of mu opiate receptors interfered with the ability of CRF to inhibit LH release (55). Consistent with these results, we subsequently obtained evidence that a similar blockade totally reversed the effect of stress on LH secretion (54). These results provided evidence that endogenous opiates also participate in the effect of stress on gonadotropins.

Taken together, the results mentioned above suggest that in the rat, the inhibition of reproductive functions caused by stress could be modulated by: 1) increased levels of circulating corticoids during chronic stress, which may interfere with LH secretion through a pituitary site of action; however, this effect appears to be mainly operative during prolonged stress; 2) an increased release of endogenous CRF, which exerts a powerful inhibitory effect on LH secretion.   The mechanisms through which CRF is presently believed to exert this effect are illustrated in Fig. 5.   The possibility that CRF inhibits LH secretion by stimulating opiate activity is supported by functional and anatomical evidence.   In particular, there is immunohistochemical evidence that CRF and β-endorphin neurons or nerve terminals are localized in the same areas of the medial basal hypothalamus and in the median eminence (16).   The mechanisms through which CRF and/or opiates inhibit LH secretion in the rat appear to include a hypothalamic site of action (56).   Indeed, β-endorphin is reported to act directly (57) or via noradrenergic pathways (54) on GnRH production by hypothalamic fragments, while CRF is also known to decrease GnRH levels in the portal vessels (58) and act directly on GnRH production by hypothalamic cells (59).   Finally, the possibility that CRF exerts an effect on GnRH neurons through the stimulation of catecholamine secretion (60.61), [hormones known to inhibit the release of this decapeptide (62)], also deserves consideration.

Modulation of ACTH Secretion During Exposure to Alcohol or Cocaine

We have observed that the acute administration of alcohol (63) or cocaine (64) caused dose-related increases in plasma ACTH and corticosteroid secretion.   Because neither drugs acutely release ACTH from cultured pituitary cells, we examined the possibility that they might depend upon endogenous CRF to activate the corticotrophs.   As reported earlier (63,64), the immunoneutralization of endogenous CRF completely abolished the acute stimulatory action of both alcohol and cocaine, suggesting that indeed an increased CRF secretion represented an essential modulator of the effect of both drugs on ACTH release.   It should be noted, however, that prior exposure of cultured pituitary cells to alcohol caused a marked decrease in the ability of the cells to respond to CRF (65,66).   These results correlate well with our earlier observation that chronic exposure of intact adult rats to alcohol vapors was not accompanied by a significant rise in plasma corticosterone concentrations (63).   Therefore, while acute exposure to alcohol causes a dramatic increase in ACTH release, long-term exposure to alcohol appears to cause some degree of diminished pituitary responsiveness to CRF.

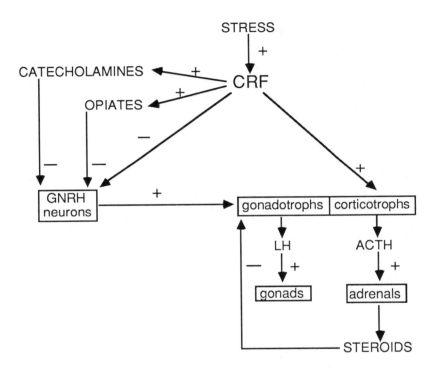

Fig. 5:   Diagram showing the mechanisms through which stress could interfere with LH secretion in the rat.

Because of the hypothesis that alcohol may release endogenous CRF, and because prior exposure to CRF causes pituitary desensitization to this factor (65-67), we examined the effect of administration of alcohol on the subsequent pituitary response to stress.   Indeed, we observed that the infusion of alcohol to intact rats for 3 h significantly blunted the secretion of ACTH induced by a subsequent 10 min exposure to mild electroshocks (68).   The observation that similar results could be obtained in adrenalectomized rats suggested that corticoid feedback did not represent an important modulator of the blunted pituitary responsiveness induced by alcohol.   On the other hand, we showed that the iv injection of CRF caused markedly smaller rises in the plasma ACTH levels of rats previously infused with alcohol, when compared to control animals. In view of all the above results, we therefore concluded that prolonged exposure to alcohol caused a state of diminished pituitary responsiveness to CRF and to stimuli which depends upon CRF to exert their pituitary effects.

By contrast to the effect of alcohol, prior exposure to cocaine induced increased pituitary sensitivity to CRF (Fig. 6) as well as to stress (Fig. 7). While at the present time, the exact mechanisms mediating this action of cocaine are not established, it may be relevant that the administration of cocaine for 6 days produced a measurable decrease in plasma corticosterone levels (unpublished), which may have altered the normal corticoid feedback signal at the level of the pituitary.

In summary, we have shown that the acute administration of both alcohol and cocaine caused marked increases in the circulating levels of ACTH and corticosteroids. By contrast, results obtained following chronic exposure to these drugs showed that alcohol induced decreased pituitary responsiveness to CRF, while cocaine caused increased sensitivity to this secretagogue.

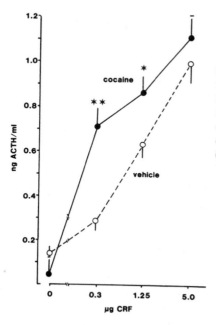

Fig. 6: Effect of the administration of cocaine (2 mg/kg/h) for 6 days on CRF-induced secretion by intact male rats. Each point represents the mean $\pm$ SEM of 5 animals. -, P > 0.05 from effect of CRF alone; *, P $\leq$ 0.05; **, P $\leq$ 0.01.

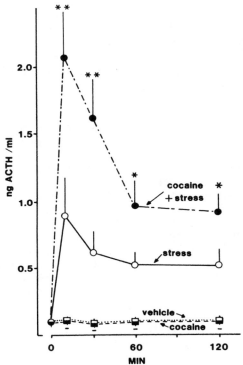

Fig. 7: Effect of the administration of cocaine (2 mg/kg/h) for 6 days on stress-induced (electroshocks: 1.5 mA; 1 sec; 2/min for 10 min) ACTH secretion by intact male rats. Each point represents the mean ± SEM of 5 rats. *, P ≤ 0.05 from effect of stress alone; **, P ≤ 0.01.

ACKNOWLEDGEMENTS

The author thanks Greta Berg, Georgia Morgan, Mary Tam, and David Hutchinson for expert technical help and Bethany Connor for secretarial assistance.

REFERENCES

1. Harris GW (1948). Neural control of the pituitary gland. Physiol Rev 28:139.
2. Rivier J, Rivier C, Spiess J, Vale W (1983). High-performance liquid chromatographic purification of peptide hormones: Ovine hypothalamic amunine (Corticotropin Releasing Factor). Analyt Biochem 127:258.
3. Rivier J, Spiess J, Vale W (1983). Characterization of rat hypothalamic corticotropin-releasing factor. Proc Natl Acad Sci (USA) 80:4851.

4.   Spiess J, Rivier J, Rivier C, Vale W (1981). Primary structure of corticotropin-releasing factor from ovine hypothalamus. Proc Natl Acad Sci (USA) 78:6517.

5.   Vale W, Spiess J, Rivier C, Rivier J (1981). Characterization of a 41 residue ovine hypothalamic peptide that stimulates the secretion of corticotropin and ß-endorphin. Science 213:1394.

6.   De Souza EB, Insel TR, Perrin MH, Rivier J, Vale WW, Kuhar MJ (1985). Corticotropin-releasing factor receptors are widely distributed within the rat central nervous system: An autoradiographic study. J Neurosci 5:3189.

7.   Vale W, Rivier C, Brown M, Plotsky P, Smith M, Bilezikjian L, Bruhn T, Perrin M, Spiess J, Rivier J (1984). Corticotropin-releasing factor. In Black PMcL, Zervas NT, Ridgway EC, Martin JB (eds): "Secretory Tumors of the Pituitary Gland," New York: Raven Press, p. 213.

8.   Vale W, Rivier C, Brown MR, Spiess J, Koob G, Swanson L, Bilezikjian L, Bloom F, Rivier J (1983). Chemical and biological characterization of corticotropin releasing factor. Proc. Laurentian 1982 Hormone Conference, In Greep RO (ed): "Recent Progress in Hormone Research," New York: Academic Press, Vol. 39, p. 245.

9.   Vale WW, Rivier C, Spiess J, Rivier (1983). Corticotropin releasing factor. In Krieger D, Brownstein M, Martin J (eds): "Brain Peptides," New York: John Wiley and Sons, p. 961.

10.   Rivier C, Brownstein M, Spiess J, Rivier J, Vale W (1982). *In vivo* CRF-induced secretion of ACTH, ß-endorphin and corticosterone. Endocrinology 110:272.

11.   Plotsky PM (1985). Hypophysiotropic Regulation of Adenohypophysial ACTH Secretion. Proc. Kroc Foundation Conference on CRF. In Federation Proceedings 44:207.

12.   Plotsky PM (1987). Regulation of hypophysiotropic factors mediating ACTH secretion. In Annals of the New York Academy of Sciences 512:205.

13.   Plotsky PM (1988). Hypophysiotropic regulation of stress-induced ACTH secretion. Proc. of Conf. on Mechanisms of Physical and Emotional Stress. In Chrousos GP (ed): "Advances in Experimental Biology and Medicine," New York: Plenum Publishing Corp., in press.

14.   Rivier CL, Plotsky PM (1986). Mediation by corticotropin-releasing factor (CRF) of adenohypophysial hormone secretion. In Annual Review of Physiology 48:475.22 .

15.   Swanson LW (1988). The Hypothalamus. In Hokfelt T, Bjorklund A, Swanson LW (eds): "Handbook of Chemical Neuroanatomy," Amsterdam: Elsevier, p. 1.

16.   Swanson LW, Sawchenko PE, Rivier J, Vale WW (1983). Organization of ovine corticotropin releasing factor (CRF)-immunoactive cells and fibers in the rat brain: An immunohistochemical study.   Neuroendocrinology 36:165.

17.   Vernikos-Danellis J, Heybach JP (1980). Psychophysiologic mechanisms regulating the hypothalamic-pituitary-adrenal response to stress.   Selye H (ed): "Selye's Guide to Stress Research," New York, Van Nostrand Reinhold Co., p. 206.

18.   Gibbs DM (1985).   Inhibition of corticotropin release during hypothermia: the role of corticotropin-releasing factor, vasopressin, and oxytocin.   Endocrinology 116:723.

19.   Plotsky PM, Bruhn TO, Vale W (1985).   Evidence for multifactor regulation of the adrenocorticotropin secretory response to hemodynamic stimuli. Endocrinology 116:633.

20.   Rivier C, Rivier J, Mormede P, Vale W (1984). Studies of the nature of the interaction between vasopressin and corticotropin-releasing factor on adrenocorticotropin (ACTH) release in the rat. Endocrinology 115:882.

21.   Rivier C, Vale W (1983). Interaction of corticotropin-releasing factor (CRF) and arginine vasopressin (AVP) on ACTH secretion *in vivo*. Endocrinology 113:939.

22.   Rivier C, Rivier J, Vale W (1982). Inhibition of adrenocorticotropic hormone secretion in the rat by immunoneutralization of corticotropin-releasing factor (CRF). Science 218:377.

23.   Rivier C, Vale W (1983). Modulation of stress-induced ACTH release by corticotropin-releasing factor, catecholamines and vasopressin.   Nature 305:325.

24.   Rivier J, Rivier C, Vale W (1984). Synthetic competitive antagonists of corticotropin releasing factor: Effect on ACTH secretion in the rat. Science 224:889.

25.   Conte-Devolx B, Rey M, Boudouresque F, Giraud P, Castanas E, Millet Y, Codaccioni JL, Oliver C (1983).   Effect of 41-CRF antiserum on the secretion of ACTH, β-endorphin and α-MSH in the rat.   Peptides 4:301.

26.   Dallman MF, Makara GB, Roberts, JL, Levin N, Blum M (1985).   Corticotrope response to removal of releasing factors and corticosteroids *in vivo*.   Endocrinology 117:2190.

27.   Giuffre KA, Udelsman R, Listwak S, Chrousos GP (1988). Effects of immune neutralization of corticotropin-releasing hormone, adrenocorticotropin, and β-endorphin in the surgically stressed rat.   Endocrinology 122:306.

28.   Linton EA, Tilders FJH, Hodgkinson S, Berkenbosch F, Vermes I, Lowry PJ (1985). Stress-induced secretion of adrenocorticotropin in rats is inhibited by administration of antisera to ovine corticotropin-releasing factor and vasopressin. Endocrinology 116:966.

29.   Ono N, Samson WK, McDonald JK, Lumpkin MD, Bedran DeCastro JC, McCann SM (1985). Effects of intravenous and intraventricular injection of antisera directed against corticotropin-releasing factor on the secretion of anterior pituitary hormones. Proc Natl Acad Sci USA 82:7787.

30.   Nakane T, Audhya T, Kanie N, Hollander CS (1985). Evidence for a role of endogenous corticotropin-releasing factor in cold, ether, immobilization, and traumatic stress. Proc Natl Acad Sci USA 82:1247.

31.   Plotsky PM, Vale W (1984). Hemorrhage-induced secretion of corticotropin-releasing factor-like immunoreactivity into the rat hypophysial portal circulation and its inhibition by glucocorticoids. Endocrinology 114:164.

32.   Gibbs DM, Vale W (1982). Presence of corticotropin releasing factor-like immunoreactivity in hypophysial portal blood. Endocrinology 111:1418.

33.   Plotsky PM, Bruhn TO, Vale W (1985). Hypophysiotropic regulation of adrenocorticotropin secretion in response to insulin-induced hypoglycemia. Endocrinology 117:323.

34.   Rivier C, Smith M, Vale W (1988). Regulation of ACTH secretion by corticotropin-releasing factor (CRF). In De Souza E, Nemeroff CB (eds): "Corticotropin-releasing factor: Basic and Clinical Studies of a Neuropeptide," Boca Raton, FL: CRC Press, Inc., in press.

35.   Rivier C, Vale W (1985). Effects of CRF, Neurohypophysial Peptides and Catecholamines on Pituitary Function. Proc. Kroc Foundation Conference on CRF. In Federation Proceedings 44:189.

36.   Tilders FJH, Berkenbosch F, Smelik PG (1985). Control of secretion of peptides related to adrenocorticotropin, melanocyte-stimulating hormone and endorphin. Front Horm Res 14:161.

37.   Antoni FA (1986). Hypothalamic control of adrenocorticotropin secretion: advances since the discovery of 41-residue corticotropin-releasing factor. Endocrine Rev 7:351.

38.   Rivier C, Vale W (1985). Neuroendocrine interaction between CRF and vasopressin on ACTH secretion in the rat. In Schrier RW (ed): "Vasopressin," New York: Raven Press, p. 181.

39.   Buckingham   JC   (1987).   Vasopressin   receptors
       influencing   the   secretion   of   ACTH   by   the   rat
       adenohypophysis.   J Endocrinol 133:389.
40.   Mormede P (1983).   The vasopressin receptor antagonist
       dPTyr(Me)AVP does not prevent stress-induced ACTH and
       corticosterone release. Nature 302:345.
41.   Mormede P, LeMoal M, Dantzer R (1985).   Analysis of the
       dual mechanism of ACTH release by arginine vasopressin
       and its analogs in conscious rats. Reg Pep 12:175.
42.   Manning M, Sawyer WH (1984).   Design and uses of
       selective   agonistic   and   antagonistic   analogs   of   the
       neuropeptidees   oxytocin   and   vasopressin.   Trends   in
       Neurosci 7:6.
43.   Rivier C, Rivier J, Vale W (1986). Stress-induced inhibition
       of   reproductive   functions: Role   of   endogenous
       corticotropin-releasing   factor.   Science   231:607.
44.   Rossier J, French ED, Rivier C, Ling N, Guillemin R, Bloom
       FE   (1977).   Foot-shock   induced   stress   increases β-
       endorphin levels in brain. Nature 270:618.
45.   Rivier   C,   Vale   W   (1985).   Effect   of   the   long-term
       administration   of   corticotropin   releasing   factor   on   the
       pituitary-adrenal   and   pituitary-gonadal   axis   in   the   male
       rat. J Clin Invest 75:689.
46.   Rivier   C,   Vale   W   (1984).   Influence   of   corticotropin-
       releasing   factor   (CRF)   on   reproductive   functions   in   the
       rat. Endocrinology 114:914.
47.   Almeida OFX, Nikolarakis KE, Herz A (1988).   Evidence for
       the involvement of endogenous opioids in the inhibition
       of luteinizing hormone by corticotropin-releasing factor.
       Endocrinology 122:1034.
48.   Cicero TJ, Schmoeker PF, Meyer ER, Miller BT, Bell RD,
       Cytron SM, Brown CC (1986).   Ontogeny of the opioid-
       mediated control of reproductive endocrinology in the
       male and female rat.   J Pharm Exper Therapeutics 236:627.
49.   Drouva SV, Epelbaum J, Tapia-Arancibia L, Laplante E,
       Kordon C (1981).   Opiate receptors modulate LHRH and
       SRIF release from mediobasal hypothalamic neurons.
       Neuroendocrinology 32:163.
50.   Forman LH, Sonntag WE, Meites J (1983).   Elevation of
       plasma LH in response to systemic injection of β-
       endorphin antiserum in adult male rats. Proc Soc Exp Biol
       Med 173:14.
51.   Gindoff PR, Ferin M (1987).   Endogenous opioid peptides
       modulate the effect of corticotropin-releasing factor on
       gonadotropin   release   in   the   primate.   Endocrinology
       121:837.

52.   Kalra SP, Kalra PS (1984). Opioid-adrenergic-steroid connection in regulation of luteinizing hormone secretion in the rat. Neuroendocrinology 38:418.

53.   Leadem CA, Kalra SP (1985). Effects of endogenous opioid peptides and opiates on luteinizing hormone and prolactin secretion in ovariectomized rats. Neuroendocrinology 41:342.

54.   Parvizi N, Ellendorff F (1980). β-endorphin alters luteinizing hormone secretion via the amygdala but not the hypothalamus. Nature 286:812.

55.   Petraglia F, Vale W, Rivier C (1986). Opioids act centrally to modulate stress-induced decrease in luteinizing hormone in the rat. Endocrinology 119:2445.

56.   Sirinathsinghji DJS, Whittington PE, Audsley A, Fraser HM (1982). β-endorphin regulates lordosis in female rats by modulating LHRH release. Nature 301:62.

57.   Rasmussen DD, Liu JH, Wolf PL, Yen SSC (1983). Endogenous opioid regulation of gonadotropin-releasing hormone release from the human fetal hypothalamus *in vitro*. J Clin Endocrinol Metab 57:881.

58.   Petraglia F, Sutton S, Vale W, Plotsky P (1987). Corticotropin-releasing factor decreases plasma luteinizing hormone levels in female rats by inhibiting gonadotropin-releasing hormone release into hypophysial-portal circulation. Endocrinology 120:1083.

59.   Gambacciani M, Yen SSC, Rasmussen DD (1986). GnRH release from the mediobasal hypothalamus: *in vitro* inhibition by corticotropin-releasing factor. Neuroendocrinology 43:533.

60.   Brown MR, Fisher LA, Rivier J, Spiess J, Rivier C, Vale W (1981). Corticotropin-releasing factor: effects on the sympathetic nervous system and oxygen consumption. Life Sci 30:207.

61.   Brown MR, Fisher LA, Spiess J, Rivier C, Rivier J, Vale W (1982). Corticotropin-releasing factor (CRF): actions on the sympathetic nervous system and metabolism. Endocrinology 111:928.

62.   McCann SM, Kalra PS, Kalra SP, Donoso AO, Bishop W, Schneider HPG, Fawcett CP, Krulich L (1972). The role of monoamines in the control of gonadotropin and prolactin secretion. In Saxena, Beling, Gandy (eds): "Gonadotropins," New York: John Wiley, p. 49.

63.   Rivier C, Bruhn T, Vale W (1984). Effect of ethanol on the hypothalamic-pituitary-adrenal axis in the rat: Role of corticotropin-releasing factor (CRF). J Pharmacol Exper Therapeutics 229:127.

64. Rivier C, Vale W (1987). Cocaine stimulates adrenocorticotropin (ACTH) secretion through a corticotropin-releasing factor (CRF)-mediated mechanism. Brain Res 422:403.

65. Reisine T, Hoffman A (1983). Desensitization of corticotropin-releasing factor receptors. Biochem Biophys Res Commun 111:919.

66. Vale W, Vaughan J, Smith M, Yamamoto G, Rivier J, Rivier C (1983). Effects of synthetic ovine CRF, glucocorticoids, catecholamines, neurohypophysial peptides and other substances on cultured corticotropic cells. Endocrinology 113:1121.

67. Rivier C, Vale W (1987). Diminished responsiveness of the hypothalamic-pituitary-adrenal axis of the rat during exposure to prolonged stress: a pituitary-mediated machanism. Endocrinology 121:1320.

68. Rivier C, Vale W (1988). Interaction between ethanol and stress on ACTH and β-endorphin secretion. Alcoholism: Clin Exper Res 12:in press.

Molecular Biology of Stress, pages 49–55

CHANGES IN CRF mRNA LEVELS FOLLOWING ADRENALECTOMY[1]

Rosalie M. Uht[2], Robert C. Thompson[*],
James O. Douglass[*], and Jeffrey F. McKelvy[3]

Department of Neurobiology and Behavior
SUNY at Stony Brook
Stony Brook, New York 11794-5230

[*]Vollum Institute for Advanced Biomedical Research
The Oregon Health Sciences University
Portland, Oregon 97201

ABSTRACT   The time course over which CRF mRNA levels
change following adrenalectomy (ADX) and the reversibility of these changes by corticosterone (CORT)
replacement were evaluated.   Analyses were performed
on rats after 1, 3 and 5 days of treatment.   CRF mRNA
and serum CORT levels were determined for the following
groups: normal, sham ADX + placebo, ADX + placebo, and
ADX + CORT, 25 mg.   CRF mRNA was clearly elevated after
3 and 5 days of ADX and the increase was attenuated by
CORT administration.

INTRODUCTION

Central nervous system regulation of the hypothalamic-
pituitary-adrenal axis involves multiple projection systems,
neuropeptides and other regulatory factors.   As a potent
ACTH secretagogue (1,2), corticotropin-releasing factor
(CRF) plays a major role in this central control.   While CRF
is widely distributed throughout the central nervous system
(3), the neurons which secrete CRF into the portal

[1]This work was supported by NSF grant BNS 84-10024 to
JFM.   RMU is an NIMH predoctoral fellow.
[2]To whom correspondence should be addressed.
[3]Present address: Abbott Laboratories, Abbott Park,
Ill. 60064

circulation, to subsequently regulate anterior pituitary ACTH secretion, are found in the medial parvocellular region of the paraventricular nucleus of the hypothalamus (PVH) (4,5). These neurons are sparsely distributed within this area in the basal state. Following ADX, the number of CRF neurons and the amount of hybridizible CRF mRNA increase (6,7). These are effects reversed by the direct adminis- tration of glucocorticoids to the PVH (8,9). Taken together with the demonstration of glucocorticoid receptor like- immunoreactivity in CRF parvocellular neurons (10,11,12) these data suggest that glucocorticoids exert at least part of their action directly within these CRF neurons of the PVH.

To completely understand the regulation of CRF, detailed analyses of the biosynthetic steps required to produce the mature peptide are necessary. Broadly defined, biosynthesis includes all those events from the initiation of CRF gene transcription to the final post translational modifications resulting in the biologically active peptide. One level of analysis includes the measurement of mRNA pools. Given the marked response of CRF neurons to ADX it is important to define the kinetics of the CRF mRNA level increase after ADX and the reversibility of this increase by glucocorticoid feedback inhibition. To date, the CRF mRNA response to ADX has been evaluated at 7 and 14 days of treatment (7,9,13). In this study, hypothalamic CRF mRNA was analyzed from rats which had been treated for 1,3 and 5 days. In addition, serum CORT levels were monitored to correlate the CRF mRNA levels of these animals with their endocrine status.

METHODS

Male Sprague/Dawley rats, 151-175 g (Taconic Farms) were studied in four groups: normal, sham ADX + placebo, ADX + placebo and ADX + CORT, 25 mg pellets (Innovative Research), s.c., implanted at the time of surgery. Animals were sacrificed at 1, 3 and 5 days after treatment and trunk blood was collected for serum CORT level measurement by a modified commercial RIA (ICN). Animals were sacrificed in the evening, at the diurnal peak of serum CORT, to permit clear differentiation between the serum CORT levels of sham ADX and ADX rats. Hypothalamic blocks were dissected using the following landmarks as points of incision: anterior, the optic chiasm; posterior, the caudal aspect of the median eminence; lateral, the hypothalamic sulci; and dorsal, just ventral to the anterior commisure. The hypothalamic blocks were frozen immediately on dry ice and stored at -70°C prior to RNA isolation.

Total RNA was isolated from individual hypothalami using a modification of Chirgwin's guanidinium thiocyanate/ cesium chloride method (14). Total RNA from each rat was denatured with glyoxal, separated by agarose gel electro- phoresis and transfered to a nylon membrane with an electroblotting apparatus. RNA was hybridized to a random primed, ^{32}P-labeled DNA probe generated from a 760 base pair Bam HI restriction fragment from the second exon of the rat CRF gene (15). After autoradiography, blots were stripped and then reprobed with v-Ha-ras (clone gift of Thomas Roberts) to correct for the amount of RNA added per lane. Autoradiographs were quantitated using an LKB Ultroscan XL densitometer with a program for two-dimensional densitometric analysis.

RESULTS

Serum Corticosterone Measurements

In administering CORT replacement, doses which achieved serum CORT values less than one half of the diurnal peak were selected. Higher levels have been shown to cause weight loss and thymic involution (16). As seen below (Table 1), 25 mg pellets administered subcutaneously resulted in initially high levels which tapered to desired levels by 3 days of administration.

TABLE 1
SERUM CORT (ng/ml)

Group	Days of Treatment		
	1	3	5
Normal	169 ± 11 (5)	214 ± 26 (5)	213 ± 28 (5)
Sham ADX	172 ± 18 (4)	184 ± 21 (6)	200 ± 40 (6)
ADX	ND (6)	ND (6)	ND (6)
Replaced	111 ± 8 (4)	70 ± 4 (6)	44 ± 2 (5)

Numbers = mean ± SEM, the numbers in parentheses = the n. Replaced: ADX + 25 mg CORT. ND = below the sensitivity of the assay (< 5.0 ng/ml).

CRF mRNA analysis

For all groups at all time points evaluated, CRF mRNA migrates as a single 1.4 kb species. CRF mRNA is elevated by 3 days of treatment (Figure 1) and remains elevated at 5 days. At both time points, the increase is attenuated by the administration of CORT. Quantitation indicates that at 3 days, CRF RNA from ADX + placebo animals is 2.3 fold and at 5 days 3.2 fold that of sham ADX rats from the same time points. The replaced rats exhibited CRF mRNA levels of 0.6 and 1.6 fold that of the sham ADX rats at 3 and 5 days, respectively.

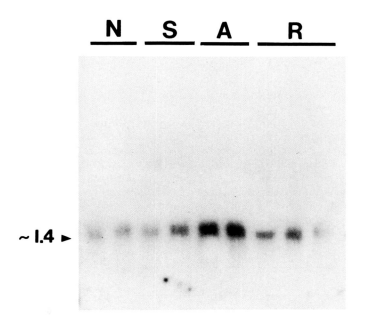

FIGURE 1.   CRF mRNA after three days of treatment. (N) normal, (S) sham ADX + placebo, (A) ADX + placebo, (R) replaced: ADX + 25 mg CORT pellets.

DISCUSSION

The response of CRF mRNA and serum corticosterone levels to ADX were followed over time. Measurement of CRF mRNA levels revealed a clear increase by 3 days of treatment which was maintained through 5 days. The administration of CORT pellets at the time of surgery attenuated the CRF mRNA increase at both time points. Under these conditions, serum CORT levels were less than 50% of the observed evening peak values and were therefore below toxic levels. Previously, Jingami et al. demonstrated a 152% increase in CRF RNA after one week of ADX by Northern analysis (13). Subsequent in situ hybridization studies at 7 days revealed an approximate two fold increase in the parvocellular regions of the PVH (7). Quantitative analyses of the data presented here indicates that the increase in hypothalamic CRF mRNA from ranges from 2-3 fold. These values are in reasonable agreement with those from Young's in situ hybridization study, given the difference in techniques.

The data presented above indicate that the effect of corticosterone withdrawal on CRF mRNA levels is detectable by 3 days of adrenalectomy. Furthermore, preliminary data indicate that CRF mRNA is increased after one day of ADX. At these early time points there are less likely to be secondary effects of ADX which might influence CRF mRNA levels as compared to 7 days of ADX, the earliest time point previously studied (7,9,13). These data are consistent, then, with a rapid and specific modulation of CRF mRNA levels by glucocorticoids.

While systemic corticosterone appears to regulate CRF mRNA levels, perhaps at the level of transcription or mRNA stabilization, the mechanism of action is incompletely understood. Systemic administration of corticosterone to ADX rats attenuates the increase in CRF mRNA levels and results in translocation of glucocorticoid receptor like-immunoreactivity from the cytoplasm to the nucleus in parvocellular neurons (11,12). In addition, glucocorticoid receptor like-immunoreactivity has been localized to CRF parvocellular neurons (10,11,12). Direct administration of dexamethasone to the paraventricular nucleus reverses the observed increase in the degree of CRF mRNA hybridization by in situ analysis. However, this effect is not observed with corticosterone (9). Therefore, the extent to which glucocorticoids exert their effect via interneurons or other projection systems in concert with a direct effect within

CRF parvocellular neurons remains to be determined.

ACKNOWLEDGEMENTS

The authors would like to thank Diane Godden for preparation of the manuscript.

REFERENCES

1. Vale W, Spiess J, Rivier C, Rivier J (1981). Characterization of a 41-residue ovine hypothalamic peptide that stimulates secretion of corticotropin and B-endorphin. Science 213:1394.
2. Rivier C, Vale W (1983). Modulation of stress-induced ACTH release by corticotropin-releasing factor, catecholamines and vasopressin. Nature 305:325.
3. Swanson LW, Sawchenko PE, Rivier J, Vale WW (1983). Organization of ovine corticotropin-releasing factor immunoreactive cells and fibers in the rat brain: an immunohistochemical study. Neuroendocrinology 36:165.
4. Merchenthaler I, Vigh S, Petrusz P, Schally AV (1983). The paraventriculo-infundibular corticotropin releasing factor (CRF) pathway as revealed by immunocytochemistry in long term hypophysectomized or adrenalectomized rats. Reg Peptides 5:295.
5. Swanson LW (1986). Organization of mammalian neuro-endocrine system. In Bloom FE (ed): "Handbook of physiology," vol IV, sect 1 (The Nervous System), Bethesda: American Physiological Society, p 317.
6. Sawchenko PE, Swanson LW, Vale WW (1984). Co-expression of corticotropin-releasing factor and vasopressin immunoreactivity in parvocellular neurocesretory neurons of the adrenalectomized rat. Proc Natl Acad Sci USA 81:1883.
7. Young III WS, Mezey E, Siegel RE (1986). Quantitative in situ hybridization histochemistry reveals increased levels of corticotropin-releasing factor mRNA after adrenalectomy in rats. Neurosci Letts 70:198.
8. Kovacs K, Kiss JZ, Makara GB (1986). Glucocorticoid implants around the hypothalamic paraventricular nucleus prevent the increase of corticotropin-releasing factor and arginine vasopressin immunostaining induced by adrenalectomy. Neuroendocrinology 44:229.

9. Kovacs KJ, Mezey E (1987). Dexamethasone inhibits corticotropin-releasing factor gene expression in the rat paraventricular nucleus. Neuroendocrinology 46:365.

10. Cintra A, Fuxe K, Harfstrand A, Agnati LF, Wikstrom A-C, Okret S, Vale W, Gustafsson J-A (1987). Presence of glucocorticoid receptor immunoreactivity in cortico-trophin releasing factor and in growth hormone releasing factor immunoreactive neurons of the rat di- and telencephalon. Neurosci Letts 77:25.

11. Liposits Zs, Uht RM, Harrison RW, Gibbs FP, Paull WK, Bohn MC (1987). Ultrastructural localization of gluco-corticoid receptor (GR) in hypothalamic paraventricular neurons synthesizing corticotropin releasing factor (CRF). Histochemistry 87:407.

12. Uht RM, McKelvy JF, Harrison RW, Bohn MC (1988). Demonstration of glucocorticoid receptor like immuno-reactivity in glucocorticoid sensitive vasopressin and corticotropin-releasing factor neurons in the hypo-thalamic paraventricular nucleus. J Neurosci Research 19:405.

13. Jingami H, Matsukura S, Numa S, Imura H (1985). Effects of adrenalectomy and dexamethasone administra-tion on the level of prepro-corticotropin-releasing factor messenger ribonucleic acid (mNRA) in the hypo-thalamus and adrenocorticotropin/B-lipotropin precursor mRNA in the pituitary in rats. Endocrinology 117:1314.

14. Chirgwin JM, Przybyla AE, MacDonald RJ, Rutter WJ (1979). Isolation of biologically active ribonucleic acid from sources enriched in ribonuclease. Biochemistry 18:5294.

15. Thompson RC, Seasholtz AF, Herbert E (1987). Rat corticotropin-releasing hormone gene: sequence and tissue-specific expression. Molec Endocrinology 1:363.

16. Akana SF, Cascio CS, Du J-Z, Levin N, Dallman MF (1986). Reset of feedback in the adrenocortical system: an apparent shift in sensitivity of adrenocorticotropin to inhibition by corticosterone between morning and evening. Endocrinology 119:2325.

Molecular Biology of Stress, pages 57–66
© 1989 Alan R. Liss, Inc.

NOREPINEPHRINE-STIMULATED CRF RELEASE MEDIATES STRESS-INDUCED CHANGES IN EXPLORATORY BEHAVIOR

Craig W. Berridge and Adrian J. Dunn

Department of Neuroscience, University of Florida
Gainesville, Florida 32610

ABSTRACT Exploratory behavior, as measured by the
time an animal spends investigating objects in a novel
environment has been shown to be sensitive to prior
exposure of the animal to stress. Using this
paradigm, the involvement of norepinephrine and CRF in
regulating stress-induced behavioral responding was
examined. Treatments that mimicked or stimulated the
the actions of endogenous CRF or norepinephrine
elicited a stress-like response in that the time spent
investigating novel objects was decreased. Further,
the effect of restraint stress on this response could
be reversed by treatments that inhibit the actions of
either CRF or norepinephrine. Inhibition of
noradrenergic activity did not alter the CRF-induced
decrease in exploratory behavior, whereas a CRF-
antagonist did reverse a noradrenegic agonist-induced
decrease in this behavior. These results suggest that
during stress there is an activation of noradrenergic
neurons which stimulates the release of CRF, which in
turn alters the behavioral response.

INTRODUCTION

The time spent investigating novel stimuli in a
complex multicompartment chamber (MCC) has been shown to be
a useful index of exploratory behavior (1). Measured in
this way, exposure of rats (1) or mice (2) to various
stressors such as restraint, tail pinch or high intensity
white noise has been shown to decrease exploratory behavior
in the absence of significant effects on locomotor activity.

Experimental evidence suggests that both norepinephrine (NE) and corticotropin-releasing factor (CRF) are
involved in regulating behavioral responding in stress. CRF
released from the hypothalamus is a potent activator of the
pituitary-adrenal system, stimulating the release of
adrenocorticotropic hormone (ACTH) from the pituitary, a
major peripheral response in stress. However, CRF (3) and
high affinity binding sites for CRF (4) have been found
throughout the central nervous system. Further, when
injected directly into the brain, CRF elicits a number of
stress-like responses (2,5,6). Noradrenergic systems are
also activated in stress (7,8,9) and NE has been implicated
in regulating behavioral responding associated with stress
and anxiety in humans, non-human primates and rodents
(10,11,12). Therefore, we examined the involvement of CRF
and NE in regulating the stressor-induced decrease in
exploratory behavior observed in the MCC.

METHODS

The testing chamber (38x38x23 cm) used in these
studies consisted of 9-interconnecting compartments within
each of which a wire mesh stimulus (3.0 cm sphere) was
recessed in a 2.5 cm hole below the floor. During a 30 min
observation period the duration and frequency of the following behaviors were recorded: Measures of contact with the
stimuli: number of contacts; duration of contacts; time per
contact (duration of contacts/number of contacts). Measures
of locomotor activity: compartment entries; rearings.

CRF and alpha-helical CRF_{9-41} (ahCRF) were provided by
Jean Rivier (Salk Institute). CRF was dissolved in saline
containing 10^{-3} M HCl. ahCRF was dissolved in water and
brought to a final concentration of 50% normal saline.
Clonidine, phenylephrine (Sigma) and prazosin (Pfizer) were
dissolved in saline. DSP-4 (Astra) was dissolved in saline
immediately before use. All drugs were administered IP
except for CRF and ahCRF which were given intracerebro-
ventricularly (ICV). Bilateral ICV cannulae were implanted
as previously described (13). ICV injections consisted of a
total volume of 4 µl divided between the cannulae.
Restraint was administered for 40 min as previously
described (2). Statistical analysis was performed using
ANOVA; comparison of individual means was made using
Duncan's multiple range test.

RESULTS

Corticotropin-Releasing Factor and the Stress-Induced
Decrease in Exploratory Behavior

ICV CRF administered 15 min prior to testing elicited
a stress-like response; a decrease in the mean time per
contact with the stimuli without significant effects on
locomotor activity (Fig 1). This effect was dose-dependent
with a minimum dose of 5 ng required to elicit a
statistically significant effect. More definitive evidence
for a role of endogenous CRF in mediating the stress-induced
change in behavior was obtained using the CRF-antagonist,
ahCRF (14). Unrestrained mice received an ICV injection of
either saline or varying doses of ahCRF (5-50 µg) 45 min
prior to testing. Restrained mice received an ICV injection
of either saline or ahCRF 5 min prior to a 40 min period of
restraint. ICV injection of ahCRF produced a dose-dependent
reversal of the restraint-induced decrease in stimulus-
contact time (Fig. 2). Unrestrained animals displayed a
slight but not statistically significant increase in the
stimulus-contact time. No consistent changes in locomotor
activity were observed in ahCRF-treated animals. These
results suggest that endogenous CRF mediates the effect of
stress on behavioral responding to the MCC.

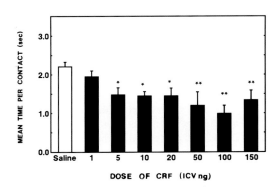

Figure 1. Effect of ICV CRF on the mean time per
contact. Mice were injected ICV with either saline or the
indicated dose of CRF. Bars represent mean ± SEM. [*]$P<0.05$,
[**]$P<0.01$ compared to saline.

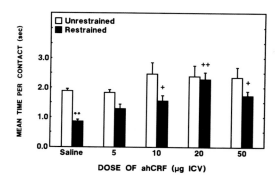

Figure 2. Effect of ahCRF on the restraint-induced decrease in the mean time per contact. Open bars represent unrestrained, and solid bars represent restrained mice. **$P < 0.01$ compared to saline-unrestrained. [+]$P < 0.05$, [++]$P < 0.01$ compared to saline-restrained.

Norepinephrine and the Stress-Induced Decrease in Exploratory Behavior

In a previous study, we had observed that the α_2-antagonist, idazoxan, elicited a stress-like decrease in stimulus-contact time (12). In contrast, the α_2-agonist, clonidine (25 µg/kg) increased the mean time per contact and partially reversed the restraint-induced decrease in the stimulus-contact time. Because α_2-receptors are known to inhibit the activity of noradrenergic neurons, these observations suggest that an increased release of NE is involved in regulating the behavioral response observed in stress. Consistent with these results, depletion of NE in the cortex and hippocampus using the noradrenergic-selective neurotoxin, DSP-4, increased the mean time per contact and inhibited the effect of prior restraint (data not shown).

Because clonidine does not completely block NE release and DSP-4 does not completely deplete NE, these two treatments were combined to produce a more effective inhibition of NE release. Animals were injected with either saline or 50 mg/kg DSP-4 3 days prior to testing. On the day of testing, mice previously injected with saline were injected with saline 45 min before testing or 5 min before being restrained. DSP-4 injected animals were injected with

25 µg/kg clonidine 45 min before testing or 5 min before being restrained. This combined treatment increased the mean time per contact in unrestrained mice and completely abolished the restraint-induced decrease in stimulus-contact time in the absence of significant effects on locomotor activity (Fig. 3).

To characterize the postsynaptic receptor involved in the restraint-induced decrease in exploration, the effect of an α_1-antagonist, prazosin was examined. Unrestrained mice were injected with either saline or varying doses (50-200 µg/kg) of prazosin 45 min prior to testing. Restrained mice were injected with saline or prazosin 5 min prior to restraint. Prazosin significantly increased the mean time per contact in the absence of significant effects on locomotor activity, with a maximal effect observed at 100 µg/kg (Fig. 4). Prazosin reversed the restraint-induced decrease in stimulus interaction in a dose-dependent manner with a complete reversal observed at 200 µg/kg. These results suggest that an α_1-receptor is involved in the effect of restraint on stimulus-contact time. Consistent with this, ICV injection of the α_1-selective agonist, phenylephrine (50 and 100 ng), decreased the mean time per contact (data not shown).

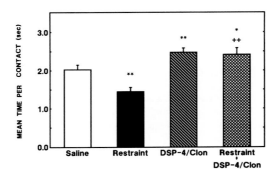

Figure 3. Effect of DSP-4 combined with clonidine on the restraint-induced decrease in the mean time per contact. *P<0.05, **P<0.01 compared to saline-unrestrained. ++P<0.01 compared to saline-restrained.

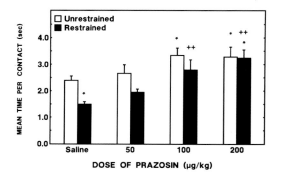

Figure 4. Effect of prazosin on the restraint-induced decrease in the mean time per contact with the stimuli. Open bars represent unrestrained, and solid bars represent restrained mice. $^*P<0.05$ compared to saline-unrestrained. $^{++}P<0.01$ compared to saline-restrained.

NE-CRF Interactions

The above experiments indicate that an increased release of both CRF and NE is involved in regulating the stress-induced change in behavior observed in the MCC. However, it is unclear whether these two systems act independently in parallel, or whether they interact. CRF could stimulate NE release or *vice versa*. Both types of interactions have been observed within the brain (6,15,16,17).

To address this question, one-half of the mice were injected IP with saline and 5 min later received an ICV injection of either saline or 20 ng CRF. The remaining mice were injected IP with prazosin and received an ICV injection of either saline or 20 ng CRF. The mice were observed 10 min following the second injection. Although both CRF and prazosin had their previously observed effects on stimulus-contact time, prazosin had no effect on the CRF-induced decrease in the mean time per contact (Fig. 5). Similarly, DSP-4 administered 3 days prior to testing increased stimulus-contact time in saline-injected animals but did not alter the action of CRF (20 ng) on this behavior (data not shown). Neither DSP-4, prazosin nor CRF significantly affected locomotor activity in these experiments.

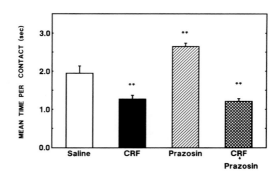

Figure 5. Effect prazosin on the CRF-induced decrease in the mean time per contact with the stimuli. **P<0.01 compared to saline-saline.

Therefore, it appears that CRF does not decrease stimulus-contact times through an activation of NE release because inhibiting noradrenergic activity did not antagonize this effect of CRF.

To test whether NE might stimulate CRF release, one-half the mice were injected ICV with saline 5 min prior to an ICV injection of either saline, 50 or 100 ng phenylephrine. The remaining animals were injected with 20 μg ahCRF 5 min after receiving an injection of either saline or 50 or 100 ng phenylephrine. The animals were tested 10 min following the second injection. As observed previously, phenylephrine decreased the mean time per contact in animals previously injected with saline (Fig. 6). The CRF antagonist tended to increase the mean time per contact in animals receiving saline, but this effect was not statistically significant. ahCRF completely blocked the phenylephrine-induced decrease in the mean time per contact. Neither phenylephrine nor ahCRF significantly affected the number of contacts, rears or compartment entries.

DISCUSSION

Both NE (10,11,12,18,19) and CRF (2,5) have been suggested to regulate behavioral responding in stress and

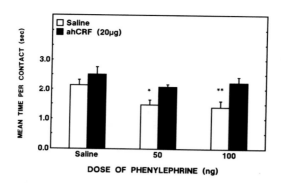

Figure 6. Effect of ICV phenylephrine and ahCRF on
the mean time per contact with the stimuli. *P<0.05,
**P<0.01 compared to saline-saline.

anxiety. Our observations are consistent with these reports
and further suggest that these two systems may interact to
regulate stress-induced behavioral responding. Thus,
stimulation of CRF- or noradrenergic-receptors resulted in a
stress-like behavioral response in the MCC, whereas
antagonists for these receptors blocked the behavioral
effect of restraint-stress. In contrast, inhibition of
noradrenergic systems, using either prazosin or DSP-4 had no
effect on the ICV CRF-induced decrease in stimulus-contact
time. However, the CRF-antagonist, ahCRF, reversed the
phenylephrine-induced decrease in stimulus-contact time.
Thus, these results suggest that NE stimulates the release
of CRF to alter the behavioral response in the MCC.
Further, because there was no additivity between a moderate
dose of CRF and either DSP-4 or prazosin, it is unlikely
that these two systems affect the behavioral response in the
MCC independently. If CRF and NE acted independently, the
combined treatment of CRF and either prazosin or DSP-4
should result in an intermediate response. A similar
noradrenergic-mediated release of CRF has been observed for
CRF release into the portal blood supply (15,16).

These results are contrary to those predicted by the
ability of CRF to stimulate NE release (6), and to increase
the action potential firing rate of the locus coeruleus
(17). However, these stimulatory effects of CRF on
noradrenergic activity were only observed at doses

significantly higher than those needed to elicit a decrease in stimulus-contact time in the MCC. At these higher doses mice display a pronounced hypoactivity and changes in posture. Thus, although both types of interactions may occur, they may regulate different responses.

ACKNOWLEDGEMENTS

We gratefully acknowledge the gift of CRF and ahCRF from Jean Rivier and of prazosin by Pfizer. This research was supported by the National Institute of Mental Health (MH25486 and a fellowship to CWB MH09680)

REFERENCES

1. Arnsten AFT, Berridge C, Segal DS (1985). Stress produces opioid-like effects on investigatory behavior. Pharmacol Biochem Behavior 22:803.
2. Berridge CW, Dunn AJ (1986). Corticotropin-releasing factor elicits naloxone sensitive stress-like alterations in exploratory behavior in mice. Reg Peptides 16:83.
3. Swanson LW, Sawchenko PE, Rivier J, Vale WW (1983). Organization of ovine corticotropin-releasing factor immunoreactive cells and fibers in the rat brain:an immunohistochemical study. Neuroendocrinol 36:165.
4. Wynn PC, Hauger RL, Holmes MC, Millan MA, Catt KJ, Aguilera G (1984). Brain and pituitary receptors for corticotropin releasing factor: localization and differential regulation after adrenalectomy. Peptides 5:1077.
5. Koob GF, Bloom FE (1985). Corticotropin-releasing factor and behavior. Fed Proc 44:259.
6. Dunn AJ, Berridge CW (1987). Corticotropin-releasing factor administration elicits a stress-like activation of cerebral catecholaminergic systems. Pharmacol Biochem Behav 27:685.
7. Stone EA (1975). Stress and catecholamines. In: Friedhoff AJ (ed): "Catecholamines and Behavior. Vol. 2 Neuropsychopharmacology", New York: Plenum Press, p 31.
8. Dunn AJ, Kramarcy NR (1984). Neurochemical responses in stress: relationships between the hypothalamic-pituitary-adrenal and catecholamine systems. In Iversen, LL, Iversen SD, Snyder SH(eds): "Handbook of Psychopharmacology" Vol. 18, New York: Plenum Press, p 455.

9.   Aston-Jones G (1985). Behavioral functions of locus coeruleus derived from cellular attributes. Physiol Psychol 13:118.

10. Charney DS, Heninger GR, Redmond DE (1983). Yohimbine induced anxiety and increased noradrenergic function in humans: effects of diazepam and clonidine. Life Sci 33:19.

11. Harris JC, Newman JD (1987). Mediation of separation distress by α_2-adrenergic mechanisms in a non-human primate. Brain Res 410:353.

12. Berridge CW, Dunn AJ (1987). α_2-Noradrenergic agonists and antagonists alter exploratory behavior in mice. Neurosci Res Comm 1:97.

13. Rivier J, Rivier C, Vale W (1984). Synthetic competitive antagonists of corticotropin-releasing factor: Effects on ACTH secretion in the rat. Science 224:889.

14. Guild AL, Dunn AJ (1982). Dopamine involvement in ACTH-induced grooming behavior. Pharmacol Biochem Behav 17:31.

15. Plotsky PM (1987). Facilitation of immunoreactive corticotropin-releasing factor secretion into the hypophysial-portal circulation after activation of catecholaminergic pathways or central norepinephrine injection. Endocrinol 121:924.

16. Szafarczyk A, Malaval F, Gibaud R, Assenmacher I (1987). Further evidence for a central stimulatory action of catecholamines on adrenocorticotropin release in the rat. Endocrinol. 121:883.

17. Valentino RJ, Foote SL, Aston-Jones G (1983). Corticotropin-releasing factor activates noradrenergic neurons of the locus coeruleus. Brain Res 270:363.

18. Redmond DE, Huang YH (1979). New evidence for a locus coeruleus-norepinephrine connection with anxiety. Life Sci 25:2149.

19. Handley SL, Mithani S (1987). Effects of alpha-adrenoceptor agonists and antagonists in a maze-exploration model of "fear"-motivated behavior. N-S Arch Pharmacol 327:1.

Molecular Biology of Stress, pages 67–76
© 1989 Alan R. Liss, Inc.

CORTICOTROPIN-RELEASING FACTOR: POSSIBLE INVOLVEMENT
IN THE PATHOGENESIS OF AFFECTIVE DISORDERS

Pamela E. Bond, Michael J. Owens, Pamela D. Butler,
Garth Bissette and Charles B. Nemeroff

Departments of Psychiatry and Pharmacology, Duke
University Medical Center, Box 3859, Durham, N.C. 27710

Corticotropin-releasing factor (CRF), a 41 amino acid peptide, has been the subject of intense interest ever since the early demonstration of hypothalamic influence upon anterior pituitary function reported by Saffran and Schally in 1955 (1). However, it was not until 25 years later that Vale and colleagues (2) elucidated the structure of CRF from nearly a half million sheep hypothalami, years after the amino acid sequences of a number of other hypothalamic hormones such as thyrotropin-releasing hormone (TRH) and somatostatin had been accomplished. This delay was largely due to the fact that: 1) CRF's amino acid sequence is considerably larger than most other hypothalamic hormones, (e.g., TRH is a tripeptide); 2) the biological potency of CRF is markedly reduced by deletion of even a small portion of the sequence; and 3) numerous endogenous substances (e.g., vasopressin, oxytocin and epinephrine) also possess CRF-like activity and therefore obscured the identity of the endogenous CRF. Shortly after the characterization of ovine CRF, Rivier (3) reported the sequence of rat CRF, which differs from ovine CRF by only seven amino acids and is identical to human CRF (4,5).

Since its characterization seven years ago, considerable data has been amassed consistent with the view that CRF is the major physiological regulator of ACTH and β-endorphin secretion from the adenohypophysis (6). Consistent with its role as a hypothalamic releasing factor regulating pituitary-adrenal activity, CRF neurons have been localized in the parvocellular region of the paraventricular nucleus (PVN) of the hypothalamus, whose main projection is to the median eminence (ME), the site of the primary plexus of the hypothalamo-hypophyseal portal system (7). Further, both autoradiographic and biochemical studies show high concentrations of CRF binding sites in the anterior and intermediate lobes of the pituitary (8).

Immunohistochemical and radioimmunoassay studies have shown that CRF-like immunoreactivity (CRF-LI) is also found in a number of extrahypothalamic areas. The extrahypothalamic distribution of CRF is compatible with an involvement in stress responses and emotionality because it is found in such forebrain limbic areas as the central and medial nuclei of the amygdala, the bed nucleus of the stria terminalis, substantia inominata, septum, preoptic area, and lateral hypothalamus, and in brainstem nuclei involved in stress responses and regulation of the autonomic nervous system such as the locus coeruleus (LC) the parabrachial nucleus, and the dorsal vagal complex (7,9). Generally, brain areas containing substantial amounts of CRF-LI also have high densities of high affinity CRF binding sites, putative CRF receptors; this high affinity specific binding is time- and temperature-dependent and is coupled to adenylate cyclase (10,11).

Not only is CRF and its receptor found in extrahypothalamic areas, but it fulfills several of the requisite criteria necessary to be considered a central nervous system (CNS) neurotransmitter. For instance, potassium-induced, calcium-dependent release has been demonstrated from slices of hypothalamus, amygdala, midbrain, striatum and cortex (12,13). Electrophysiological studies have revealed that microinfusion of CRF alters the firing rate of CNS neurons in the LC (14), the major noradrenergic cell population that projects to the forebrain, a circuit long implicated in the pathogenesis of both depression and anxiety (15,16). CRF also alters hippocampal neuronal firing rates (17) and produces EEG changes suggestive of increased arousal in the hippocampus and cortex (18,19).

Studies examining the effects of CRF administration into the CNS have shown that it produces behavioral and autonomic effects that are dissociated from its activation of the hypothalamic-pituitary-adrenocortical (HPA) axis and are insensitive to glucocorticoid feedback. Acting at several CNS sites, CRF increases sympathetic nervous system activity as demonstrated by increased plasma concentrations of epinephrine and norepinephrine with concomitant elevations in heart rate, blood pressure, plasma glucagon and glucose concentrations (20). These autonomic changes produced by CRF are accompanied by behavioral changes typical of stress responses. Central administration of CRF in rats in a familiar non-stressful environment produces a dose-dependent increase in locomotion, sniffing, rearing and grooming, consistent with increased behavioral arousal (21). When placed in a novel environment such as an open-field, CRF-treated animals exhibit a marked decrease in exploratory behavior and rearing and accompanying increases in grooming and freezing behavior (22). Tazi et al. (23), reported that intraventricular administration of CRF increased the frequency of stress-induced fighting induced by mild electric footshock, whereas frequency of fighting was decreased with administration of a CRF antagonist. CRF thus appears to increase sensitivity to the stressful or anxiogenic nature of the environment. In addition, like chronic stress, centrally administered CRF causes decreased appetite and decreased sexual behavior (24,25).

To investigate the effects of stress on endogenous CRF, we measured the concentration of CRF-LI in 36 microdissected rat brain regions following exposure to either acute immobilization/cold stress for 3 hours, or chronic exposure to a series of unpredictable stressors for fourteen days (26). There was a 50% decrease in CRF-LI in the ME of both acute and chronically stressed animals as well as a two-fold increase in the concentration of CRF-LI in the LC. Acute stress also decreased CRF-LI in the medial pre-optic area, whereas chronic stress decreased CRF-LI in the dorsal vagal complex but increased it in the periventricular nucleus. All of these brain areas have been implicated in the stress response. The decrease in CRF-LI in the ME is presumably due to the stress-enhanced release of CRF-LI from nerve terminals in the ME into the hypothalamo-hypophysial portal circulation which activates the HPA. It appears that the rate of synthesis of CRF in neurons that project to the ME is unable to keep up with the increased demands for release. The finding that chronic stress decreased CRF-LI in the dorsal vagal complex is consistent with a role for CRF in regulation of the autonomic nervous systems and its response to stress described above. The increased CRF-LI in the LC is of particular interest because CRF increases firing rates in this area and, as mentioned above, the LC contains the cell bodies of NE neurons which project throughout the neuraxis. Thus CRF may modulate the major noradrenergic cell group in the brain, one which has long been implicated in the pathophysiology of stress, anxiety and affective disorders.

Also of interest is the possibility that antidepressant and/or anxiolytic drugs may in part produce their therapeutic effects via interactions with CRF-containing neurons. In a recent study (27), we measured plasma ACTH and regional brain CRF concentrations in imipramine-, alprazolam-, and adinazolam-treated rats killed 1 hour after a single intraperitoneal injection. While other benzodiazepines do not consistently reduce plasma stress hormones, treatment with either of the triazolobenzodiazepines alprazolam or adinazolam, produced significant reductions in plasma ACTH concentrations when compared to either controls or imipramine-treated rats. The reduction in plasma ACTH concentrations by alprazolam has recently been confirmed in humans after parenteral administration. Both the alprazolam- and adinazolam-treated animals exhibited significantly higher hypothalamic concentrations of CRF-LI, indicative of decreased release of CRF into the hypothalamo-hypophyseal portal vessels when compared to vehicle and imipramine-treated rats. Most intriguing, however, was the finding of a large reduction in the concentration of CRF-LI in the LC of both the alprazolam- and adinazolam-treated animals. Acute imipramine treatment did not change CRF-LI concentrations in any of the brain areas studied. Thus, the two triazolobenzodiazepines exert effects on CRF concentrations in the hypothalamus and LC opposite to the effects of stress.

These preclinical findings provided the rationale for our clinical studies examining the role of CRF in affective disorders. As shown in Table 1, the behavioral changes observed in CRF-treated rats are very similar to symptoms seen in patients with major depression. Further, it is well-established that the HPA axis is hyperactive in the majority of patients with depression. Thus CRF hypersecretion in both hypothalamic and extrahypothalamic areas may contribute to both the hypercortisolemia characteristic of the majority of depressed patients, as well as several of the signs and symptoms of depression.

TABLE 1

Similarities Between Signs and Symptoms of Major Depression (DSM III-R Criteria) and the Behavioral Effects of Centrally Administered Corticotropin-Releasing Factor (CRF) in Laboratory Animals.

DSM III-R Major Depression   Effects of CRF
(At least 5 of the following
are present for at least two
weeks)

1. Depressed mood (irritable mood in children and adolescents) most of the day, nearly every day, as indicated either by subjective account or observations by others.

1. Centrally administered CRF in infant rhesus monkeys mimics the behavioral despair syndrome observed after maternal separation.

2. Markedly diminished interest or pleasure in all or almost all activities most of the day, nearly every day.

2. Centrally administered CRF decreases the incidence of sexual behavior in male and female rats.

3. Significant weight loss or weight gain when not dieting or decrease or increase in appetite nearly every day.

3. Centrally administered CRF decreases food consumption in rats.

4. Insomnia or hyposomnia nearly every day.

4. Centrally administered CRF disrupts normal sleep with concomitant EEG changes.

5. Psychomotor agitation or retardation nearly every day.

5. Centrally administered CRF increases locomotor activity in a familiar environment but produces "stress-like" alterations in locomotion in a novel environment.

6. Fatigue or loss of energy nearly every day.

6. NO DATA.

(Continued)

7. Feelings of worthless-   7. NO DATA.
   ness or excessive or
   unappropriate guilt
   nearly every day.

8. Diminished ability to   8. NO DATA.
   think or concentrate, or
   indecisiveness, nearly
   every day.

9. Recurrent thoughts of   9. NO DATA.
   death, recurrent suicidal
   ideation or a suicide
   attempt.

We have carried out several studies showing elevated cerebrospinal fluid (CSF) concentrations of CRF in patients with major depression as compared to patients with schizophrenia, Alzheimer's disease, or normal controls. In our first study, 11 of the 23 depressed patients exhibited higher CSF CRF concentrations than the highest value in the control group (28). In a subsequent study in collaboration with Banki and colleagues (29) (54 depressed patients, 138 controls), we confirmed our earlier findings; CSF CRF concentrations were nearly two-fold that of the control group. While our group has not found a correlation between CSF CRF concentrations and dexamethasone non-suppression, Gold and colleagues (30) have recently found a significant correlation between post-dexamethasone plasma cortisol concentrations and CSF CRF concentrations. Moreover, in their depressed patient population the DST non-suppressors had higher CSF CRF concentrations than the DST suppressors.

If CRF is chronically hypersecreted in depressed patients, there should be a concomitant reduction in the density of CRF binding sites, so-called receptor down-regulation. To examine this hypothesis, we, in collaboration with Stanley and Andorn (31), measured the affinity (K_d) and number (Bmax) of high affinity CRF binding sites in the frontal cortex of suicide victims and compared them to age- and sex-matched controls (Figure 1). A 23% decrease in CRF receptor density in the frontal cortex was present in the suicide group. These findings support the hypothesis that CRF of both hypothalamic and extrahypothalamic origin may be hypersecreted in suicide victims.

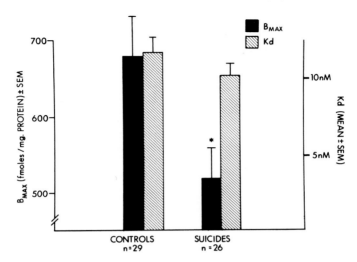

Figure 1. Bmax and K_d of ^{125}I-Tyr^0-oCRF binding sites in frontal cortex in suicide victims and controls. Suicide victims exhibited a 23% decrease (*p = .020 by Student's t-test) in receptor binding.

To determine whether the elevated CSF CRF concentrations represents a trait marker (a genetic predisposition for depression) or a state marker of depression, we measured CSF CRF concentrations before and after a course of six electroshock therapy treatments (ECT). In this pilot study, CSF CRF concentrations were reduced in most patients after the ECT. This indicates that elevated concentrations of CSF CRF in depressed patients may, like hypercortisolemia, represent a state, rather than a trait marker.

Given the available preclinical and clinical findings, CRF remains a strong candidate as a neurotransmitter underlying the pathogenesis of depression, and perhaps anorexia nervosa. To complement our studies, vide supra, investigating changes in CRF concentrations and receptor density in these disorders, we are also using in situ hybridization and Northern analysis to examine changes in CRF gene expression in both laboratory animals and post-mortem tissue from depressed patients.

ACKNOWLEDGEMENTS

We are grateful to Shelia Walker for preparation of this manuscript. Supported by NIMH MH-42088.

REFERENCES

1. Saffran M, Schally AV, Benfey BG (1955). Stimulation of release of corticotropin from adenohypophysis by neurohypophysial factor. Endocrinology 57:439.
2. Vale W, Spiess J, Rivier C, Rivier J (1981). Characterization of a 41-residue ovine hypothalamic peptide that stimulates secretion of corticotropin and β-endorphin. Science 213:1394.
3. Rivier J, Spiess J, Vale W (1983). Characterization of rat hypothalamic corticotropin-releasing factor. Proc Natl Acad Sci USA 80:4851.
4. Furatani Y, Morimoto Y, Shibahara S, Noda M, Takahashi H, Hirose T, Asai M, Inayama S, Hayashida H, Miyata T, Numa S (1983). Cloning and sequence analysis of cDNA for ovine corticotropin-releasing factor precursor. Nature 301:537.
5. Shibahara S, Morimoto Y, Furutani Y, Notake M, Takahashi H, Shimuzu S, Horikawa S, Numa S (1983). Isolation and sequence analysis of the human corticotropin-releasing factor precursor gene. EMBO J 2:775.
6. Rivier J, Rivier C, Vale W (1982). Inhibition of adrenocorticotropic hormone secretion in the rat by immunoneutralization of corticotropin-releasing factor. Science 218:377.
7. Swanson LW, Sawchenko PE, Rivier J, Vale W (1983). Organization of ovine corticotropin-releasing factor immunoreactive cells and fibers in the rat brain: an immunohistochemical study. Neuroendocrinology 36:165.
8. DeSouza EB, Perrin MH, Rivier J, Vale WW, Kuhar MJ (1984). Corticotropin-releasing factor receptors in rat pituitary gland: autoradiographic localization. Brain Res 296:202.
9. Merchenthaler I (1984). Corticotropin releasing factor (CRF)-like immunoreactivity in the rat central nervous system. Extrahypothalamic distribution. Peptides 5:53.
10. DeSouza EB (1987). Corticotropin-releasing factor receptors in the rat central nervous system:

characterization and regional distribution.   J Neurosci
7:88.

11.   DeSouza EB, Insel TR, Perrin MH, Rivier J, Vale WW,
Kuhar MJ (1985).   Corticotropin-releasing factor
receptors are widely distributed within the rat central
nervous system: an autoradiographic study.   J Neurosci
5:3189.

12.   Smith MA, Bissette G, Slotkin TA, Knight DL, Nemeroff
CB (1986).   Release of corticotropin-releasing factor
from rat brain regions in vitro.   Endocrinology
118:1997.

13.   Owens MJ, Maynor B, Nemeroff CB (1987).   Release of
corticotropin-releasing factor (CRF) from rat
prefrontal cortex in vitro.   Soc Neurosci Abst 13:1110.

14.   Valentino RJ, Foote SL, Aston-Jones G (1983).
Corticotropin-releasing factor activates noradrenergic
neurons of the locus coeruleus.   Brain Res 270:363.

15.   Redmond DE Jr., Huang YW (1979).   Current concepts II.
New evidence for a locus coeruleus-norepinephrine
connection with anxiety.   Life Sci 25:2149.

16.   Svensson TH (1987).   Peripheral, autonomic regulation
of locus coeruleus noradrenergic neurons in brain:
putative implications for psychiatry and
psychopharmacology.   Psychopharmacology 92:1.

17.   Aldenhoff JB, Giuol PL, Rivier J, Vale W, Siggins GR
(1983).   Corticotropin-releasing factor decreases
postburst hyperpolarizations and excites hippocampal
neurons.   Science 221:875.

18.   Ehlers CL, Henriksen SJ, Wang M, Rivier J, Vale W,
Bloom FE (1983).   Corticotropin releasing factor
produces increases in brain excitability and convulsive
seizures in rats.   Brain Res 278:332.

19.   Marrosu F, Mereu G, Fratta W, Carcangiu P, Camarri F,
Gessa GL (1987).   Different epileptogenic activities of
murine and ovine corticotropin-releasing factor.   Brain
Res 408:394.

20.   Brown MR, Fisher LA (1985).   Corticotropin-releasing
factor: effect on the autonomic nervous system and
visceral systems.   Fed Proc 44:243.

21.   Sutton RE, Koob GF, LeMoal M, Rivier J, Vale W (1982).
Corticotropin releasing factor produces behavioral
activation in rats.   Nature 297:331.

22.   Britton DR, Koob GF, Rivier J, Vale W (1982).
Intraventricular corticotropin-releasing factor
enhances behavioral effects of novelty.   Life Sci
31:363.

23. Tazi A, Bantzer R, LeMoal M, Rivier J, Vale W, Koob GF (1987). Corticotropin-releasing factor antagonist blocks stress-induced fighting in rats. Reg Peptides 18:37.

24. Morley JH, Levine AS (1982). Corticotrophin releasing factor, grooming and ingestive behavior. Life Sci 31:1459.

25. Sirinathsinghji DJS, Rees LH, Rivier J, Vale W (1983). Corticotropin-releasing factor is a potent inhibitor of sexual receptivity in the female rat. Nature 305:232.

26. Chappell PB, Smith MA, Kilts CD, Bissette G, Ritchie J, Anderson C, Nemeroff CB (1986). Alterations in corticotropin-releasing factor-like immunoreactivity in discrete brain regions after acute and chronic stress. J Neurosci 6:2908.

27. Owens MJ, Bissette G, Lundberg D, Nemeroff CB (1987). Acute effects of antidepressant and anxiolytic drugs on CRF-LI in microdissected rat brain regions. Proc 26th Ann Meeting of the Amer College of Neuropsychopharmacology 167.

28. Nemeroff CB, Widerlov E, Bissette G, Walleus H, Karlsson I, Eklund K, Kilts CD, Loosen PT, Vale W (1984). Elevated concentrations of CSF corticotropin-releasing factor-like immunoreactivity in depressed patients. Science 226:1342.

29. Banki CM, Bissette G, Arato M, O'Connor L, Nemeroff CB (1987). Cerebrospinal fluid corticotropin-releasing factor-like immunoreactivity in depression and schizophrenia. Am J Psychiatry 144:873.

30. Roy A, Pickar D, Paul S, Doran A, Chrousos GP, Gold PW (1987). CSF corticotropin-releasing hormone in depressed patients and normal control subjects. Am J Psychiatry 144:641.

31. Nemeroff CB, Owens MJ, Bissette G, Andorn AC, Stanley M (1988). Reduced corticotropin-releasing factor (CRF) binding sites in the frontal cortex of suicides. Arch Gen Psychiatry 45:577.

Molecular Biology of Stress, pages 77–86
© **1989 Alan R. Liss, Inc.**

OPIOIDS, STRESS, AND THE DEVELOPING BRAIN

Ian S. Zagon and Patricia McLaughlin

Department of Anatomy, Pennsylvania State University College
of Medicine, M.S. Hershey Medical Center, Hershey, PA, 17033

ABSTRACT   The use of opioid antagonist and agonist
paradigms has revealed that endogenous opioid systems
(i.e., endogenous opioids and opioid receptors)
modulate growth.   One of the targets for this
regulation is cell proliferation.   Experiments
demonstrate that methionine enkephalin is a prototypic
opioid involved with growth processes.   Preliminary
binding studies show a distinct and novel opioid
receptor related to developmental events.

INTRODUCTION

Perinatal exposure to exogenous opioid agonists such
as methadone, morphine, and heroin is known to alter the
growth of the developing organism (1,2).   In vitro
experiments using cultured cells and exogenous opioids
concur with this finding (3,4).   In vivo and in vitro
investigations demonstrated that opioid-induced growth
alterations can be blocked by concomitant exposure to an
opioid antagonist such as naloxone (3-6), suggesting that
opioid-receptor interactions underlie the influence of
exogenous opioids on development.   Unfortunately, a host of
confounding variables (e.g., lack of prenatal/postnatal
care, malnutrition) makes it difficult to establish the
etiology of the perinatal opioid syndrome (7).   No doubt
that exposure to exogenous opioids, not to mention
withdrawal from these drugs, is stressful to the organism.
It is well-known that a clear association exists between
stressful conditions and the release of opioid peptides (8-
10).   Given that the opioid receptor mediates the growth

altering properties of exogenous opioids, and that opioid peptides are released during exposure/withdrawal, it is intriguing to inquire whether endogenous opioid peptides are involved with growth.

There are at least two basic experimental paradigms that can be used to examine the role of endogenous opioids in growth. The first approach takes advantage of compounds that are antagonistic to opioid action, and disrupt opioid-receptor interaction. These compounds include naloxone, a short-acting antagonist, and naltrexone, a more potent and longer-acting drug. The second approach utilizes endogenous opioids. However, the instability of these peptides in vivo, not to mention the expense, make these compounds less desirable for investigation. An important consideration in studies with opioid antagonists or agonists relates to interpretation as to whether a direct drug effect is being observed, or if one is witnessing the repercussion of drug activity (11). Thus, action and reaction to agonists and antagonists must always be considered.

In an initial series of studies, naltrexone was used to interrupt endogenous opioid-opioid receptor interactions in the developing rat. Preweaning development in the rat (birth to day 21) is characterized by extraordinary body and brain growth, and serves as a good model to examine the influence of various agents on developmental events. Utilizing chronic (daily) subcutaneous injections of naltrexone ranging from 0.1 to 50 mg/kg (dosages that were 2.5% or less of the LD_{50}), a dosage dependent effect on somatic and neurobiological development was noted. Dosages of 10 mg/kg and less inhibited growth, whereas dosages of 20 mg/kg and greater enhanced growth. Subsequent experiments that closely examined the relationship between growth, drug dosage, and the pharmacological properties of naltrexone revealed that the duration of opioid receptor blockade determined the course of body and brain growth (12). It appeared that short daily (intermittent) exposures to opioid antagonists retarded growth, whereas continuous opioid receptor blockade (either by a single daily injection of a "high" dosage of naltrexone, or repeated daily injections of a "lower" dosage) accelerated growth. Further exploration with the stereoisomers of naloxone showed that opioid antagonist action was distinctly at the level of the opioid receptor. In contrast to the alteration in growth produced by chronic daily injection of (-) naloxone, (+) naloxone had no effect on growth (Zagon and McLaughlin, in preparation).

In view of the changes in body and brain development induced by perturbing endogenous opioid-opioid receptor interfacing, the question arose as to whether endogenous opioid systems (i.e., opioids and receptors) play a role in the appearance of physical characteristics and neurobehavioral ontogeny. To address this question, detailed examination of preweaning rats given either 1 or 50 mg/kg naltrexone, which produced an intermittent and continuous receptor blockade, respectively, was conducted (12,13). Animals given 50 mg/kg naltrexone exhibited a significantly earlier appearance of eye opening, whereas the 1 mg/kg group showed a delay in eye and ear opening. The patterns for spontaneous motor and sensorimotor behaviors were similar. For example, measurement of the appearance of walking, a behavioral milestone, revealed that the 50 mg/kg naltrexone group was able to walk between postnatal days 8 to 12, while the animals in the 1 mg/kg naltrexone group walked between days 13 to 15; the range for control subjects was 10 to 13 days. Furthermore, at the age when only half of the controls were able to walk, no rat in the 1 mg/kg naltrexone group could walk, and all of the animals in the 50 mg/kg naltrexone group could walk. Therefore, perturbation of endogenous opioid systems not only influences somatic and neurobiological development, but also the timetable of neurobehavioral ontogeny.

A series of histological, histochemical, and morphometric studies was conducted to ascertain more fully the role of endogenous opioid systems in regulating brain development (14-17). In the first study (15), the developing cerebella of 21-day old rats given a temporary (1 mg/kg naltrexone) or complete (50 mg.kg naltrexone) blockade of opioid receptors throughout the first 3 weeks of postnatal life were investigated. In general, 50 mg/kg naltrexone had a stimulatory action on cerebellar ontogeny, while 1 mg/kg naltrexone had an inhibitory influence. Both sexes were affected in a similar fashion. Limits to the ability of naltrexone to modulate cerebellar ontogeny were noted, with more latitude existing toward growth enhancement than impairment. The temporal course of neurogenesis was not delayed in naltrexone-treated rats; a shortening of the timetable of cerebellar neurodevelopment remains to be determined. The events that transpired over the preweaning period were dramatically affected. The most notable alterations in the 1 mg/kg naltrexone-treated rats were marked decreases in dimensions of cerebellar area, the content of internal granule neurons, and cellular and tissue differentiation. Characteristics of the 50 mg/kg naltrexone group included increases in dimensions of cerebellar area, neural cell number, content, and size, and structural changes consistent with acceleration in growth and differentiation. Naltrexone influenced both neurons and glia, but only neural cells generated during the first 21 days after birth were altered in regard to quantity. Investigations (16) using electron microscopy revealed that no subjective changes at the ultrastructural level could be detected in the developing cerebellum of animals given naltrexone. This suggests that neither opioid antagonist modulation - nor the repercussions of opioid changes - alters the structural integrity of the nervous system, at least qualitatively; quantitative evaluation remains to be conducted.

In a companion study (17) on opioid antagonist modulation of cerebral and hippocampal development, the same experimental design was employed. As with the cerebellum, 50 mg/kg naltrexone had a stimulatory effect on growth of cortical and hippocampal regions, whereas 1 mg/kg naltrexone had an inhibitory effect, with both males and females being affected comparably. Opioid antagonist action was especially directed at cellular and tissue differentiation, with marked changes in macroscopic dimensions of area and histotypic organization recorded in the cerebral cortex. A notable effect on the cerebrum of the 1 mg/kg naltrexone group was a substantial increase in packing density of neural cells, reflecting a reduced area for accommodating neural elements. Changes in the hippocampus were largely restricted to the 1 mg/kg group. However, the number of granule cells was increased in the dentate gyrus of the 50 mg/kg group, suggesting that opioid receptor blockade affects cell types undergoing postnatal proliferation. As in the cerebellum, cellular elements derived prior to naltrexone treatment (e.g., pyramidal neurons) were capable of being influenced in only their capacity to differentiate.

It is possible that the establishment of neuronal organization and intricacy in the developing brain is dependent on endogenous opioid/opioid receptor interactions. To address the role of endogenous opioids in neuroplasticity, developing neurons in the cerebral cortex, hippocampus, and cerebellum were structurally examined in 10- and 21- day old rats subjected to continuous or intermittent receptor blockade (18,19). Pyramidal cells from frontoparietal cortex (layer III) and hippocampal field CA1, and cerebellar Purkinje cells, were impregnated using the Golgi-Kopsch method; total and mean dendrite segment length, branch frequency and spine concentration were analyzed morphometrically. Perturbations in endogenous opioid systems caused region-dependent alterations in dendrite complexity and/or spine concentration in all brain areas. Continuous opioid receptor blockade resulted in dramatic increases in dendrite and/or spine elaboration compared to controls at 10 days; however, these increases were only evident in the hippocampus at 21 days. With intermittent blockade, dendrite and/or spine growth were often subnormal, being most prominent at day 21. These results indicate that endogenous opioid systems are critical regulators of neuronal differentiation, and control growth through an inhibitory mechanism.

In view of the changes in cell number induced by disturbing the endogenous opioid systems, it would appear that opioid-receptor interactions may be involved in cell proliferative events. To examine the role of endogenous opioid systems in modulating the proliferation of developing neural cells, autoradiographic studies examining the cerebellar cortex of 6-day old rats were undertaken (20). The blockade of endogenous opioid-opioid receptor interfacing by naltrexone was accompanied within 1-2 hr by an increased proportion of cells incorporating radiolabeled thymidine. When high doses of naltrexone (50 mg/kg) were administered, this index was still elevated 12 hr later; however, when low doses of naltrexone (1 mg/kg) were administered the index of labeled cells was decreased markedly. A key factor in using the opioid antagonist paradigm was to determine the action of endogenous opioids by disturbing their action. The results from experiments with naltrexone would suggest that endogenous opioids are inhibitory factors that tonically regulate proliferative processes through an inhibitory mechanism. To confirm the action of opioids on cell replication, methionine enkephalin

(a natural opioid peptide) was injected directly
(systemically) into 6-day old rats. A subnormal number of
cells incorporating radiolabeled thymidine was observed.
Concomitant injection of 1 mg/kg naloxone, however, blocked
the inhibitory effects of methionine enkephalin on cell
division but did not itself affect cell generation. These
studies demonstrate that endogenous opioids are indeed
regulators of cell proliferation, serving as inhibitory
agents.

Further evidence of a direct involvement of endogenous
opioids in the control of brain development comes from a
variety of other quarters. β-endorphin and enkephalin
levels in the cerebellum were found to reach their highest
levels in the first postpartum week and to decline
subsequently to low levels (21,22). Recently, the
distribution of enkephalin in the cerebellum was examined
with immunocytochemistry (23). Methionine and leucine
enkephalin-like material were found to be concentrated in
the external germinal cells of the 10-day old rat cerebellum
and localized throughout the cortical cytoplasm.
Enkephalin-like immunoreactivity was not detected by
immunocytochemistry in differentiated neural cells
originating from this layer (e.g., internal granule
neurons). Immunoelectron microscopic studies (25) confirmed
these findings and revealed that enkephalin-like
immunoreactivity was localized in the soma of proliferating,
migrating, and differentiating neural cells, and was
associated with the plasma membrane, microtubules,
filaments, mitochondria, endoplasmic reticulum, and nuclear
envelope in 10-day old rats. Neurons and glia displayed a
similar staining profile. Enkephalin-like material was also
detected in the dendrites and dendritic spines of Purkinje
cells, and was concentrated in postsynaptic densities.
Methionine enkephalin-like immunoreactivity was not
associated with axons, glial processes, or presynaptic
elements, with the exception of mossy fiber terminals.
Shortly after weaning (day 40), methionine enkephalin-like
immunoreactivity was mainly related to the soma of Purkinje,
Purkinje cell dendrites, and synaptic spines.

In earlier studies using receptor binding assays,
radiolabeled methionine enkephalin and naloxone both bound
to homogenate preparations of the developing rat cerebellum
(22,24), with the highest levels recorded during the first

few days of life and declining to low levels shortly thereafter. Detailed studies in our laboratory reveal that at postnatal day 6, specific and saturable binding could be detected with prototypic ligands (and appropriate methodology) for mu, delta, and kappa receptors. It was noted in competition assays that compounds like methionine enkephalin which were extremely potent as growth regulators, were not extremely potent in displacing any of the ligands to known receptor types. Further work showed that radiolabeled methionine enkephalin had high affinity and saturable binding to cerebellar homogenates of 6-day old rats. This binding was dependent on time, temperature, and pH, and was sensitive to proteolysis. Even when a cocktail of ligands prototypic for mu, delta, and kappa receptors was added to the radiolabeled methionine enkephalin assay, specific and saturable binding still occurred. These results would suggest that a methionine enkephalin binding site exists in the developing cerebellum. Moreover, this binding site is proteinaceous in character.

If, indeed, methionine enkephalin is a prototypic ligand for growth and identifies a new receptor type, then one would expect differential response in assays for growth between ligands prototypic for opioid receptors. For example, using [^{3}H]-thymidine as a marker for cell proliferation as described earlier, methionine enkephalin, but not equimolar quantities of ligands prototypic for other receptors such as mu, delta, and kappa, would be predicted to alter thymidine incorporation. We conducted such a study using the model of the 6-day old cerebellar cortex, and evaluated the external germinal layer. Injection of methionine enkephalin suppressed [^{3}H]-thymidine incorporation, but equimolar quantities of [D-Ala^2, MePhe^4, Glyol^5] enkephalin (DAGO), [D-Ala^2, D-Leu^5] enkephalin (DADLE), or ethylketocyclazocine (EKC) had no effect on incorporation (Zagon and McLaughlin, in preparation).

CONCLUSIONS

The perinatal opioid syndrome involves a complex series of events including opioid receptor mediation of drug effects, that may lead to growth retardation. The exposure to drugs and/or such processes as drug withdrawal may be stressful to the organism. Since stressful conditions cause the release of opioid peptides and, given that exogenous opioids can adversely influence growth via opioid receptors, the possibility that endogenous opioids are involved in growth has been explored. Evidence gathered from pharmacological, structural, and biochemical experimentation strongly suggests that endogenous opioids play an important role in growth regulation. It appears that methionine enkephalin is a prototypic ligand for growth, and that a new opioid receptor has been identified that mediates this action. The mechanism of the trophic influence of endogenous opioid systems involves the regulation of cell proliferative events.

ACKNOWLEDGEMENTS

The technical skills of Laura Nagy, Sue Pileggi, and Sue Ditty are gratefully acknowledged, as is the manuscript preparation by Ms. Terri Segneri. This work was supported in part by Grants NS-20500, NS-20623, and NS-21246 from the National Institutes of Health.

REFERENCES

1.   Zagon IS, McLaughlin PJ, Weaver DJ, Zagon E (1982). Opiates, endorphins and the developing organism: A comprehensive bibliography. Neurosci Biobehav Rev 6:439-479.
2.   Zagon IS, McLaughlin PJ, Zagon E (1984). Opiates, endorphins, and the developing organism: A comprehensive bibliography 1982-1983. Neurosci Biobehav Rev 8:387-403.
3.   McLaughlin PJ, Zagon IS (1984). Opioid regulation of neuromotor cell growth in vitro. Soc Neurosci 10:1111.
4.   Zagon IS, McLaughlin PJ (1984). Opiates alter tumor cell growth and differentiation in vitro. In Harris LS (ed): "Problems of Drug Dependence",National Institute on Drug Abuse Research Monograph 49, DHHS Pub No 83-1316, Washington DC: Supt of Docs, US Govt Print Off, pp 344-350.

5.   Smith AA, Hui FW, Crofford MJ (1977). Inhibition of growth in young mice treated with d,1-methadone. Eur J Pharmacol 43:307-314.

6.   Crofford M, Smith AA (1973).   Growth retardation in young mice treated with d,1-methadone. Science 181:947-949.

7.   Zagon IS (1985).   Opioids and development: New lessons from old problems.   In Chiang CN and Lee CC (eds): "Prenatal Drug Exposure: Kinetics and Dynamics. National Institutes on Drug Abuse Research Monograph 60, DHHS Pub No ADM 85-1413, Washington, DC: Supt of Docs, US Government Print Off, pp 58-78.

8.   Viveros OH, Diliberto EJ, Hazum E, Chang KJ (1979). Opiate-like materials in the adrenal medulla: Evidence for storage and secretion with catecholamines. Mol Pharmacol 16:1101-1108.

9.   Wilson SP, Klein RL, Chang KJ, Gasparis MS, Viveros OH, Yang UH (1980).   Are opioid peptides co-transmitters in noradrenergic vesicles of sympathetic nerves? Nature (London) 288:707-709.

10. Guillemin R, Vargo T, Rossier J, Minck S, Ling N, Rivier C, Vale W, Bloom F (1977). β-endorphin and adrenocorticotropin are selected concomitantly by the pituitary gland.   Science 197:1367-1369.

11. Zagon IS, McLaughlin PJ (1988).   Endogenous opioid systems and neurobehavioral development.   In Rodgers RJ, Cooper SJ (eds): "Endorphins; Opiates, and Behavioral Processes", New York, John Wiley and Sons, pp 287-309.

12. Zagon IS, McLaughlin PJ (1984). Naltrexone modulates body and brain development in rats: A role for endogenous opioids in growth. Life Sci 35:2057-2064.

13. Zagon IS, McLaughlin PJ (1985).   Naltrexone's influence on neurobehavioral development.   Pharmacol Biochem Behav 22:441-448.

14. Zagon IS, McLaughlin PJ (1983).   Increased brain size and cellular content in infant rats treated with an opiate antagonist.   Science 221:1179-1180.

15. Zagon IS, McLaughlin PJ (1986).   Opioid antagonist (naltrexone) modulation of cerebellar development: Histological and morphometric studies. J Neurosci 6:1424-1432.

16.   Hess GD, Zagon IS (in press). Endogenous opioid systems and neural development: Ultrastructural studies in the cerebellar cortex of infant and weanling rats. Brain Res Bull.

17.   Zagon IS, McLaughlin PJ (1986). Opioid-antagonist-induced modulation of cerebral and hippocampal development: Histological and morphometric studies. Brain Res 28:233-246.

18.   Hauser KF, McLaughlin PJ, Zagon IS (1987). Endogenous opioids regulate dendritic growth and spine formation in developing rat brain. Brain Res 416:157-161.

19.   Hauser KF, McLaughlin PJ, Zagon IS (in press). Endogenous opioid systems and the regulation of dendritic growth and spine formation. J Comp Neurol.

20.   Zagon IS, McLaughlin PJ (1987). Endogenous opioid systems regulate cell proliferation in the developing rat brain. Brain Res 412:68-72.

21.   Maseda C, Aguado EG, Mena MA, DeYevenes JG (1983). Ontogenetic development of β-endorphin immunoreactivity in rat brain regions. Neurosci Lett [Suppl] 14:S237.

22.   Tsang D, Ng SC, Ho KP, Ho WKK (1982). Ontogenesis of opiate binding sites and radioimmunoassayable β-endorphin and enkephalin in regions of rat brain. Brain Res 5:257-261.

23.   Zagon IS, Rhodes RE, McLaughlin PJ (1985). Localization of enkephalin immunoreactivity in germinative cells of developing rat cerebellum. Science 227:1049-1051.

24.   Tsang D, Ng SC (1980). Effect of antenatal exposure to opiates on the development of opiate receptors in rat brain. Brain Res 188:199-206.

25.   Prouty SM, Zagon IS (1987). Met-enkephalin immunoreactivity in developing rat cerebellum: Immunoelectron microscopic studies. Soc Neurosci 13:1702.

Molecular Biology of Stress, pages 87–96
© **1989 Alan R. Liss, Inc.**

EFFECTS OF STRESS INTENSITY AND MODALITY ON
CARDIOVASCULAR SYSTEM: AN INVOLVEMENT OF OPIOID SYSTEM[1]

H. M. Rhee and D. W. Hendrix

Department of Pharmacology
Oral Roberts University School of Medicine
Tulsa, OK 74137

ABSTRACT To define the role of stress on cardiovascular
parameters, and plasma and adrenal concentrations of
catecholamines, several groups of rats were subjected to
either immobilization, heat or treadmill exercise
stress. Intensity of the stresses was increased gradually by an increase in the duration of the stresses.
The animals were chronically catheterized two days
before each stress. At the end of different stress for
given duration blood was collected and both adrenal
glands were pooled for the assay of catecholamine content by HPLC. Immobilization stress increased blood
pressure and heart rate, which was attenuated by the
treatment of naloxone (1 mg/kg, i.p.). The immobilization stress also increased adrenal content of
norepinephrine, epinephrine, and dopamine. The adrenal
content of epinephrine was reduced by naloxone treatment. Heat stress also increased blood pressure with a
little change in heart rate. Treadmill exercise
increased the plasma concentrations of norepinephrine
and epinephrine, which was not affected by naloxone
pretreatment. The data suggest that opioid receptors
play a significant role in different types of stress by
the modulation of synthesis and release of adrenergic
neurotransmitters.

---

[1]This work was supported in part by Oklahoma Center for
the Advancement of Science and Technology.

INTRODUCTION

Hypertension, smoking, diabetes, arteriosclerosis, and high cholesterol are the important risk factors for cardiac diseases. However, individuals who do not have such risk factors still suffer from many cardiovascular diseases (1). In a fast-moving society, psychological and physical stressors are known to be key factors that are responsible for sympathetic overdrive with an elevated level of plasma catecholamines. A certain degree of stress is beneficial and even needed to maintain our normal health. However, it is not clear what type of stressors is ideal and what intensity of the stress would be beneficial. Mental, psychological and various other stressful conditions such as exercise release epinephrine, steroids, and enkephalins and endorphins (2-4).

We now know that enkephalin has profound cardiovascular effects in anesthetized and conscious animals, which influence blood pressure, heart rate and sympathetic nerve activity (5-8). Nowadays, millions of healthy persons as well as patients are involved in one kind of exercise or another without knowing the exact molecular mechanism by which the exercise produces various beneficial results. Therefore, it is imperative to examine the role of this peptide in health and stressful conditions. Thus, the main purpose of the research was to characterize several types of stresses in terms of their effects on cardiovascular and opioid systems.

METHODS

Experiments were performed on young adult Sprague-Dawley male rats (200-250 g). Animals were divided into 4 major groups: I. control non-stress group; II. Group for immobilization stress model; III. Group for heat stress model; and IV. Group for treadmill exercise. The rats were singly housed in suspended wire-bottom cages and were given water (purified by reverse osmosis) and food ad libitum except group IV as indicated below. A 12-h light-dark cycle was maintained (light on 0630-1830). Rats in group I were control, which did not participate in any types of stress. Rats in Group II received immobilization stress for the duration up to 60 minutes. In order to produce psychological stress with a minimal of physical activity the rats

were placed in a restraining cage (Fisher Scientific), of
which size was adjustable depending on the size of animals.

Rats in Group III received heat stress for 5 minutes
three times with 5 minute-cool off period. The source of
heat was an infrared lamp, which was equipped to maintain
39°C near the animals in the cage. For the Group IV rats
diet was fixed at 15 g per day per rat and the rats in this
group were subdivided into sedentary control, exercise
control and exercise stress. Sedentary control group did
not participate in any type of treadmill exercise. Exercise
control rats ran daily treadmill up to 3 weeks with a
gradual increase in the speed as well as in the duration of
running. However, the rats did not run on the day when the
blood was withdrawn for catecholamine assay. Exercise
stress rats ran as the exercise control rats did and, in
addition, they ran prior to the withdrawing of blood. In
the first week the rats ran 7.5 to 30 meters per min for 5
or 10 minutes, which was increased up to 40 meters per min
for 15 min in the second week. In the third week speed was
increased to 45 meters per min for 15 minutes. The treadmill with 10 tracks was manufactured by Quinton Instrument
Company (Seattle, WA). In all groups 50% of animals were
given naloxone (1 mg/kg i.p.) 10 minutes before the stress
of either immobilization, heat or treadmill exercise.

All animals in Groups I through IV were anesthetized
(pentobarbital 30 mg/kg) for chronic surgical implantation
of catheters. The right carotid artery and the left jugular
vein were cannulated, using two micro-renathane tubes (Brain
Tree Sci.). After 2-3 days healing of surgical wound,
either sham control, immobilization or exercise stress were
applied to the rats. The arterial catheter was connected
directly to a Statham p23 pressure transducer via a kinking
free swivel device rodent jacket (Harvard Instrument).
Measurement of blood pressure and heart rate were described
elsewhere (5,6), and in some rats, the cardiovascular parameters were analyzed indirectly by a tail cuff method, using
a programmed electrosphygmomanometer (Narco Biosystem, Model
PE 300).

As indicated in text arterial blood was collected in
EDTA (1 mg/ml blood) containing tube during or at the end of
specific stresses. To minimize the unnecessary effect of
blood withdrawal on catecholamines release 1 ml of saline
with reconstituted rat red cells was slowly infused during
the withdrawal of the blood. The blood was quickly centrifuged in a refrigerated centrifuge and the plasma was stored
at -70°C freezer until catecholamines assay.

On the day an analysis was to be performed, 0.5 ml of
the plasma was added 50 µl of 3,4-dihydroxybenzylamine
(DHBA) as an internal standard. After mixing 10 mg of alum-
inum oxide was added along with 400 µl of 2M Tris-EDTA buffer (pH 8.7) and the mixture was shaken for 15 minutes on an
overhead shaker (Labindustries, Inc. Cat. No. 400-110). The
plasma layer was discarded after a centrifugation for one
minute, which procedure was repeated after an addition of 1
ml of 0.2% of Tris-EDTA buffer (pH 8.1). Glacial acetic acid
(100 µl), 50 µl of 10% sodium disulfite and 50 µl of 5% EDTA
were diluted into distilled water to a final volume of 10
ml. To the alumina 100 µl of the mixture was added and shaken ventrically for 15 minutes. Subsequently it was centrifuged for 1 minute and the supernate was saved to assay as
described below. An aliquot (usually 20 µl) of eluted plasma sample was injected (Waters Associates, Injector Model
U6K), which was pumped by a solvent delivery pump (Model
590). Using an electrochemical detector (Model 460), the
peaks of norepinephrine, epinephrine, DHBA and dopamine were
detected and integrated (Model 745B Integrator). By comparing the integrated areas of catecholamine standard and those
of unknown sample, concentrations of plasma catecholamines
were expressed as picogram of catecholamines per ml of plasma. The left and the right adrenal glands were pooled and
homogenized in 10% perchloric acid to make a final 10% homogenate. The homogenate was centrifuged and the supernate
was filtered through a Millex HB4 filter before an injection
to the injector.

RESULTS

In chronically catheterized rats systolic blood was
115.6 ± 4.7 mmHg (N=16) (Table 1). The immobilization procedure increased systolic and diastolic blood pressure including the heart rate. Mean pressure was also increased
significantly within 10 minutes after the onset of immobilization stress. Naloxone (1 mg/kg, i.p.), which was given 10
minutes before the onset of immobilization stress effectively, blocked the elevation of blood pressure as well as
heart rate (data not shown). Table 2 shows the concentrations of adrenal catecholamines in the three groups of
rats. Immobilization for 60 minutes increased norepinephrine and epinephrine, which was attenuated by the treatment
of naloxone.

Heat stress increased blood pressure rapidly, which was gradually reduced upon turning off the infrared lamp. Naloxone reduced the rate of rise of systolic blood pressure and the peak systolic pressure was also low after naloxone treatment (data not shown). Heat stress had a slow effect on heart rate, compared to its effect on systemic blood pressure. A treatment with naloxone increased the rate of rise in heart rate (Table 3).

Treadmill exercise increased both blood pressure and heart rate (data not shown). Exercise stress after the pretreatment with naloxone did not prevent from the elevation of blood pressure and heart rate after the identical treadmill exercise. Before any exercise or experiment at 0 week the levels of plasma norepinephrine or epinephrine were not statistically different in the 4 groups of rats (Table 4). Treadmill exercise control group norepinephrine level was 450.5 ± 47.1 pg/ml plasma, which was significantly higher than the level in the sedentary control, which were handled identically without actual run. A single additional run prior to the withdrawal of blood raised both norepinephrine and epinephrine. However, the standard error was large enough it appears statistically not significant. Naloxone treatment produced a nonsignificant decrease in the level of epinephrine. The level of epinephrine was further increased even after 3 weeks of exercise, although the level of norepinephrine was not really altered in third week (data not shown).

TABLE 1

EFFECTS OF IMMOBILIZATION ON BLOOD PRESSURE AND
HEART RATE IN SPRAGUE-DAWLEY RATS[1]

Immobiliza-Duration (min)	n[2]	Systolic pressure (mmHg)	Diastolic pressure (mmHg)	Heart rate (bpm)
0	16	115.6 ± 4.7[3]	100.4 ± 4.2[4]	419.1 ± 16.2[4]
10	8	128.9 ± 6.1[4]	116.2 ± 4.4[4]	465.0 ± 17.5[4]
30	8	141.7 ± 9.6[4]	123.3 ± 9.0[4]	476.1 ± 11.4[4]
60	8	141.0 ± 6.1[4]	121.5 ± 4.1[4]	488.3 ± 21.9[4]

[1] Rats were restrained in a small adjustable cage for immobilization stress as in "Methods."
[2] Indicates number of animals used.
[3] All values are expressed in mean ± S.E.
[4] Indicates $p < 0.05$, compared to 0 minute control.

TABLE 2
ADRENAL CONTENT OF CATECHOLAMINES AFTER[1]
IMMOBILIZATION STRESS: NALOXONE EFFECTS[1]

Experiments	n	NE[2]	Epi	DA
Control	9	8.3 ± 0.6[3]	39.9 ± 1.8	0.6 ± 0.2
Immobilization	10	11.8 ± 1.3[3]	47.2 ± 4.4	1.1 ± 0.1
Immobilization plus naloxone	10	9.1 ± 0.5	29.7 ± 2.9[4]	1.2 ± 0.2

[1]Duration of immobilization was for 1 hour.
[2]Indicates number of animal used.
[3]NE, Epi and DA stand for norepinephrine, epinephrine and dopamine, respectively, and unit is µg/g tissue.
[3]Indicates $p < 0.05$, compared to the control.
[4]Indicates $p < 0.05$, compared to immobilization group.

TABLE 3
EFFECTS OF HEAT STRESS ON HEART RATE IN CONSCIOUS
SPRAGUE-DAWLEY RATS: NALOXONE EFFECT[1]

Treatment	Duration	n	Heart Rate (beats per minute) Control	n	Naloxone
Heat on	0 min.	32	418 ± 15.4	32	418 ± 15.4
	1 min.	20	392 ± 23.0	12	464 ± 16.7[2]
	2 min.	20	416 ± 19.4	12	468 ± 15.7[2]
	3 min.	20	431 ± 21.9	12	478 ± 17.5[2]
	4 min.	20	441 ± 17.8	12	488 ± 18.4[2]
	5 min.	20	453 ± 15.6	12	498 ± 18.3[2]
Heat off	1 min.	12	416 ± 22.4	12	487 ± 20.2[2]
	2 min.	12	406 ± 22.3	12	476 ± 23.0[2]
	3 min.	12	398 ± 24.3	12	467 ± 23.1
	4 min.	12	397 ± 24.2	12	460 ± 22.0
	5 min.	12	397 ± 27.2	12	457 ± 20.3

[1]Naloxone dose was 1 mg/kg, body weight, i.p., which was given 10 min before the stress.
[2]Indicates $p < 0.05$, compared to control stress group.
[3]All values are expressed in mean $\pm$ S.E.

TABLE 4

EFFECTS OF TREADMILL EXERCISE STRESS ON PLASMA
EPINEPHRINE CONCENTRATIONS IN RATS: NALOXONE EFFECTS[1]

Treatment	n	Plasma epinephrine (pg/ml)		
		0 Week	Second Week	Third Week
Sedentary Control	5	52.2 ± 7.5	113.6 ± 18.6[2]	98.6 ± 27.7
Exercise Control	6	79.6 ± 8.3	224.5 ± 17.7[2]	226.2 ± 54.3
Exercise Stress	6	53.6 ± 6.0	587.7 ± 189.3	1076.6 ±299.3
Exercise Stress plus Naloxone	7	62.5 ± 7.9	498.0 ± 96.3	379.1 ±104.2

[1]Duration of treadmill exercise was gradually increased with
an appropriate increase in the speed of running daily for 2
to 3 weeks.
[2]Indicate $p < 0.05$, compared to sedentary control group.

DISCUSSION

     Recently there has been tremendous research interest in
opioid peptides since they have diverse physiological effects in analgesia, thermoregulation, reproduction, appetite
and obesity, and cellular metabolism, in addition to its
pulmonary and cardiovascular actions (9,10). Particularly,
met-enkephalin decreases sympathetic nerve activity which
subsequently reduces systemic blood pressure and heart rate
in intact anesthetized animals (5,6). Especially, it is
remarkable that met-enkephalin decreased diastolic pressure
to a great extent than the reduction of systolic pressure so
that there was a net increase in pulse pressure. The peptide is distributed in the central nervous system as well as
in the peripheral tissues (11,12) such as autonomic ganglia
(13,14) and adrenal medulla (15,16). It is released stoichi-
ometrically with catecholamines into the blood stream from
the adrenal glands on stressful situations such as exercise. All these suggest that met-enkephalin has an effect on
the cardiovascular system in normal and stressed conditions.
     In the present studies naloxone, an opioid antagonist,
effectively prevented immobilization-induced elevation of
systolic blood pressure. This suggests an involvement of
opioid receptors in this type of stress. The immobilization
stress was designed to produce a psychological stress with a
minimal muscular movement. Although there was difference in

the degree of immobilization of the rats due to difference in body weight, this stress increased quantitatively plasma norepinephrine more than the plasma epinephrine (data not shown). Synaptic release of norepinephrine may be a dominant species of norepinephrine than that from the adrenal gland after the immobilization stress.

In Kvetnansky's type immobilization by fixing all four limbs of a rat to a board, repeated immobilization stress reduced the content of adrenal catecholamine (17) with an elevation of its plasma concentration (18). This suggests the release of catecholamines is stimulated to a rate exceeding the rate that the catecholamines are replaced. In this present study a mild immobilization for 60 minutes increased the adrenal content of norepinephrine (Table 2). This means there must be either an increase in adrenal catecholamine synthesis or a decrease in the release of adrenal catecholamines. Since the latter is not likely true, naloxone may play a role in the synthesis of adrenal catecholamines.

Heat stress under an infrared lamp increased heart rate with little increase in blood pressure (Table 3). This may indicate that the stress may affect baroreceptors-mediated reflexogenic component of hemodynamic consequence. Although naloxone has little or no effects on either blood pressure or heart rate in control animals, naloxone blocked the elevation of pressure induced by the heat stress and it increased heart rate in the heat stressed animals. This modulatory action of naloxone is difficult to explain without further experiments, although opiates are known to play a role in thermoregulation (19).

In treadmill exercise the plasma level of epinephrine was usually higher than the level of norepinephrine, which suggests that, depending on the nature of stress, there must be differential release of norepinephrine from the synapses and epinephrine from the adrenal gland. The plasma epinephrine was continuously increased even after the three weeks of stress, which indicates that the animals were not trained to run for such a short period of time. Even trained rats to run at the speed of 45 meters per minute might be stressful. Continuous exercise for a long period of time might show signs of adaptation to the exercise stress in terms of biochemical indicators such as catecholamines. It would be profitable to determine the specific types(s) of opioid receptors involved in the distinctly different kinds of stresses that were used in this study.

ACKNOWLEDGMENTS

The authors thank Mr. Graeham White for his excellent technical assistance for the assay of catecholamines.

REFERENCES

1. Kaplan NM (1984). An overview of hypertension, the clinical problem and its possible relationship to nutrition. In Horan MJ et al, (eds): "NIH workshop on nutrition and hypertension," Biomed Inform. Corp., New York, pp. 1-8.
2. Gambert SR, Garthwaite TL, Pontzer CH, Cook EE, Tristani FE, Duthie EA, Martinson DR, Hagen TH, McCarty DJ (1981). Running elevates plasma β-endorphin immunoreactivity and ACTH in unstrained human subjects. Proc Soc Exp Biol Med 168:1-4.
3. Carr DB, Bullen BA, Skrinar GS, Arnold MA, Rosenblat M, Beitins IZ, Martin JB, McArthur JW (1981). Physical conditioning facilitates the exercise-induced secretion of β-endorphin and β-lipotropin in women. New Eng J Med 305:560-563.
4. Fraioli F, Moretti C, Paolucci D, Alicicco E, Crescenzi F, Fortunio G (1980). Physical exercise stimulates marked concomitant release of β-endorphin and adrenocorticotropic hormone (ACTH) in peripheral blood in man. Experientia 36:987-989.
5. Eulie P, Rhee, H (1984). Reduction by phentolamine of the hypotensive effect of methionine enkephalin in anesthetized rabbits. Brit J Pharmacol 83:783-790.
6. Rhee HM, Eulie PJ, Peterson DF (1985). Suppression of renal nerve activity by methionine enkephalin in anesthetized rabbits. J Pharmacol Exp Ther 234 (No. 2):534-537.
7. Rhee HM (1986). Suppression of sympathetic nerve activity by methionine enkephalin: additive interaction with clonidine in intact anesthetized rabbits. In Holaday JW et al. (eds): "Proc. 1986 International Narcotics Research Conference, NIDA Research Monograph Series Nr. 75, USDHHS, PHS, Washington, DC, pp. 327-330.
8. Schaz K, Stock G, Simon W, Schlör K-H, Unger T, Rockhold R, Ganten D (1980). Enkephalin effects on blood pressure, heart rate, and baroreceptor reflex. Hypertension 2:395-407.

9. Martin GE, Bacino CB, Papp, NL (1981). Action of selected serotonin antagonists on hyperthermal evoked by intracerebrally injected β-endorphin. Peptides 2:213-217.

10. Sapru HN, Willette RN, Krieger AJ (1981). Stimulation of pulmonary J receptors by an enkephalin analogue. J Pharmacol Exp Ther 217:228-234.

11. Tang J, Yang H-Y T, Costa E (1982). Distribution of met-enkephalin Arg-phe in various tissues of rats and guinea pigs. Neuropharmacol 21:595-600.

12. Giraud P, Eiden LE, Audigier Y, Gillioz, P, Conte-Devolx B, Bourdouresque F, Eskay R, Oliver C (1981). Enkephalins, ACTH, α-MSH and β-endorphin in human pheochromocytomas. Neuropeptides 1:237-252.

13. Di Giulio AM, Yang H-YT, Lutold B, Fratta W, Jong J, Costa E (1978). Characterization of enkephalin-like material extracted from sympathetic ganglia. Neuropharmacology 17:989-992.

14. Schultzberg M, Hökfelt T, Lundberg JM, Terenius L, Elfvin L-G, Elde R (1978). Enkephalin-like immunoreactivity in nerve terminals in sympathetic ganglia and adrenal medulla and in adrenal medullary gland cells. Acta Physiol Scand 103:475-477.

15. Kimura S, Lewis RV, Stern AS, Rossier J, Stein S, Udenfriend, S (1980). Probable precursors of [leu] enkephalin and [met] enkephalin in adrenal medulla: peptides of 3-5 kilodaltons. Proc Natl Acad Sci USA 77:1681-1685.

16. Lewis RV, Stern AS, Kimura S, Rossier J, Stein S, Udenfriend S (1980). An about 50,000-dalton protein in adrenal medulla: a common precursor of [met]- and [leu]-enkephalin. Science 208:1459-1461.

17. Kvetnansky R, Mikulaj L (1970). Adrenal and urinary catecholamines in rats during adaptation to repeated immobilization stress. Endocrinol 87: 737-743.

18. Kvetnansky R, Sun CL, Lake CR, Thoa N, Torda T, Kopin LJ (1978). Effect of handling and forced immobilization of rat plasma levels of epinephrine, norepinephrine and dopamine-beta-hydroxylase. Endocrinol 103:1868-1874.

19. Martin GE, Bacino CB, Papp NL (1981). Action of selected serotonin antagonists on hyperthermia evoked by intracerebrally injected β-endorphin. Peptides 2:213-217.

Molecular Biology of Stress, pages 97–106
© 1989 Alan R. Liss, Inc.

IN VIVO STUDIES OF SOMATOSTATIN BIOSYNTHESIS IN THE HYPOTHALAMUS: EFFECTS OF CYSTEAMINE ADMINISTRATION[1]

John D. Fernstrom, Judy L. Cameron,
and Roland P.S. Kwok

Departments of Psychiatry and Behavioral Neuroscience
University of Pittsburgh School of Medicine
Pittsburgh PA 15213

ABSTRACT The in vivo biosynthesis of somatostatin-14 and somatostatin-28 was estimated in rat hypothalamus following injection of ^{35}S-cysteine into the third ventricle. Cysteamine administration caused an almost complete depletion of immunoreactive levels of total somatostatin in hypothalamus. Recovery occurred in 3 days. The drug also substantially suppressed labeling of the somatostatin peptides, but labeling returned to normal within 8–10 hr after cysteamine injection. The rapid recovery of somatostatin synthesis suggests that new peptide synthesis may make an important contribution to the the repletion of endogenous somatostatin stores in hypothalamus.

INTRODUCTION

Somatostatin was originally described as a hypothalamic neuroendocrine peptide of 14 amino acids (somatostatin-14; SRIF-14) that inhibits pituitary growth hormone (GH) secretion[1]. During the decade following its discovery, other peptides were identified in hypothalamus that contained the SRIF-14 sequence, but were of higher molecular weight. One such peptide was an n-terminally-extended form of SRIF-14 containing 28 amino acids, somatostatin-28 (SRIF-28). Another consisted of about 100 amino acids, with SRIF-14 at its c-

---

[1]These studies were supported by a grant from the NIH (NS20017). JDF is the recipient of an NIMH Research Scientist Development Award (MH00254).

terminus. This latter peptide, prosomatostatin (proSRIF), is the translation product of proSRIF mRNA, less the signal sequence [2]. ProSRIF is thought to be processed in hypothalamic neurons to smaller peptides, including SRIF-14 and SRIF-28. SRIF-28 may be the immediate precursor of SRIF-14. However, SRIF-28 is as potent biologically as SRIF-14, and is released into the pituitary portal circulation [3,4]. It is thus presumably a biologically-important peptide in its own right.

Although the basic design of the somatostatin biosynthetic pathway is known, almost nothing is known about the factors that govern the rate of somatostatin (SRIF-14 and SRIF-28) production. Some studies have described changes in the levels of the proSRIF mRNA or of immunoreactive (IR) SRIF in response to particular treatments [5,6]. Such information can provide useful clues as to how such treatments alter SRIF synthesis. But the results must be interpreted cautiously, since measurements of levels often do not provide accurate reflections of synthesis rates. An illustration of this general notion can be made using catecholamine synthesis in the autonomic nervous system. Treatments that greatly stimulate catecholamine synthesis in and release from sympathetic nerve endings and the adrenal medulla produce no change in endogenous catecholamine levels [7]. To study catecholamine synthesis, therefore, one must study it directly, and not use measurements of levels as indices of synthesis rates.

Such may also be the case for peptides like the somatostatins. We have therefore sought to develop a method for studying hypothalamic somatostatin synthesis in vivo. The SRIF peptides seemed to us to be appealing candidates for study, for three reasons: First, those peptides that include the SRIF-14 domain contain two cysteine residues. Cysteine can be labeled to very high specific activity with ^{35}S, such that the incorporation of this label into peptide is readily measurable. Second, a major fraction of the SRIF neurons in the central nervous system (CNS) is concentrated in a very small brain region, the hypothalamus [8]. In addition, the SRIF-producing cells in this region are located directly adjacent to the third ventricle, making the delivery of ^{35}S-cysteine to these cells anatomically simple and effective. These anatomic features optimize the chance that sufficient label will be incorporated into SRIF peptides to be detected. And third, a great deal is already known about the function of SRIF-producing cells in the hypothalamus. This information provides a useful starting point to begin to explore for factors that might influence SRIF synthesis.

THE EXPERIMENTAL PARADIGM

Our method for quantitating synthesis currently focuses on SRIF-14 and SRIF-28, the biologically-active end-products of the synthetic pathway [9,10]. In a typical study, animals are anesthetized and placed in a stereotaxic device. A small hole is bored in the skull, and a microliter syringe is lowered into the third ventricle. The ^{35}S-cysteine is then administered in one-minute, 0.1 microliter volumes over a ten minute period. At the end of this period, the wound is closed, and animals are returned to their cages. They are subsequently sacrificed, and hypothalami quickly removed and homogenized. (Typically, four hypothalami are pooled to make one sample; using two stereotaxic devices, sixteen animals can easily be administered label in a few hours.) The supernatants prepared from these homogenates are then spiked with carrier peptides (SRIF-14 and SRIF-28), and passed through Sep-Pak© cartridges. The Sep-Pak© eluates are subjected to reversed-phase, high-pressure liquid chromatography (HPLC). In order to isolate labeled SRIF-14 and SRIF-28, two sequential HPLC separations are typically employed. The first is a gradient-elution method, utilizing trifluoroacetic acid and a linear gradient of acetonitrile [9,10]. Fractions containing SRIF-14 and SRIF-28 are identified via absorbance peaks generated by the carrier peptides, and are collected, pooled, and lyophilized. The pooled material is then reconstituted and run on a second, isocratic separation using a buffer of either triethylammonium phosphate or heptafluorobutyric acid containing about 20% acetonitrile. In these second separations, radioactive peaks are readily identified that are authentic SRIF-14 and SRIF-28 [9,10].

Because our goal is to study the effects of different treatments on ^{35}S-cysteine incorporation into SRIF-14 and SRIF-28, we felt it important to be able to quantitate precursor (i.e., cysteine) specific activity. Such measurements would insure that changes in peptide labeling following particular treatments were not the spurious result of a difference in cysteine specific activity, rather than the actual rate of label incorporation into peptide. In the method we developed, hypothalamic samples are homogenized, and supernatants prepared and subjected to performic acid oxidation (to convert cysteine to cysteic acid) [10]. The oxidized samples are reacted with o-phthalaldehyde [OPT] (cysteic acid, but not cysteine produces a highly-fluorescent product on reaction with OPT), and then subjected to an HPLC procedure to isolate cysteic acid. Using our HPLC method [10], a fluorescence peak corresponding to cysteic acid emerges within 17 minutes; fractions are collected and counted. Cysteine specific activity is then directly calculated for each sample using the fluorescent peak to measure the amount of cold cysteine, and the radioactive peak to quantitate hot cysteine.

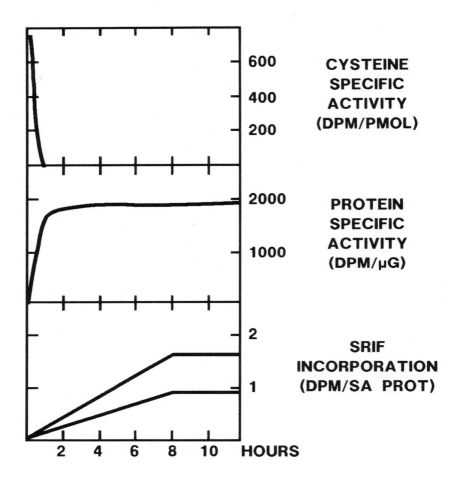

FIGURE 1. Schematic of the time-course in hypothalamus of the changes in cysteine and protein specific activities and in ^{35}S-cysteine incorporation into SRIF-14 and SRIF-28. The units for SRIF incorporation (DPM peptide/specific activity of protein) were developed to allow comparisons of labeling results across studies, by taking into account variations in the actual amount of ^{35}S-cysteine injected (see [11]). This figure is a composite derived from several studies [10,12].

Using these methods, we have found that (a) hypothalamic cysteine specific activity falls to very low values within 30 min of ^{35}S-cysteine administration; (b) ^{35}S-cysteine incorporation into acid-precipitable protein in hypothalamus rises rapidly to attain a plateau around 1 hr after termination of label administration; and (c) ^{35}S-cysteine incorporation into SRIF-14 and SRIF-28 rises linearly to attain plateau values 8 hr following label administration (**see figure 1**) [10]. These results are very fortunate. First, since cysteine specific activity falls to very low values soon after its administration, especially when compared to the timecourse of SRIF-14 and SRIF-28 labeling, the method appears to produce a "pulse" labeling of the SRIF pathway. Pulse labeling is a useful technique when attempting to follow the progression of a molecule through its synthetic (in this case, post-translational processing) pathway. And second, since label appearance in SRIF-14 and SRIF-28 is initially linear (for 8 hr), it is possible to estimate peptide synthesis rate (label incorporation/time). In practice, given linearity, a single timepoint can be used for such estimates; we typically make measurements 4 hr after label injection, a timepoint in the middle of the linear portion of the curve, and one associated with easily detectable levels of radioactivity in SRIF-14 and SRIF-28. It is also interesting to note that the labeling of acid-precipitable protein plateaus early in relation to that of SRIF-14 and SRIF-28. This result may indicate that the labeling of other polypeptides, such as proSRIF also plateaus at this early timepoint, suggesting that a significant timeperiod is involved in processing propeptide to final peptide(s). A significant time-lag between the labeling of precursor and product peptides is experimentally useful when trying to study peptide processing.

EFFECTS OF CYSTEAMINE ON SRIF-14 AND SRIF-28 SYNTHESIS

The rationale for conducting studies with cysteamine (CSH) derives from a simple pharmacologic strategy. When one does not initially know how sensitive his/her method is for measuring a biologic/biochemical variable, he/she first attempts to alter the variable with the most robust conditions possible. If the variable is not responsive to such a treatment, it is unlikely that it will be responsive to more modest (i.e., physiologic) treatments. In the case of CSH (2-aminoethanethiol), this drug was observed some years ago to produce a profound, though not permanent depletion of IR-SRIF levels throughout the CNS [13,14]. In the hypothalamus, IR-SRIF levels fall in a few hr to below 50% of normal values, and are not restored for 3-7 days [14]. The action of CSH is also reported to be selective for SRIF: no other small peptides are apparently depleted in the CNS [15].   Given these facts, it seemed to us possible that

TABLE 1

EFFECTS OF CYSTEAMINE INJECTION ON IN VIVO INCORPORATION OF ^{35}S-CYSTEINE INTO HYPOTHALAMIC PROTEIN, SRIF-14 AND SRIF-28[a]

Variable and Group	Time after cysteamine injection		
	1 hr	4 hr	1 wk
Protein Specific Activity			
Vehicle	2205 + 253(3)	1663 + 324(5)	2038 + 159(3)
Cysteamine	2191 + 291(3)	1781 + 437(5)	2146 + 329(3)
SRIF-14 Incorporation			
Vehicle	1.90 + 0.58(3)	1.99 + 0.26(5)	3.24 + 1.20(3)
Cysteamine	0.15 + 0.09(3)*	0.41 + 0.29(5)*	3.31 + 1.20(3)
SRIF-28 Incorporation			
Vehicle	1.01 + 0.29(3)	1.16 + 0.11(5)	1.91 + 0.60(3)
Cysteamine	0.11 + 0.10(3)*	0.22 + 0.10(5)*	1.76 + 0.70(3)

[a]Data are presented as the means + sem. The units are dpm [^{35}S]/microgram protein for protein specific activity, and [dpm(^{35}S)-peptide]/[protein specific activity] for incorporation values. The numbers in parentheses are the group sizes, where each member represents a pooled sample of 4 hypothalami. * Group mean differs significantly from that in the vehicle group, P < 0.025. From [16].

CSH might inhibit SRIF biosynthesis. We therefore examined this notion, by administering CSH (300 mg/kg sc) or vehicle to rats, and studying its effects on ^{35}S-cysteine incorporation into SRIF-14 and SRIF-28. In our initial series of experiments [16], we looked at three timepoints after CSH injection: 1 hr, 4 hr, and one week. These times were selected, since the effects of CSH on IR-SRIF levels are known to be robust 1 and 4 hr post-injection, and gone by 7 days [14]. First, we confirmed that CSH did deplete the IR levels of SRIF in hypothalamus, but not those of two other peptides (oxytocin and vasopressin). We then quantitated SRIF-14 and SRIF-28 labeling. As shown in **table 1**, CSH-treated groups showed a profound suppression of ^{35}S-cysteine-labeling of chromatographically-identified SRIF-14 and SRIF-28. These effects were apparent when label was administered 1 or 4 hr after CSH (all animals were then killed 4 hr after ^{35}S-cysteine injection), but not one week after CSH injection. They were not the result of an action of CSH to suppress cysteine specific activity: cysteine specific activity was measured in hypothalami at the end of the label administration period (when the specific activity is high [10]), and found to be similar between treatment groups [16]. Moreover, protein specific activities were also similar between vehicle and CSH groups 4 hr after ^{35}S-cysteine injection, suggesting again that initial ^{35}S-cysteine specific activities were the same (table 1).

These results led us to conclude tentatively that the synthesis of SRIF-14 and SRIF-28 might be suppressed and restored in parallel with the reduction in IR-SRIF levels. Given these initial results with CSH, we decided to study the drug's actions in greater detail. In particular, we wondered whether and/or how the inhibition of ^{35}S-cysteine labeling of SRIF-14 and SRIF-28 (i.e., presumed synthesis) might participate in the production of the apparent loss and recovery of endogenous SRIF pools. First, in this regard, it seemed clear that a CSH-induced suppression of SRIF synthesis could not account for the very rapid, dramatic drop in endogenous SRIF stores: despite the rapid change, SRIF synthesis rate is probably too small in comparison to total hypothalamic SRIF content to produce an immediate effect on endogenous pool size. (Indeed, another mechanism is more likely to produce this effect [17]). Second, however, the question of how the endogenous SRIF pool is eventually repleted is not as readily answered, particularly given the limited data we had thus far collected (synthesis measurements for only a few times after drug injection: 1 and 4 hr, and 1 week). If, as has been suggested [17,18], CSH chemically modifies endogenous SRIF molecules without actually causing their loss from cells (through disulfide exchange reactions), then one possible mechanism of repletion might be the gradual, spontaneous reversion of these modified SRIF molecules to normal. A second mechanism might simply be that normal synthesis is restored soon after CSH injection, and provides new SRIF molecules at a rate sufficient to restore endogenous pools over the timeperiod typically observed (several days). We therefore undertook studies to obtain more detailed information regarding the temporal effects of CSH on SRIF-14 and SRIF-28 labeling. In particular, we sought to determine how soon after CSH injection SRIF-14 and SRIF-28 labeling returned to normal. If it took several days, we hypothesized, then new synthesis could not be an important contributor to the rebuilding of IR-SRIF pools; if less, then perhaps it might be. For these experiments, we injected CSH, and then at multiple times thereafter, administered ^{35}S-cysteine and quantitated labeling of SRIF-14 and SRIF-28 4 hr later. The results were straight-forward [19]. The labeling of SRIF-14 and SRIF-28 returned to normal within 10 hr of CSH injection. In these studies, we also performed a time-course of the CSH-induced depletion of IR-SRIF. The maximal depletion (to about 10% of control values) was attained 24 hr post-injection; IR-SRIF stores returned to normal within 72 hr.

The finding that somatostatin synthesis rapidly returns to normal following CSH injection, while endogenous pools are only very slowly restored, suggests that new synthesis may be an important contributor to the restoration of hypothalamic SRIF pools. It is presently unknown whether this is the only mechanism by which SRIF stores are eventually replenished. An additional source might conceivably derive from the proposed mechanism by which CSH is thought to deplete SRIF pools initially. That is, if the drug mediates disulfide exchange reactions between the cysteine residues of SRIF-14 moieties and other sulfhydryl-containing molecules, the result would be to alter the tertiary structure of SRIF-14 fragments, making them unreactive with anti-SRIF-14 antibodies directed at the c-terminus (most antisera) [17]. Consequently, following CSH treatment, hypothalamic cells would contain their original complement of SRIF-14 (and SRIF-28) molecules, though these molecules would have been chemically altered, and thus rendered undetectable [17,18] and biologically inert [20]. In this case, if these altered molecules were not completely metabolized or otherwise discarded, then perhaps some would eventually return to their original structures, and be restored to functional somatostatin pools. If so, then these pools of modified somatostatin molecules might be a significant source for replenishing hypothalamic somatostatin stores. At present, we do not know if SRIF molecules are recoverable, once modified by CSH. Current work in our lab is focused on this issue.

CONCLUSIONS

These studies show that SRIF-14 and SRIF-28 synthesis in hypothalamus can readily be estimated in vivo, and is found to change in response to a pharmacologic treatment (CSH) known to alter endogenous SRIF levels. In other studies, we have also noted that SRIF-14 and SRIF-28 labeling is suppressed by a pathophysiologic treatment, hypophysectomy [12]. This latter effect is consistent with the known SRIF action to inhibit pituitary GH secretion. It will now be interesting to explore for effects of more physiologic treatments on the synthesis of these peptides. In this regard, stress is an obvious candidate for study: it is known to be a potent suppressor of GH secretion, an effect that appears to be mediated by an enhancement of SRIF release [21,22]. Perhaps the stress-induced increase in hypothalamic SRIF release also increases SRIF-14 and/or SRIF-28 synthesis rates. If so, then stress would become a useful model for dissecting the possible physiologic mechanisms that might govern the SRIF-14 and SRIF-28 biosynthetic pathway(s).

REFERENCES

1. Burgus R, Ling N, Butcher M, Guillemin R (1973). Primary structure of somatostatin, a hypothalamic peptide that inhibits the secretion of pituitary growth hormone. Proc Natl Acad Sci US 70: 684.
2. Goodman RH, Aron DC, Roos BA (1983). Rat pre-prosomatostatin. J Biol Chem 258: 5570.
3. Millar RP, Sheward WJ, Wegener I, Fink G (1983). Somatostatin 28 is a hormonally active peptide secreted into hypophyseal portal vessel blood. Brain Res 260: 334.
4. Brazeau P, Ling N, Esch F, Bohlen P, Benoit R, Guillemin R (1981). High biological potency of the synthetic replicates of somatostatin-28 and somatostatin-25. Reg Peptides 1: 255.
5. Rogers KV, Vician L, Steiner RA, Clifton DK (1987). Reduced preprosomatostatin messenger ribonucleic acid in the periventricular nucleus of hypophysectomized rats determined by quantitative in situ hybridization. Endocrinology 121: 90.
6. Berelowitz M, Firestone SL, Frohman LA (1981). Effects of growth hormone excess and deficiency on hypothalamic somatostatin content and release and on tissue somatostatin distribution. Endocrinology 109: 714.
7. Cooper JR, Bloom FE, Roth RH (1986). "The Biochemical Basis of Neuropharmacology (Fifth Edition)". New York: Oxford, p 226.
8. Brownstein M, Arimura A, Sato H, Schally AV, Kizer JS (1975). The regional distribution of somatostatin in the rat brain. Endocrinology 96: 1456.
9. Van Itallie CM, Fernstrom JD (1982). Hypothalamic somatostatin-14 and -28 biosynthesis: effects of anesthetics and hypophysectomy. Brain Res 249: 177.
10. Van Itallie CM, Fernstrom JD (1983). In vivo studies of somatostatin-14 and somatostatin-28 biosynthesis in rat hypothalamus. Endocrinology 113: 1210.
11. Wetsel WC, Fernstrom JD (1987). In vivo biosynthesis of arginine vasopressin and oxytocin in hypothalami from intact and hypophysectomized rats. Endocrinology 120:   2562.
12. Wetsel WC, Fernstrom JD (1986). Effect of hypophysectomy on somatostatin-14 and somatostatin-28 biosynthesis in the rat hypothalamus. Brain Res 370: 315.
13. Szabo S, Reichlin S (1981). Somatostatin in rat tissues is depleted by cysteamine administration. Endocrinology 109: 2255.
14. Sagar SM, Landry D, Millard WJ, Badger TM, Arnold MA, Martin JB (1982). Depletion of somatostatin-like immunoreactivity in the rat central nervous system by cysteamine. J Neurosci 2: 225.
15. Palkovits M, Brownstein MJ, Eiden LE, Beinfeld MC, Russell J,

Arimura A, Szabo S (1982). Selective depletion of somatostatin in rat brain by cysteamine. Brain Res 240: 178.

16. Cameron JL, Fernstrom JD (1986). Effects of cysteamine administration on the in vivo incorporation of [^{35}S]Cysteine into somatostatin-14, somatostatin-28, arginine vasopressin, and oxytocin in rat hypothalamus. Endocrinology 119: 1292.

17. Patel YC, Pierzchala I (1985). Cysteamine induces a loss of tissue somatostatin-28 when measured as somatostatin-28(15-28)-like immunoreactivity but not when assessed as somatostatin-28(1-14)-like immunoreactivity: evidence for the importance of the disulfide bond for cysteamine action. Endocrinology 116: 1699.

18. Ceccatelli S, Hokfelt T, Hallman H, Nylander I, Terenius L, Elde R, Brownstein M (1987). Immunohistochemical analysis of the effects of cysteamine on somatostatin-like immunoreactivity in the rat central nervous system. Peptides 8: 371.

19. Kwok RPS, Cameron JL, Fernstrom JD (submitted). Rapid recovery of hypothalamic somatostatin, vasopressin and oxytocin biosynthesis following cysteamine administration to rats.

20. Millard WJ, Sagar SM, Badger TM, Martin JB (1983). Cysteamine effects on growth hormone secretion in the male rat. Endocrinology 112: 509.

21. Terry LC, Willoughby JO, Brazeau P, Martin JB, Patel Y (1976). Antiserum to somatostatin prevents stress-induced inhibition of growth hormone secretion in the rat. Science 192: 565.

22. Arimura A, Smith WD, Schally AV (1976). Blockade of the stress-induced decrease in blood GH by anti-somatostatin serum in rats. Endocrinology 98: 540.

Molecular Biology of Stress, pages 107–120

IMMUNE MODULATION OF THE HYPOTHALAMIC-PITUITARY ADRENAL AXIS: CELLULAR EFFECTS OF THYMOSIN ON CLONAL CORTICOTROPES

JM Farah[1], Jr, JF Bishop[2], J Michel[1], AL Goldstein[3], NR Hall[3,4] and TL O'Donohue[1]

[1]Central Nervous System Diseases Research
G. D. Searle and Company, St. Louis, Missouri 63198
and
[2]Experimental Therapeutics Branch, National Institute of Neurological and Communicative Disorders and Stroke, Bethesda, Maryland 20892
and
[3]Department of Biochemistry, The George Washington University School of Medicine and Health Sciences, Washington, DC 20037

ABSTRACT Recent reports suggest that the thymus may be one source of substances which mediate interactions between the immune system and the hypothalamic-pituitary adrenal (HPA) stress axis. Thymosin, a purified thymic extract, is known to increase the activity of the HPA axis in vivo. In the present study, the in vitro effects of thymosin on hormone secretion by clonal pituitary corticotropes were examined with particular emphasis on the intracellular basis for TSN-5 actions.

INTRODUCTION

Hypothalamic and adrenal hormones are known regulators of endocrine secretions by anterior pituitary corticotropes. In recent years, there has been increasing focus on the possibility that factors produced by cells of the immune system also participate in controlling the release of adreno-corticotropic hormone (ACTH), beta-endorphin (β-E) and other biologically active peptides derived from the

---

[4]Present address: Departments of Psychiatry and Immunology, University of South Florida, Tampa, FL 33613

corticotrope precursor molecule, pro-opiomelanocortin
(POMC). For example, interleukin-1 (IL-1) is a cytokine
produced principally by activated monocytic cell types to
promote an appropriate immunologic response to infection
(1). Among its pleiotropic actions, IL-1 stimulates the
activity of the hypothalamic-pituitary adrenal (HPA) axis
(2) either by direct effects on the pituitary (3,4) or
through hypothalamic release of corticotropin-releasing
factor (CRF) (5,6). A recent immunocytochemical study
supports the latter possibility since IL-1 containing
neurons appear to innervate the hypothalamic paraventricular nucleus from which CRF nerves emanate (7).
Whatever the specifics of the IL-1 effects, observations
like these indicate that substances normally thought to be
involved with lymphocyte proliferation and the cellular
immune response might also participate in governing
secretion of pituitary hormones derived from POMC.

One organ critical to the development of normal
cell-mediated immunity is the thymus (8,9). In addition to
its role as a primary organ of the immune system, the
thymus may act as a key source for immunologic modulators
of the HPA axis, presumably through release of hormones
produced by the thymic epithelium (10). Thymectomy lowers
serum levels of ACTH, β-E or adrenal steroids in young
primates and rodents (11, 12) and these effects are
reversed by replacement therapy with thymic extracts (11).
Conversely, thymosin fraction five (TSN-5), a preparation
of bovine thymus containing numerous active polypeptides
(13), selectively increases circulating ACTH and
glucocorticoids in both species (12, 14). The effects of
TSN-5 on the HPA axis do not appear to be mediated through
direct actions on adrenal steroidogenesis (15) and are not
associated with neurochemical changes in the brain typical
of the stress response in rodents (16). Together, these
findings indicate that the thymus might produce factors
that directly influence anterior pituitary release of
POMC-derived hormones. Consistent with this, TSN-5 and a
purified thymic hormone, thymopoietin, were shown to
increase the secretion of immunoreactive β-E (iβ-E) and
ACTH from corticotropic tumor cells and from primary
cultures or explants of the anterior pituitary (17, 18,
19). These results support the view that corticotropic
peptide(s) from the thymus mediate secretion of POMC-
derived hormones through direct stimulation of the
pituitary.

The purpose of the present study was to explore the cellular basis for TSN-5 stimulation of hormone secretion. Mouse clonal corticotropic cells were treated with TSN-5 alone or in combination with agents known to regulate secretion of POMC-derived hormones through defined intracellular mechanisms. Preliminary results indicate that the corticotropic activity of TSN-5 may involve mechanisms parallel to, but not independent of, adenylate cyclase and protein kinase C activation.

METHODS

AtT-20/D16-16 corticotropic tumor cells were grown as described (17) and for experimental purposes, subcultured at 300,000 cells/well in 6-well cluster plates.

Stock solutions were prepared as follows: human, rat corticotropin releasing factor (CRF; Peninsula Labs, Belmont, CA), TSN-5 (Alpha 1 Biomedicals, Gaithersburg, MD), thymopoietin (Ortho Pharmaceuticals, Raritan, NJ), and the purified human cytokines (IL-1, Advanced BioTechnologies, Inc, Silver Spring, MD; IL-2, Boehringer Mannheim Biochemicals, Indianapolis, IN) were prepared in sterile distilled water. Dexamethasone, forskolin, nifedipine, phorbol 12-myristate 13-acetate and 4-alpha phorbol (Sigma Chemical Co., St. Louis, MO) were dissolved in absolute ethanol; ethylene glycol-bis (β-aminoethyl ether) N,N,N^1,N^1-tetraacetic acid (EGTA, Sigma), in alkaline water (0.1 M NaOH).

For release experiments, nearly confluent monolayers of AtT-20 cells received a fresh change of 1 ml Dulbecco's Modified Eagles Medium supplemented with charcoal-stripped fetal bovine serum and antibiotics (DMEM) and were immediately treated as described in RESULTS (17). After a 4 h incubation, aliquots of cell- and debris-free media were frozen at -70 C. For cyclic nucleotide experiments, cells were preincubated for 30 min in DMEM containing 0.5 mM isobutylmethylxanthine (IBMX, Sigma). After 30 min treatment, cells were rinsed with phosphate buffered saline and extracted by freezing and thawing in 0.1 M hydrochloric acid followed by sonication. For phosphorylation experiments, cells were preincubated for 60 min in a phosphate-free modified Krebs Ringer (MKR) buffer containing 50 μCi of 32P-orthophosphate (Dupont/NEN, Boston, MA). After 5-15 min treatment, cells were extracted; acid-precipitated, cytosolic proteins were analyzed by two dimensional electrophoresis and autoradiography as described (20).

Immunoreactive β-endorphin (iβ-E) was measured by radioimmunoassay (21) and radioimmunoassay for cAMP was obtained from Dupont/NEN (Boston, MA) and used as described. Protein values were determined using a modified Lowry method (22).

Significant differences between treatment effects were accepted for p<0.05 using Duncan's or least significant difference comparisons after one- or two-way analysis of variance (23).

RESULTS

AtT-20 cells exhibit a high rate of constitutive release which is distinct from regulated vesicular release of hormone (24). The enhanced release of iβ-E which is induced by TSN-5 treatment was tested for calcium dependence and, as shown in Table 1, found to be inhibited by cotreatment of the cultures with either an antagonist of voltage-dependent calcium channels, nifedipine, or a chelator of free calcium, EGTA. These results indicate that TSN-5 promotes hormone release through calcium-dependent mechanisms characteristic of regulated exocytosis.

TABLE 1

NIFEDIPINE AND EGTA EFFECTS ON HORMONE RELEASE EVOKED BY TSN-5

	VEH	TSN-5
VEH	16.6 ± 1.2^a	43.3 ± 2.7^c
NIFED	12.8 ± 0.8^b	21.9 ± 1.5^c
EGTA	4.6 ± 0.3^b	7.3 ± 0.4^c

Cells were incubated for 4 h with the indicated combinations of vehicle (VEH), TSN-5 (600 ug/ml), nifedipine (NIFED; 1 μM) or EGTA (5 mM).
[a] Values as ng iβ-E/ml/4 h, mean ± SE; N=6
[b] p<0.05 vs VEH
[c] p<0.05 vs TSN-5

Corticotropes are normally balanced between the inhibitory control of adrenal glucocorticoids and the stimulatory effects of hypothalamic corticotropin-releasing factor (CRF) (25). Therefore the interactions of TSN-5 effects with those of these principal regulators were explored. As shown in Table 2, pretreatment of AtT-20 cultures with the synthetic glucocorticoid, dexamethasone, inhibited TSN-5 stimulated hormone secretion. Dexamethasone lowered basal release of iβ-E by 55% and prevented the TSN-5 induced increase relative to controls. Conversely, the stimulatory effects of TSN-5 and of CRF were synergistic resulting in a 5-fold increase hormone secretion.

The stimulatory effects of TSN-5 on basal and CRF-evoked iβ-E secretion were compared with those of other immmunomodulatory agents. As shown in Figure 2 both thymopoeitin (TP) and purified human interleukin-1 (IL-1) increased basal secretion of hormone yet, in combination with CRF, neither increased secretion comparable to effects mediated by TSN-5. Additional concentrations of TP and IL-1 were no more effective that those illustrated in Figure 1 (not shown). Unlike the other agents tested, the lymphocte activating factor, interleukin-2 (IL-2) had no effect alone or in combination with CRF. Interestingly,

TABLE 2

EFFECTS OF DEXAMETHASONE AND CORTICOTROPIN RELEASING FACTOR ON TSN-5 INDUCED HORMONE SECRETION

	VEH	TSN-5
VEH	24.1 ± 2.1^a	51.1 ± 5.7^b
DEX	10.9 ± 1.4^b	23.2 ± 1.6
CRF	42.2 ± 2.8^b	128.8 ± 16.4^{bc}

Cells were pretreated for dexamethasone (DEX; 0.1μM) or vehicle (VEH; 0.01% ethanol) 7 h and then treated for an additional 4 h with VEH, corticotropin releasing factor (CRF; 0.1μM) or thymosin fraction 5 (TSN-5; 600 μg/ml) in the absence or presence of added DEX.
[a] Values as ng iβ-E/ml/4 h, mean ± SE; N=6
[b] p<0.05 vs VEH
[c] p<0.05 vs TSN-5 or CRF

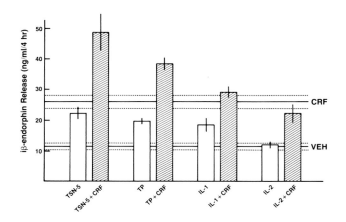

FIGURE 1.   Effects of immunomodulatory compounds
on hormone secretion by AtT-20 corticotropes.   Cells were
incubated in medium containing vehicle (VEH) or CRF
(0.1 µM) plus additional VEH, TSN-5 (600 µg/ml),
thymopoietin (TP; 0.6 µg/ml), purified human IL-1 (10 U/ml)
or purified human IL-2 (20 U/ml).   Group means ± SEM are
represented as bars and vertical lines or as solid and
dashed horizontal lines (VEH controls and CRF), n=6.

neither the alpha nor beta forms of recombinant human
IL-1 influenced basal or CRF-stimulated hormone secretion
in AtT-20 cells (unpublished results).   Perhaps different
preparations of this cytokine could account for the
discrepancy between laboratoris regarding direct pituitary
effects of IL-1 (3, 4, 5, 6).
       Since the degree of cooperativity with CRF for iβ-E
release was greatest in cells treated with TSN-5, the
cellular mechanisms underlying this response were explored
using selected activators of the secretory response.   Cells
were treated with TSN-5 alone or in combination with CRF or
forksolin, the diterpene activator of adenylate cyclase.
As shown in Figure 2, a 10 µM dose of forskolin increased
release of iβ-E to 350% of control levels (5.7 ± 0.4
ng/ml/4h), a rise comparable to that stimulated by either
TSN-5 or CRF treatment.   Like CRF, forskolin's effects were
synergistic with those of TSN-5 resulting in a 9-fold

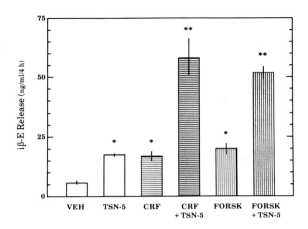

FIGURE 2. Effects of TSN-5 on CRF and forskolin
stimulated hormone secretion. AtT-20 cells were incubated
for 4 h in medium containing appropriate vehicle (VEH)
treatments or TSN-5 (600 μg/ml), CRF (0.1 μM) or FORSK (10
μM) alone or in combination. Bars and vertical lines
represent the group mean ± SE; N=6
     *p<0.05 vs VEH
     **p<0.05 vs TSN-5, CRF or FORSK

increase in the 4 h release of iβ-E. Also like CRF
treatment (17), forskolin reduced the intracellular hormone
content of AtT-20 cells after 24 h of treatment (Controls,
178 ± 12; TSN-5, 187 ± 14; CRF, 118 ± 6; FORSK, 86 ± 6 ng
iβ-E/mg protein). These data support the notion that
forskolin mimics most if not all actions of CRF on
corticotropes.
     The effects of CRF and forskolin on corticotrope
secretions are mediated primarily by cyclic adenosine
monophosphate (cAMP), the second messenger generated by the
activity of adenylate cyclase (25, 26). Cells were
treated with combinations of TSN-5 and forskolin to
determine if the synergistic effects of these agents on
hormone secretion might be accounted for by similar actions
on cAMP. As shown in Figure 3, however, TSN-5 had no
effect on basal levels of cAMP and inhibited, rather than
potentiated, the accumulation of cAMP induced by forskolin

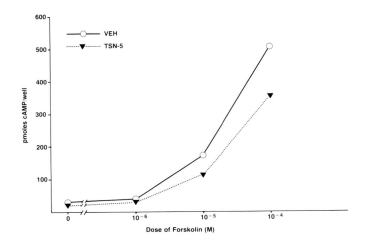

FIGURE 3. Effects of TSN-5 on forskolin-dependent accumulation of intracellular cAMP. Cells were treated for 30 min with release medium containing TSN-5 (600 µg/ml) or vehicle with or without forskolin at the concentrations indicated. Symbols indicate the group mean, n=6 (SEMs less than symbol dimensions).

by as much as 35%. These findings indicate that coordinate actions of TSN-5 with forskolin (and probably CRF) occur despite reduced intracellular free cAMP.

Stimulation of normal corticotropes with vasopressin is associated with phosphatidylinositol (PI) metabolism (27) which is a signal transduction system utilizing the second messengers, inositol trisphosphate and diacylglycerol, to promote the release of sequestered intracellular calcium (28) and activation of protein kinase C (29), respectively. Although AtT-20 cells are unresponsive to vasopressin, pharmacologic stimulation of protein kinase C with phorbol esters has been shown to increase hormone secretion and POMC gene expression in clonal corticotropes (30,31). In order to explore the possibility that TSN-5-evoked iβ-E secretion is mediated via protein kinase C, AtT-20 cells were treated with TSN-5 in the presence or absence of phorbol myristate acetate (PMA), 4-alpha phorbol (an inactive phorbol ester) or CRF. As illustrated in Figure 4, PMA elicited a similar amount of hormone secretion as treatments with CRF or TSN-5.

Furthermore, when TSN-5 treatment was combined with either CRF or PMA, the effect on iβ-E release was additive. The effect of PMA was apparently associated with normal kinase activation since the inactive phorbol had no effect on hormone secretion in vehicle or TSN-5 treated cells. These findings indicated that the corticotropic actions of TSN-5 might be dissociated from the effects of protein kinase C activity.

Regulatory mechanisms usually require modifications of cellular phosphoproteins which may then function as "third messengers" is signal transduction (32). Since protein phosphorylation in AtT-20 cells has been linked to control of hormone secretion by activators of cAMP-dependent as well as C kinase (20,33), the effects of TSN-5 on cytosolic phosphoproteins were examined relative to the reported effects of forskolin and PMA. As shown in

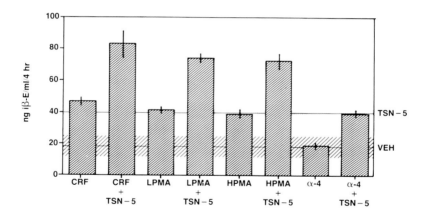

FIGURE 4.   Effects of phorbol esters and CRF on basal and TSN-5 evoked hormone secretion. Corticotropes were incubated with medium containing vehicle (VEH) or TSN-5 in the absence or presence of CRF (0.1 μM), 100 nM low dose phorbal myristate acetate (LPMA), 600 nM high dose phorbal myristate acetate (HPMA) or 600 nM 4-alpha phorbal (α-4). Group means ± SEM are represented as bars and vertical lines or as solid horizontal lines with crosshatching (VEH- and TSN-5-treated groups), n=6.

Figure 5, a characteristic pattern of phosphorylated
cytosolic proteins were resolved by two-dimensional
electrophoresis. Compared to phosphoproteins in the
cytosolic extracts of vehicle-treated cells, TSN-5
increased the amount of 32 phosphate incorporated into
87 kDa (pI~4.4), 43 kDa (pI~4.9), 39 kDa (pI~5.0), a pair
of ~19 kDa (pI 5.7-6.0) and a 14.5 kDa (pI~5.2) phosphoproteins. Alterations in the phosphorylation of the 14.5
kDa and the pair of ~19 kDa proteins have been significantly
correlated with hormone secretion evoked by both forskolin
and PMA (20,33), however, TSN-5 increased, whereas PMA and
forskolin decreased, the phosphorylation of 14.5 kDa.
Also, TSN-5 increased ^{32}P incorporation into the 43 kDa
protein whereas neither forskolin nor PMA significantly
altered the phosphorylation state of this molecule (20).

DISCUSSION

The multihormonal regulation of anterior pituitary
corticotropes is dominated normally through stimulatory
regulation by hypothalamic CRF and inhibitory regulation

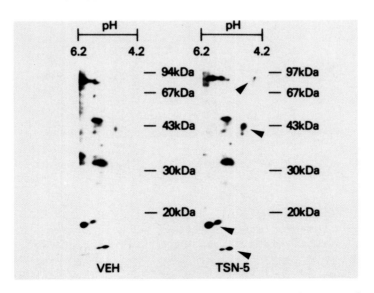

FIGURE 5. Effects of TSN-5 on phosphorylation of
cytosolic proteins in AtT-20 cells. ^{32}P-loaded cells were
treated for 15 min with vehicle (VEH) or TSN-5 (600 µg/ml).

by adrenal glucocorticoids. As this study demonstrates, other factors derived from immune sources also directly influence hormone secretion from corticotropic cells and, thereby, may participate in modulating the activity of the HPA axis during stress.

A preparation of thymic hormones called thymosin (TSN-5), purified thymopoietin (TP), which is not represented in TSN-5 (10,13), and the purified cytokines, IL-1 and IL-2, were examined for their effects on basal and stimulated hormone secretion from AtT-20 corticotropes. TP and IL-1, but not IL-2, increased basal release of iβ-E consistent with their effects on primary cultures of anterior pituitary (4,18). Neither TP nor IL-1, however, augmented CRF-stimulated hormone secretion like TSN-5, which has been found to act synergistically with CRF in the anterior pituitary (19). Like CRF, TSN-5 increased calcium-dependent release of iβ-E and its effects were antagonized by pretreating the AtT-20s with glucocorticoid. The cellular basis for the cooperative actions of TSN-5 and CRF was explored and the stimulatory effects on hormone secretion were found to be mimicked by cotreatment with TSN-5 and forskolin. Nevertheless, unlike CRF or forskolin, TSN-5 did not lower cellular hormone contents or increase basal levels of cAMP and reduced, rather than augmented, the synthesis of cAMP evoked by forskolin treatment. The tumor promotor, phorbol myristate acetate, increased hormone secretion to levels comparable to release induced by CRF or TSN-5 but its additive effects in combination with TSN-5 suggested that, like CRF-mediated secretion, TSN-5 probably promotes secretion of POMC-derived hormones from corticotropes through some mechanism independent of protein kinase C activation. In fact, two-dimensional gel analysis of phosphoproteins in AtT-20 cells revealed that TSN-5 induced 32P incorporation into cytosolic proteins, some which were shared and others, distinct from those in PMA- and forskolin-stimulated corticotropes (20,33).

Together, these findings indicate that the corticotropic constituent(s) of TSN-5 increases hormone secretion through unique mechanisms perhaps parallel to the adenylate cyclase cascade and protein kinase C phosphorylation. The results presented here and elsewhere (17, 18, 19) support the possibility that thymic hormones normally involved with cellular immunity may modulate the activity of the hypothalamic-pituitary adrenal axis through novel actions on pituitary corticotropes.

ACKNOWLEDGEMENTS

This paper is dedicated to the memory of Dr. Thomas O'Donohue whose leadership and contagious enthusiasm inspired these and many other enlightening scientific endeavors. This work was supported in part by the Monsanto Company and Alpha 1 Biomedicals. We appreciate the generous gift of cells provided by Dr. Steven Sabol and of C-55 antiserum from Dr. Gregory Mueller. The authors are grateful to Dianne Dickherber for preparation of the manuscript.

REFERENCES

1. Dinarello CA (1988). Biology of interleukin 1. FASEB J 2:108.
2. Besedovsky HO, del Ray A, Sorkin E, Dinarello CA (1986) Immunoregulatory feedback between inter-leukin-1 and glucocorticoid hormones. Science 233:652.
3. Woloski BMRNJ, Smith EM, Meyer WJ III, Fuller GM, Blalock JE (1985). Corticotropin-releasing activity of monokines. Science 230:1035.
4. Bernton EW, Beach JE, Holaday JW, Smallridge RC, Fein HG (1987). Release of multiple hormones by a direct action of interleukin-1 on pituitary cells. Science 238:519.
5. Berkenbosch FJ, van Oers J, del Rey A, Tilders F, Besedovsky H (1987). Corticotropin-releasing factor-producing neurons in the rat activated by interleukin-1. Science 238:524.
6. Sapolsky R, Rivier C, Yamamoto G, Plotsky P, Vale W (1987). Interleukin-1 stimulates secretion of hypothalamic corticotropin-releasing factor. Science 238:522.
7. Breder CD, Dinarello CA, Saper CB (1988). Interleukin-1 immunoreactive innervation of the human hypothalamus. Science 240:321.
8. Scollay R, Bartlett P, Shortman K (1984). T Cell development in the adult murine thymus: changes in the expression of the surface antigens Ly2, L3T4 and B2A2 during development from early precursor cells to emigrants. Immunol Rev 82:79.
9. Haars R, Kronenberg M, Gallatin WM, Weissman IL, Owen PL, Hood L (1986). Rearrangement and expression of T cell antigen receptor and genes during thymic development. J Exp Med 164:1.

10. Dardenne M, Bach JF (1988). Functional biology of thymic hormones. In Kendall MD, Ritter MA (eds): "Thymus Update 1: The Microenvironment of the Human Thymus," Chur: Harwood Academic, p 101.
11. Deschaux P, Massengo B, Fontages R (1979). Endocrine interaction of the thymus with the hypophysis, adrenals and testes: Effects of two thymic extracts. Thymus 1:95.
12. Healy DL, Hodgen GD, Schulte HM, Chrousos GP, Loriaux DL, Hall NR, Goldstein AL (1983). The thymus-adrenal connection: thymosin has corticotropin-releasing activity in primates. Science 222:1353.
13. Spangelo, B.L., Hall, N.R., Goldstein, A.L. (1987). Biology and chemistry of thymosin peptides-modulators of immunity and neuroendocrine circuits. Proc NY Acad Sci 496:196.
14. McGillis JP, Hall NR, Vahouny GV, Goldstein AL (1985). Thymosin fraction 5 causes increased serum corticosterone in rodents in vivo. J Immunol 134:3952.
15. Vahouny GV, Kyeyune-Nyombi E, McGillis JP, Tare NS, Huang K-Y, Tombes R, Goldstein AL, Hall NR (1983). Thymosin peptides and lymphokines do not directly stimulate adrenal corticosteroid production in vitro. J Immunol 30:791.
16. Dunn AJ, Hall NR (1987). Thymic extracts and lymphokine-containing supernatant fluids stimulate the pituitary-adrenal axis, but not cerebral catecholamine or indolamine metabolism. Brain Behav Immun 1:113.
17. Farah JM Jr, Hall NR, Bishop JF, Goldstein AL, O'Donohue TL (1987). Thymosin fraction 5 stimulates secretion of immunoreactive B-endorphin in mouse corticotropic tumor cells. J Neurosci Res 18:140.
18. Malaise MG, Hazee-Hagelstein MT, Reuter AM, Vrinds-Gevaert Y, Goldstein G, Franchimont P (1987). Thymopoietin and thymopentin enhance the levels of ACTH, β-endorphin and β-lipotropin from rat pituitary cells in vitro. Acta Endocrinol 115:455.
19. McGillis JP, Hall NR, Goldstein AL (1988). Thymosin fraction 5 stimulation of in vitro ACTH release from superfused cultured rat pituitary. Life Sci 42:2259.
20. Bishop JF, Farah JM, Patel J, O'Donohue TL (1987). Activation of distinct second messenger systems in anterior pituitary corticotrophic tumor cells alters the phosphorylation states of both shared and distinct cytosolic proteins. Mol Cell Endocrinol 52:17.

21. Mueller GP, Pettibone DJ, Farah JM Jr, Sapun-Malcolm D (1985). Glucocorticoid inhibition of immunoreactive beta-endorphin release fromthe anterior lobe of the rat pituitary: in vitro and in vivo studies. Proc Soc Exp Biol Med 179:338.
22. Lowry OH, Rosebrough NJ, Farr AL, Randall RJ (1951). Protein measurement with the Folin phenol reagent. J Biol Chem 193:265.
23. Winer BJ (1971). "Statistical Principles in Experimental Design." 2nd Ed, New York:McGraw-Hill.
24. Gumbiner B, Kelly R (1982). Two distinct intracellular pathways transport secretory and membrane glycoproteins to the surface of pituitary tumor cells. Cell 28:51.
25. Axelrod J, Reisine TD (1983). Stress hormones: their interaction and regulation. Science 224:452.
26. Heisler S, Reisine T (1984). Forskolin stimulates adenylate cyclase activity, cyclic AMP accumulation, and adrenocorticotropin secretion from mouse anterior pituitary tumor cells. J Neurochem 42:1659.
27. Bilezikjian LM, Vale WW (1987). Regulation of ACTH secretion from corticotrophs: the interaction of vasopressin and CRF. Ann NY Acad Sci 512:85.
28. Berridge MJ, Irvine RF (1984). Inositol trisphosphate, a novel second messenger in cellular signal transduction. Nature 312:315.
29. Nishizuka Y (1984). The role of protein kinase C in cell surface signal transduction and tumor promotion. Science 233:305.
30. Heisler S (1984). 12-O-tetradecanoylphorbol-13-acetate-induced ACTH secretion in pituitary tumor cells. Eur J Pharmacol 98:177.
31. Affolter H-U, Reisine T (1985). Corticotropin releasing factor increases proopiomelanocortin messenger RNA in mouse anterior pituitary tumor cells. J Biol Chem 260:15477.
32. Nestler EJ, Greengard P (1984). "Protein Phosphorylation in the Nervous System." New York: Wiley.
33. Pasmantier R, Danoff A, Fleischer N, Schubart UK, (1986). P19, a hormonally regulated phosphoprotein of peptide hormone-producing cells: secretagogue-induced phosphorylation in AtT-20 mouse pituitary tumor cells and in rat and hamster insulinoma cells. Endocrinology 19:1229.

II. THE ADRENAL MEDULLA
AND STRESS

Molecular Biology of Stress, pages 123–132
Published 1989 Alan R. Liss, Inc.

ADRENERGIC RESPONSE FOLLOWING RECOGNITION OF STRESS

Irwin J. Kopin, Graeme Eisenhofer, David Goldstein

National Institutes of Health, National Institute of Neurological and Communicative Disorders and Stroke, Bethesda, Maryland 20892

ABSTRACT

The responses of an organism to stressors which are perceived as threats to the preservation of conditions essential for life are mediated by a complex hierarchal network of neuroendocrine systems. The initial manifestations of such stress responses are usually mediated by the sympathoadrenal medullary system and include stimulus-specific responses targetted to correct or compensate for the disturbance.

Sympathoadrenal medullary activity is the efferent limb of many homeostatic reflexive responses, but these reflexes are modulated or overridden by afferents from higher brain regions to alter bodily functions in anticipation of physiological requirements or with emotional state. Failure of homeostasis or severe stress elicit more generalized responses which include physiological changes which do not enhance homeostasis and may indeed be harmful.

Because catecholamines from the adrenal are released directly into the circulation, plasma epinephrine levels reflect adrenal medullary activity. Although activation of sympathetic nerve terminals results in release of norepinephrine (NE), inactivation of NE is mainly by reuptake into the neuron and differences in regional patterns of responses, blood flow changes, and anatomical factors influence how much of the released NE reaches the systemic circulation. Thus plasma NE levels may not reflect changes in sympathetic neuronal activity. Furthermore, alterations in receptors and the mechanisms they activate may influence responses. Alternative methods for assessing sympathetic neuronal responses from NE metabolites and by examining receptors are being studied.

INTRODUCTION

Our understanding of the mechanisms by which the body responds to various disturbances began with Claude Benard's concept of an internal environment - the *milieu interne* - which must be maintained to preserve life. As organisms evolved to become independent of their environment, they developed complex mechanisms to maintain the constancy of their internal environment. This concept was expanded by Walter Cannon, who coined the term "homeostasis" to characterize the "coordinated physiological reactions which maintain the steady states of the body" by the integrated cooperative activity of a wide range of organs. He recognized that emotional as well as physiological disturbances could elicit sympathoadrenomedullary (SAM) responses which are characteristic of physiological changes seen in preparation for "fight or flight". The physiological components of the "fight or flight" responses include cardiovascular, renal, visceral, cutaneous, pulmonary and metabolic changes which may be reasonably interpreted as having survival value in critical situations; the body rapidly is prepared for action.

To examine adrenergic responses to stress it is necessary first to have a clear understanding of what is meant by stress and to have suitable models or situations which can be studied. Second, appropriate parameters of responses of the SAM must be available for measurement. It is the purpose of this presentation to review briefly our present concepts of stress, the measures which have been used to assess SAM responses, and the results which have been obtained in studies of various stressors in experimental animals and humans.

WHAT IS STRESS?

Hans Selye popularized the notion of "Stress" and defined a syndrome produced in response to a variety of stressors. The first stage of the syndrome is an "alarm reaction" associated with SAM discharge. This is followed by a "stage of resistance" during which the hypothalamic-pituitary-adrenal cortical axis is activated and adrenal hypertrophy, lymphoid shrinkage, and gastrointestinal ulceration - the General Adaptation Syndrome - develop. The last stage of Selye's stress response is exhaustion and death. It has become apparent, however, that although there are many common features in SAM initial responses to a variety of stressors, responses to different stressors are not identical (see below).

Definitions of stress have lacked precision and generally have not been sufficiently inclusive. For instance, one definition states that stress is "pressure outside that makes you feel tense inside". This psychologically-oriented subjective definition may be applicable to competitive situations, deadlines, anticipation of disaster or exciting events, etc., but excludes many environmental or biological stressors. In common usage, stress refers to a force or stimulus which tends to disturb a steady state; the obvious biological equivalent is any event, stimulus, or agent which threatens or is perceived to threaten homeostasis. Stressors include disturbances of the internal environment (anoxia, hypoglycemia, etc.), external extremes (heat, cold, centrifugation, etc.), psychological disturbances (fear, anger, surprise, etc) and distress of various types (pain, depression, etc.). Combinations of stressors (e.g., pain and anxiety) are not uncommon.

RESPONSES TO STRESSORS

Although the central theme in Selye's concept of "Stress" is that of a single entity with characteristic responses independent of the stressor, it has become evident that there are differences in the responses elicited by various stressors. Responses to any stressor are complex and have features which are homeostatic and specific to that stressor, as well as components which are non-specific and common to the responses to a variety of other stressors. The responses are not necessarily attended by emotional distress. Generally the more severe, prolonged or frequent the stressor, the greater is enlistment of generalized responses.

Homeostatic and Generalized Responses

The characteristics of homeostatic and generalized responses are listed in Table 1. Homeostatic responses are specific for the stimulus and serve useful adaptive functions. They are generally mediated by the autonomic nervous system and are quite similar among different individuals. The functional changes require energy, but there are few if any structural alterations or pathological changes. When the disturbances are severe, persistent, and/or not corrected adequately by the homeostatic mechanisms, the responses become more generalized; although generalized responses may not appear to contribute to the amelioration of the specific disturbance, they may be important in resisting the potential damages which result from failure of homeostasis. Generalized responses include both SAM and adrenal cortical activation. The intensity of disturbance required to trigger a generalized response appears to vary widely and may in part be determined genetically. When persistent, generalized responses may be attended by structural changes including hypertrophy, dysfunction (related to receptor changes) or tissue damage.

Table 1

Homeostatic Responses

- Stimulus-specific with useful adaptive function
- Mediated by the autonomic nervous system.
- Relatively predictable with small individual variations
- "Cost" is energy utilization for functional change.

Generalized Responses

- Non-specific, with drastic or persistent disturbances
  (failure of homeostasis)
- Sympathoadrenomedullary and adrenal cortical activation
- Wide individual differences in threshold
- "Cost" is cellular component change
  (hypertrophy, dysfunction, tissue damage)

Stressors which affect many tissues and create metabolic disturbances which threaten life (anoxia, hypoglycemia, hemorrhage, circulatory collapse, etc.) elicit the most marked generalized responses; they are mediated mostly by adrenal medullary discharge, predominantly of epinephrine (EPI). This hormonal response increases blood glucose, stimulates the heart, increases blood pressure, increases pulmonary ventilation, activates platelets, etc. Attending sympathetic neuronal responses are highly variable and at times may even be absent.

Psychological responses are frequently generalized but are highly variable in intensity; they appear to be a continuum between a relaxed state and extremes of the "fight or flight" responses (Fig. 1). Alerting reactions progress to alarm or irritation and then to fear or anger and aggression. With progressively more intense attendant physiological and biochemical responses with failure to escape, avoid, or reverse a disturbance, responses progress to the extremes of panic or rage. In these states neither behavior nor physiological responses serve to achieve the desired goal. Abnormalities in the levels of stimulus which elicit these patterns of response occur in various psychiatric and psychosomatic disorders.

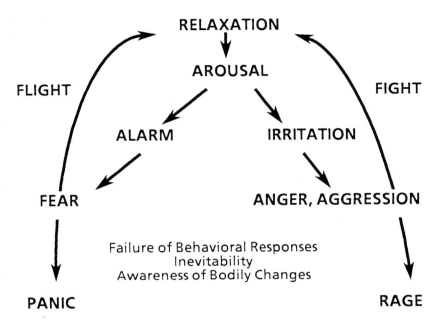

Fig. 1 Arousal States in Response to Environmental Stimuli or Internal Needs

Central Nervous System Regulation of Sympathoadreno-medullary Activity

The final common pathway for the initial responses to various stressors is regional activation of the sympathetic neurons and discharge from the adrenal medulla. The pattern of response depends upon nerve impulses which originate from preganglionic cholinergic neurons located in the intermediolateral gray matter of the thoracic and upper lumbar segments of the spinal cord. Activity of these preganglionic neurons is regulated by descending fibres from the medulla and brain stem as well as by local spinal innervation. The involved pathways and the hierarchal systems which influence SAM activity include components in the cerebral cortex, limbic system, hypothalamus, brainstem and medulla. Their neurotransmitters and their roles have been described by others in this symposium and are beyond the scope of this presentation, but it is important to recognize that the patterns of response to different stressors are determined by psychological as well as physiological factors and that this integration occurs by complex regulatory systems in the brain.

EVALUATION OF ADRENERGIC RESPONSES TO STRESS

Studies of adrenergic responses to stress require selection of experimental or naturally occurring situations which are believed to be stressful and to have available appropriate methods to measure parameters which reflect with adequate precision the characteristics and the intensity of SAM responses.

Table 2

Stress Studies

Animal Models of Stress

Slight Disturbances (*turn on light, open cage, handle gently*)
Major Stressors
Physical (*shock, immobilization, heat, cold*)
Pharmacological (*ether, 2DG*)
Tissue damage (*fracture, hemorrhage, anoxia*)
Psychological (*threaten, predator or anticipation of shock*)

Human Volunteers

Laboratory Situations (*games, interviews, shock*)
On-the-job (*piece work, air traffic controllers*)
Opportunistic
Patients (*trauma, surgery, disaster*)
Disaster (*patient relative*)

Numerous models have been used to examine the effects of stress in experimental animals and human volunteers; examples are listed in Table 2. In animals, studies have varied from use of slight disturbances to major stressors simulating psychological as well as non-psychological disturbances. In humans, voluntary participation in laboratory experimental stress studies may not adequately reflect real life situations.

To obtain more meaningful information, studies have been designed to examine responses of individuals subjected to stress during the course of their daily activities or who, because of an unfortunate circumstance, are exposed to unusual stress.

Assessment of SAM Activity

Although various physiological changes which attend SAM activation provide evidence of the body's response to stressors, only a few of these (heart rate, blood pressure, skin conductivity changes with sweating) can be quantified; they provide coarse indirect measures of autonomic responses.

Activity of sympathetic fibers in peripheral motor nerves can be recorded directly and clearly provides an immediate and useful measure of function in a particular segment of the sympathetic nervous system. However, this procedure requires considerable technical expertise, has been used only in humans and does not necessarily provide an index of overall SAM activity. Recording of sympathetic activity has also been possible in anesthetized small animals, but this method has limitations in the study of stress.

Biochemical measures of the substances secreted at sympathetic terminals and from the adrenal medulla are widely used to assess SAM activity. It had been known since the turn of the century that epinephrine (EPI) is the pressor substance released into the blood from the adrenal medulla, but it was not until about 50 years later that norepinephrine (NE) was proven to be the neurotransmitter substance released at sympathetic nerve terminals.

Development of sensitive and specific methods for measurement of these catecholamines and their metabolites in urine and plasma provided the means for direct biochemical assessment of SAM activation. The first fluorimetric method based on measurements of oxidation products of catecholamines were exacting, tedious, and required relatively large quantities of plasma. More precise and sensitive radioenzymatic methods suitable for measurements of catechols in small volumes of plasma made possible studies in experimental animals. Subsequent introduction of high performance liquid chromatography with electrochemical detection allowed rapid convenient measurements of O-methylated and deaminated metabolites, as well as the catecholamines, in plasma and urine. These developments facilitated studies of SAM responses and encouraged critical assessment of the validity of biochemical indices of SAM activity.

Inactivation of NE released from sympathetic nerve terminals into the synaptic cleft of neuroeffector junctions involves mainly reuptake (uptake 1) into the nerve terminal where it is either destroyed by monoamine oxidase to form dihydroxyphenylglycol (DHPG) or recaptured by synaptic vesicles for reuse. NE which escapes reuptake into the nerve terminal is taken up (uptake 2) into extraneuronal cells or diffuses into the circulation. Depending upon the width of the synaptic cleft and the tissue, only 2-10% of the released NE reaches the effluent blood. Furthermore, a large portion (80%) of NE released into the portal venous blood is removed during a single passage through the liver. Thus, mixed venous blood contains only a small portion of the NE released at peripheral sympathetic nerve terminals and the visceral components are vastly under represented.

Further modifications of plasma NE levels occur as blood traverses the lungs and peripheral tissues. Precise assessment of regional differences in release of NE into the circulation requires infusion of radiolabelled NE and measurement of arterial and regional venous plasma levels of endogenous and isotopically labelled NE. The total body "spillover" of NE can be calculated from the rate of infusion of labelled NE and the specific activity of arterial NE; regional release of NE can be calculated for those vascular beds from which effluent venous blood is sampled. Net NE release is determined from its extraction (which varies with flow rate), venous-arterial differences in concentration and estimates of blood flow. Thus, plasma levels of NE in blood obtained from the antecubital vein have limited value in assessing regional changes in sympathetic activity, but sometimes may reflect changes in generalized sympathetic nerve activity. Since NE taken up into the nerves is largely metabolized to DHPG and then to MHPG, plasma levels of these metabolites may be useful adjuncts to assess sympathetic activation. Because DHPG and MHPG are metabolized more slowly than NE and because DHPG may be formed from NE, which leaks out of vesicles without having been released, the metabolites are less sensitive indices of rapidly changing levels of sympathetic activity.

In contrast to NE, EPI is derived almost wholly from the adrenal medulla and is secreted directly into the circulation.

Although a considerable portion of EPI is removed during the passage of blood through the lungs and tissues, its plasma levels in antecubital venous blood appear to reflect adequately adrenal medullary activity. The basal levels of EPI in plasma are low (<50 pg/ml), but even small increments (>100 pg/ml) elicit physiological responses, whereas increments of NE do not elicit direct responses until the basal levels (about 250 pg/ml) increase more than 5-fold, presumably because of the gradient in NE concentration between plasma and the synaptic clefts. In Table 3, stress-induced increments in plasma catecholamine levels are shown for several representative stressors in humans. The increments in NE levels during standing, hyperthermia, and moderate exercise are relatively greater (expressed as percent basal) than the increments in EPI. Under these conditions compensatory changes in the distribution of the cardiac output are homeostatic mechanisms. The predominant increment in EPI levels during hypoglycemia may also be considered homeostatic since EPI causes glucose release. During public speaking, the increment in EPI probably represents an "alerting" reaction.

Table 3
Stress-induced Increments in Arterial
Plasma Catecholamines (% basal)

	NE	EPI
Standing	+ 110	+ 10
Public Speaking	+ 60	+ 140
Hyperthermia (41.5 °C)	+ 350	+ 30
Mild Hypoglycemia (60 mg %)	+ 50	+ 550
Moderate Exercise	+ 500	+ 200
Strenuous Exercise	+ 700	+ 1800
Severe Hypoglycemia (<30 mg %)	+ 280	+ 2000
Diabetic Ketosis	+ 500	+ 1000
Myocardial Infarction	+ 1000	+ 2000
Shock, Hemorrhage	+ 1500	+ 3000

Elevations in arterial plasma levels of NE are not necessarily attended by equal increments in NE levels in plasma from venous blood in different regions. During hyperthermia the pattern of response facilitates heat loss (cutaneous vasodilation with a regional decrease in sympathetic activity) whereas during exposure to cold a reverse pattern may be encountered. In hypoglycemia, the responses of the sympathetic component may be minimal, most NE and all EPI being derived from the adrenal medulla. During strenuous exercise, components of both sympathetic and adrenal medullary activation are evident. Myocardial infarction, shock or hemorrhage elicit marked increases in adrenal medullary secretion as well as sympathetic neuronal activity. Thus there are multiple patterns of SAM activity which vary with the nature and severity of the stressor. The responses are coordinated with the parasympathetic nervous system, hypothalamic-pituitary-adrenal cortex axis, and other neuroendocrine responses.

When stress is prolonged or repeated, adaptive changes occur in some receptors (usually down regulation), there is induction of catecholamine biosynthetic enzymes in adrenals and sympathetic nerves and processes which alter structure (e.g., hypertrophy of cardiac and vascular smooth muscle) are initiated. The mechanisms which are involved in the disorders which are related to chronic stress remain to be defined, but it is clear that such effects may be of importance in influencing cardiovascular, gastrointestinal, and immune function.

Molecular Biology of Stress, pages 133–142
© 1989 Alan R. Liss, Inc.

CATECHOLAMINES AND STRESS IN THE NEWBORN[1]

Theodore A. Slotkin and Frederic J. Seidler

Department of Pharmacology
Duke University Medical Center
Durham, North Carolina 27710

ABSTRACT. Catecholamines released into the fetal and neonatal circulation play key roles in the adaptation of the organism to extrauterine life. At term, the adrenal medulla secretes large amounts of epinephrine and norepinephrine, utilizing a specialized mechanism which is independent of innervation by the central nervous system, and which is responsible for acute cardiovascular, respiratory and metabolic responses necessary to survive birth. Subsequently, catecholamines released from sympathetic neurons provide trophic signals regulating end-organ cellular development and maturation of sensitivity to neuronal input. Environmental factors which interfere with these mechanisms (stress, drugs, hormonal imbalances) compromise neonatal viability and have adverse effects on cell replication and differentiation.

INTRODUCTION

The release of catecholamines by the adrenal medulla is an integral part of the physiological and metabolic response to "fight-or-flight" situations. In the mature organism, stress results in centrally-derived activation of the splanchnic nerve, which innervates the chromaffin cells of the adrenal medulla. Acetylcholine released by the splanchnic nerve then stimulates nicotinic receptors on the cells to elicit the catecholamine secretory response. Thus, the adrenal medulla behaves like a sympathetic neuronal projection, except that the catecholamines are discharged into the bloodstream instead of a synaptic cleft, and that, in most species the predominant compound released is

---

[1]Supported by USPHS NS-06233 and HD-09713.

epinephrine as opposed to norepinephrine. Adrenal catecholamines, once released into the circulation, are free to act upon adrenergic receptors throughout the periphery, initiating events which are designed to enhance the ability of the organism to survive or to respond appropriately to stress situations.

Studies from a number of laboratories indicate that the adrenal medulla of the fetal and neonatal organism plays a relatively more important role in adaptations to stress than it does in the adult and that adrenal catecholamines may subserve unique functions during critical periods of development. Studies with newborn humans indicates a rise in adrenomedullary activity at the approach of parturition, culminating in a profound surge of catecholamine release at delivery (1-3); the latter phase appears to result from increased intracranial pressure acting alone or in combination with the hypoxia associated with the birth process (4). The marked elevation of circulating catecholamines is thought to assist the neonate in adapting metabolic, cardiovascular and respiratory function to the demands of extrauterine life (5-6), and interference with the catecholamine surge is associated with decreased survival potential (1,2,7). In many species, including the rat, and to a somewhat lesser extent, man, sympathetic innervation of autonomic end-organs is absent or non-functional at birth, and in these cases the neonate is predominantly dependent upon adrenomedullary catecholamines for achieving adrenergic responses to stress. Historically, the rat has provided a convenient model in which to study the development of the adrenal medulla and of sympatho-adrenal function, and much of the information concerning the biochemical and morphological processes occurring in this tissue have been evaluated in that species. On the other hand, classical physiological evaluations are more readily performed on large animals, such as the sheep, pig and cow, species whose sympathetic nervous systems are generally more mature at birth. It is only relatively recently that comparable studies have been feasible in the rat, but available evidence suggests that very similar processes delineate the development of sympatho-adrenal function in all species, with major differences only in the time frame over which maturation occurs.

DEVELOPMENT OF INNERVATION

To a large extent, the mechanisms controlling catecholamine secretion during development are determined by the functional ontogeny of splanchnic innervation. In the rat, splanchnic control of adrenomedullary function is absent at birth, appears towards the end of the first week postnatally, and becomes fully mature by 10 days of age (7-10). Thus, the catecholamine secretory response to insulin-induced hypoglycemia, a stimulus which ordinarily produces reflexly-mediated catecholamine release, is absent. In order for this reflex to take place, four components must be present: (a) the central nervous system must sense the hypoglycemia and send stimuli down the efferent sympathetic pathway, (b) splanchnic nerve connections to the adrenal medulla must be functional, (c) the adrenal medulla must contain nicotinic receptors, and (d) the receptors must be coupled to the secretory response. Studies with excised neonatal adrenals incubated _in vitro_ with depolarizing concentrations of potassium indicate that neonatal chromaffin cells contain all the machinery necessary for exocytotic release of granule contents (11-13); high potassium evokes profound release of catecholamines which is completely prevented by removing calcium from the incubation medium, thus fulfilling the major criteria for exocytosis. Similarly, administration of a test dose of nicotine _in vivo_ readily causes a catecholamine secretory response, indicating that the receptors and receptor-mediated responses are present in the adrenal and are linked to the exocytotic release mechanisms even at 2 days of age, well before the onset of neurally-evoked response capabilities. Nerve recordings in neonatal rats also indicate that the central nervous system is fully responsive to stimuli which evoke sympatho-adrenal reflexes; both hypoglycemia and asphyxia in 2 day olds can elicit activation of preganglionic sympathetic efferents equivalent to that seen in more mature animals (14). It is therefore likely that the neonatal adrenal is unresponsive to neurogenic stimuli because of deficiencies in the function of splanchnic connections to the tissue.

ADRENAL FUNCTION AND NEONATAL SURVIVAL

Despite the absence of functional neuronal connections to the immature adrenal medulla, the tissue is, in fact, not passive to stressful stimuli. Instead, catecholamine release may proceed by a non-neurogenic mechanism which is not present in mature animals. The differences between neurogenic and non-neurogenic release mechanisms can be illustrated by the acute effects of hypoxia (7). In mature animals, stress-induced catecholamine secretion is reflexly-mediated and can therefore be blocked by chlorisondamine, a nicotinic antagonist which prevents splanchnic nerve signals from reaching the chromaffin cells of the adrenal medulla. In neonatal rats, hypoxia produces a catecholamine secretory response, but chlorisondamine cannot block the effect. Additionally, the proportion of norepinephrine and epinephrine released by non-neurogenic stimulation exactly duplicates their ratio in the immature adrenal; in contrast, mature, neurogenic secretion is characterized by selective release of either amine, attendant upon excitation of specific populations of descending spinal neurons which provide afferent input to the splanchnic nerve.

The unique mechanism for catecholamine release from the immature adrenal disappears concurrently with the onset of neurogenic control (7,9,10,15). Studies from our laboratory support the view that the onset of nerve stimuli is responsible for terminating the phase in which non-neurogenic responses are possible. First, acceleration of the onset of splanchnic nerve function caused either by repeated maternal stress during late gestation, or by neonatal hyperthyroidism, is invariably accompanied by the loss of non-neurogenic catecholamine secretory responses. A definitive proof that it is the development of neural competence which initiates the switchover of secretory mechanism has been provided by recent studies in which neonatal rats were subjected to surgical denervation of the adrenals at 3 days of age, prior to the onset of splanchnic function (9). The denervated group maintained the ability to release catecholamines non-neurogenically in response to hypoxia, whereas the response was entirely neurogenic in the innervated cohort. Finally, rats denervated in adulthood also showed the reappearance of non-neurogenic response capabilities after 3 weeks without neural input to the adrenal. Thus, the development of neural stimulation itself appears to be responsible for the ontogenetic loss of the unique response pattern in the fetus and neonate.

An important question is whether the non-neurogenic release of catecholamines in response to hypoxia is of physiological significance to the organism. Interference with adrenal catecholamine actions, either through adrenalectomy (with or without corticosteroid replacement) or through blockade of the effects of circulating catecholamines, leads to loss of the ability of the neonate to survive hypoxia (7,9). In contrast, prevention of catecholamine release from sympathetic nerves (bretylium administration) has no discernible effect, a finding in concert with the relative immaturity of sympathetic neuronal function. Similarly, chlorisondamine, which blocks neural input to the adrenal, does not influence hypoxic survival time until the development of neural competence after the first postnatal week.

The reasons for the dependence of survival on adrenal catecholamines appear to involve both respiratory and cardiovascular components (7,9,16). First, the necessary respiratory adjustments are mediated through β_2-receptors; thus administration of a β_2-antagonist to neonatal rats results in the loss of the ability to survive hypoxia in the immediate neonatal period, but not at later stages of development, when respiratory adaptations to air-breathing are complete. Interestingly, β-receptors do not appear to be critical to the maintenance of cardiac function during neonatal hypoxia: atenolol, a cardiac-specific β_1-receptor blocking agent, does not cause an increase in hypoxia-induced mortality. Instead, survival requires catecholamine effects mediated through cardiac α-receptors and which are unique to the immature animal (16,17). In the heart, α-receptors are present in concentrations exceeding those found in the adult, and this population declines as the tissue acquires β-receptors. So long as catecholamine release and α-receptors remain intact, hypoxia does not cause any significant alteration of heart rate, and cardiac conduction characteristics are well-maintained. However, administration of phenoxybenzamine, an α-receptor blocking agent, results in loss of hypoxia tolerance, marked by a progressive decline in sinus rhythm and appearance of marked atrioventricular conduction defects, culminating in frank cardiac failure. Again, these responses are not present by 8 days of age, when non-neurogenic catecholamine secretory mechanisms have disappeared and cardiac receptor populations lose their immature characteristics. Even when hypoxic exposure occurs at a level insufficient to compromise survival, catecholamines still act on cardiac α-adrenergic receptors to aid in metabolic recovery from low oxygen conditions (18).

A final issue concerning non-neurogenic secretion is the potential for teratologic alteration of the timetable for replacement of immature with mature response mechanisms. Because of the crucial role played by adrenal catecholamines in neonatal survival, perinatal factors which affect catecholamine actions, development of sympathetic nerves, or ontogeny of central regulation of sympathetic outflow all have adverse impact on the development of the organism. The separation of neonatal adrenergic function into non-neurogenic and neurogenic phases produces corresponding differences in the vulnerability to insult by stress, drugs, hormonal imbalance or toxic chemicals. In general, situations which accelerate the onset of nerve competence lead to the premature loss of non-neurogenic response mechanisms and their protective effect toward neonatal hypoxia (7,9). These include neonatal hyperthyroidism (10), exposure to heavy metals (19), maternal drug abuse (8) and maternal stress (7).

Acceleration of neural development is thus neither beneficial, nor innocuous. This has been readily demonstrated for late gestational maternal stress and neonatal hyperthyroidism (7), both of which cause premature onset of innervation and a consequent loss of non-neurogenic secretory mechanisms. Because of the dependence on neural function, these animals are more susceptible to hypoxia-induced death, especially under conditions which compromise neural conduction. If CNS development is at a sufficient level to process appropriate sensory input and stimulate sympathetic nerve supplies, then a problem might not necessarily exist. However, if for any reason CNS function is compromised, then the neonate will be more vulnerable in situations where peripheral neural development has been accelerated. Hypoxia itself may be one of those cases, since prolonged oxygen deprivation results in failure of neural conduction. Maternal opiate abuse is even more likely to produce these conditions, as opiates accelerate peripheral sympathetic synaptogenesis, while slowing CNS development (24-26). The combination of these neural effects may contribute to the increased perinatal mortality and Sudden Infant Death Syndrome which have been noted in the offspring of opiate addicts.

CATECHOLAMINES AND CELLULAR DEVELOPMENT

The development of sympathetic neuronal function occupies two distinct phases during the postnatal period (20). Initially, while terminals are forming in their target tissues, neural activity and transmitter turnover are measurable, but low. After the establishment of fully-functional physiological connections of neurons to their targets, there is a period of pronounced hyperactivity, in which impulse frequency and turnover may reach twice the adult value (14,21). Both these stages appear to be important in determining the maturation of cells in the innervated tissues. First, exposure of postsynaptic sites to norepinephrine mediates the developmental pattern of receptors and receptor-mediated processes (10,20,22,23). In addition, sympathetic neurons appear to coordinate cell replication and differentiation in a manner linked to the two phases of neuronal activity. Low degrees of sympathetic input are required to maintain normal rates of cell replication in peripheral tissues (27). Conversely, the later period of sympathetic hyperactivity initiates the switchover of postsynaptic cells from the replication phase to the differentiation phase (28), thus enhancing the developmental decline in DNA synthesis. These events are coupled to the maturation of sympathetic neural activity and are mediated through β-receptors (28); the specific linkage of the receptors to DNA synthesis disappears immediately after the period of sympathetic hyperactivity.

Thus, in situations where sympathetic neuronal development is compromised, one would expect to see an eventual deficit in cell acquisition. Studies in which sympathetic neurons were destroyed by neonatal administration of 6-hydroxydopamine confirm that low levels of neuronal input are required to maintain cell replication (27). Because high levels of sympathetic activity terminate replication (later phase of development), premature development of sympathetic synapses and/or elevation of sympathetic tone should also have adverse effects on cellular development. Indeed, administration of isoproterenol early in development has been shown to duplicate the shut-down of cell replication which ordinarily attends sympathetic hyperactivity (28). Even more dramatic is the demonstration that abnormalities of kidney growth caused by a teratogen (methylmercury) can be prevented by neonatal sympathectomy (29), confirming that premature arrival of neuronal signals and elevated sympathetic activity caused by this heavy metal compound are responsible for the effects on end-organ development.

Finally, the same programming of responsiveness and cellular development appear to extend to catecholamines within the central nervous system itself. Early interference with transmitter actions compromises the development of receptors and receptor-mediated behavioral and biochemical effects (30,31). Similarly, central denervation of adrenergic pathways in neonates has an adverse effect on structural organization of the brain (32), and high levels of adrenergic input can terminate cell replication (33) just as in the periphery. The findings in the sympathetic nervous system may thus provide a model for demonstrating the linkage between adverse environmental effects on central neuronal development and behavioral teratology (26).

CONCLUSIONS

Release of catecholamines from the adrenal medulla by specialized mechanisms provide a critical signal necessary to survive the stress of birth. Adrenergic target tissues also possess unique receptor populations and response patterns which are required to mediate the adaptation to extrauterine life. The release mechanism and end-organ responses lose their fetal/neonatal characteristics and acquire the adult pattern as a result of the development of sympathetic projections from the CNS to the periphery. Different phases of sympathetic neuronal activity (low at birth, transiently hyperactive immediately after neuronal competence is established) participate in the programming of postsynaptic responsiveness to stimulation and in the timing of cell replication and differentiation. Factors which interfere with neuronal development can thus increase neonatal mortality and evoke permanent changes in physiological response patterns and in structure of innervated tissues.

REFERENCES

1. Lagercrantz H, Bistoletti P (1973). Catecholamine release in the newborn infant at birth. Pediat Res 11:889.
2. Lagercrantz H, Slotkin TA (1986). The "stress" of being born. Sci Am 254(4):100.
3. Slotkin TA, Seidler FJ (1988). Adrenomedullary catecholamine release in the fetus and newborn: secretory mechanisms and their role in stress and survival. J Devl Physiol 10:1.
4. Bistoletti P, Nylund L, Lagercrantz H, Hjemdahl P, Strom H (1983). Fetal scalp catecholamines during labor. Am J Obstet Gynecol 147:785.
5. Jones CT (1980). Circulating catecholamines in the fetus, their origin, actions, and significance. In Parvez H, Parvez S(eds): "Biogenic Amines in Development," Amsterdam: Elsevier, p. 63.
6. Silver M, Edwards AV (1980). The development of the sympathoadrenal system with an assessment of the role of the adrenal medulla in the fetus and neonate. In Parvez H, Parvez S (eds): "Biogenic Amines in Development," Amsterdam: Elsevier, p. 147.
7. Seidler FJ, Slotkin TA (1985). Adrenomedullary function in the neonatal rat: Responses to acute hypoxia. J Physiol 358:1.
8. Slotkin TA, Smith PG, Lau C, Bareis DL (1980). Functional aspects of development of catecholamine biosynthesis and release in the sympathetic nervous system. In Parvez H, Parvez S (eds): "Biogenic Amines in Development," Amsterdam: Elsevier, p. 29.
9. Seidler FJ, Slotkin TA (1986). Ontogeny of adrenomedullary responses to hypoxia and hypoglycemia: Role of splanchnic innervation. Brain Res Bull 16:11.
10. Slotkin TA (1986). Development of the sympatho-adrenal axis. In Gootman PM (ed): "Developmental Neurobiology of the Autonomic Nervous System," Clifton, NJ: Humana, p. 69.

11. Slotkin TA (1973). Maturation of the adrenal medulla. I. Uptake and storage of amines in isolated storage vesicles of the rat. Biochem Pharmacol 22:2023.

12. Slotkin TA (1973). Maturation of the adrenal medulla. II. Content and properties of catecholamine storage vesicles of the rat. Biochem Pharmacol 22:2033.

13. Rosenthal RN, Slotkin TA (1977). Development of nicotinic responses in the rat adrenal medulla and long-term effects of neonatal nicotine administration. Brit J Pharmacol 60:59.

14. Smith PG, Slotkin TA, Mills E (1982). Development of sympathetic ganglionic transmission in the neonatal rat: Pre- and postganglionic nerve response to asphyxia and 2-deoxyglucose. Neuroscience 7:501.

15. Chantry CJ, Seidler FJ, Slotkin TA (1982). Non-neurogenic mechanism for release of catecholamines from the adrenal medulla of neonatal rats: Possible modulation by opiate receptors. Neuroscience 7:673.

16. Seidler FJ, Brown KK, Smith PG, Slotkin TA (1987). Toxic effects of hypoxia on neonatal cardiac function in the rat: α-Adrenergic mechanisms. Toxicol Lett 37:79.

17. Slotkin TA, Kavlock RJ, Cowdery T, Orband L, Bartolome M, Whitmore WL, Bartolome J (1986). Effects of neonatal methylmercury exposure on adrenergic receptor binding sites in peripheral tissues of the developing rat. Toxicology 41:95.

18. Slotkin TA, Orband-Miller L, Queen KL (1987). Do catecholamines contribute to the effects of neonatal hypoxia on development of brain and heart? Influence of concurrent α-adrenergic blockade on ornithine decarboxylase activity. Intl J Devl Neuroscience 5:135.

19. Slotkin TA, Bartolome J (1987). Biochemical mechanisms of developmental neurotoxicity of methylmercury. Neurotoxicology 8:65.

20. Slotkin TA (1986). Endocrine control of synaptic development in the sympathetic nervous system: The cardiac-sympathetic axis. In Gootman PM (ed): "Developmental Neurobiology of the Autonomic Nervous System," Clifton, NJ: Humana Press, p. 97.

21. Seidler FJ, Slotkin TA (1981). Development of central control of norepinephrine turnover and release in the rat heart: Responses to tyramine, 2-deoxyglucose and hydralazine. Neuroscience 6:2081.

22. Seidler FJ, Slotkin TA (1979). Presynaptic and postsynaptic contributions to ontogeny of sympathetic control of heart rate in the preweanling rat. Brit J Pharmacol 65:531.

23. Lau C, Slotkin TA (1980). Maturation of sympathetic

neurotransmission in the rat heart. II. Enhanced development of presynaptic and postsynaptic components of noradrenergic synapses as a result of neonatal hyperthyroidism. J Pharmacol Exp Ther 212:126.

24. Slotkin TA, Whitmore WL, Salvaggio M, Seidler FJ (1979). Perinatal methadone addiction affects brain synaptic development of biogenic amine systems in the rat. Life Sci 24:1223.

25. Slotkin TA, Thadani PV (1980). Neurochemical teratology of drugs of abuse. In Persaud TVN (ed): "Neural and Behavioural Teratology, Advances in the Study of Birth Defects, vol. 4," Lancaster: MTP Press, p. 199.

26. Slotkin TA (1988). Perinatal exposure to methadone: How do early biochemical alterations cause neurofunctional disturbances? Progr Brain Res 73:in press.

27. Slotkin TA, Levant B, Orband-Miller L, Queen KL, Stasheff S (1988). Do sympathetic neurons coordinate cellular development in the heart and kidney? Effects of neonatal central and peripheral catecholaminergic lesions on cardiac and renal nucleic acids and proteins. J Pharmacol Exp Ther 244:166.

28. Slotkin TA, Whitmore WL, Orband-Miller L, Queen KL, Haim K (1987). Beta-adrenergic control of macromolecule synthesis in neonatal rat heart, kidney and lung: Relationship to sympathetic neuronal development. J Pharmacol Exp Ther 243:101.

29. Bartolome J, Trepanier PA, Chait EA, Barnes GA, Lerea L, Whitmore WL, Weigel SJ, Slotkin TA (1984). Neonatal methylmercury poisoning in the rat: Effects on development of peripheral sympathetic nervous system. Neuronal participation in methylmercury-induced cardiac and renal overgrowth. Neurotoxicology 5:45.

30. Friedhoff AJ, Miller JC (1983). Prenatal psychotropic drug exposure and the development of central dopaminergic and cholinergic neurotransmitter systems. Monogr Neural Sci 9:91.

31. Deskin R, Seidler FJ, Whitmore WL, Slotkin TA (1981). Development of α-noradrenergic and dopaminergic receptor systems depends on maturation of their presynaptic nerve terminals in the rat brain. J Neurochem 36:1683.

32. Lovell J (1982). Effects of 6-hydroxydopamine-induced norepinephrine depletion on cerebellar development. Devl Neuroscience 5:359.

33. Slotkin TA, Windh R, Whitmore WL, Seidler FJ (1988). Adrenergic control of DNA synthesis in developing rat brain regions: Effects of intracisternal administration of isoproterenol. Neuroscience, in press.

Molecular Biology of Stress, pages 143–151

INTEGRATED NEUROENDOCRINE STRESS RESPONSES IN FETAL SHEEP

James F. Padbury, Alma M. Martinez,
Siang L. Thio, and Elizabeth Burnell

Department of Pediatrics, Harbor-UCLA Medical Center
UCLA School of Medicine, Torrance, CA 90509

ABSTRACT

Catecholamines and endogenous opiate peptides, including enkephalins, are co-stored in many regions of the central and peripheral nervous system. We demonstrate that blockade of endogenous opiates with naloxone augments the fetal epinephrine response to hypoxia, geometric mean epinephrine 990 pg/ml during hypoxia alone versus 5500 pg/ml during hypoxia plus naloxone. We further demonstrate that hypoxia evokes simultaneous increases in catecholamines and a high molecular weight form of enkephalins. There is no change in circulating methionine enkephalin peptide. These results suggest that endogenous opiate peptides exert a limit on catecholamine release during hypoxic stress in the fetus. Further, the results suggest that enkephalin peptides are co-secreted with catecholamines and that post-translation processing of high MW enkephalins takes place post-secretion.

INTRODUCTION

Endogenous opiate peptides (OP), opiate receptors and catecholamines are co-localized throughout many regions of the central and peripheral nervous system. OP are localized

This work was supported by grants from the USPHS HD 22003 and HD 18014.

to brain-stem nuclei and pathways importantly involved in autonomic regulation. Enkephalins (ENK), a major class of OP, are found in sympathetic ganglia (1), preganglionic neurons (2) and the adrenal medulla (2). This co-localization with the sympathoadrenal system has been suggested to indicate an important role in the regulation of autonomic function (3). Indeed, OP have been demonstrated to block ganglionic transmission (4) and release of norepinephrine from central and peripheral noradrenergic neurons (5,6) and to inhibit adrenal catecholamine release (7). These interactions with the sympathoadrenal system are most evident during periods of increased sympathoadrenal activity. Blockade of OP with the antagonist naloxone has little effect during quiescence but greatly augments stimulated sympathetic nerve firing rate and catecholamine release.

In addition to co-localization with catecholamines, enkephalins are co-secreted in response to cholinergic or depolarizing stimuli (8,9). Enkephalins are best studied in adrenal medullary chromaffin cells where they are co-stored with CA in intact chromaffin granules in a molar ratio of 1 to 750 to 1000 (10). Enkephalins are stored as the pro-enkephalin pro-hormone, carboxy-extended portions of the pro-hormone of varying intermediate length and as the free penta-peptides methionine and leuceine enkephalin (met & leu-ENK). The pro-enkephalin molecule contains four copies of met-ENK, one of leu-ENK and one each of met-arg-phe and met-arg-gly-leu. The penta, hepta and octa peptides represent only 10-20% of the total enkephalin equivalents demonstrable after proteolytic cleavage of the total adrenal enkephalins (8-10).

There is relatively little data on the interaction of OP systems with the sympathoadrenal system during fetal life. We have demonstrated naloxone augments even further the surge in catecholamines at birth (11). However, interpretation of these results is difficult because dose response data were not available. There are no data on co-secretion of catecholamines and enkephalins in developing animals in vivo. We therefore designed experiments to determine the dose response effect of naloxone on fetal catecholamine release and to simultaneously measure circulating enkephalin levels. To evoke catecholamine and enkephalin release, we chose hypoxia in the chronically catheterized fetal sheep. A portion of these results have been presented in detail elsewhere (12).

METHODS

The details of fetal catheterization and post-operative care have been presented (12). In this series of experiments, seven singleton fetuses were catheterized at 115-118 days gestation (term = 150 days). Beginning at 122 days, the fetuses were randomly assigned to one of seven treatment protocols: saline infusion, naloxone infusion alone, or hypoxia plus naloxone infusion at 0.1, 0.5, 1.0 and 2.0 mg/kg. The naloxone was administered at the start of hypoxia as a bolus (mg/kg) followed by a continuous infusion (mg/kg/hr). Hypoxia was induced by placing a clear plastic bag over the head of the ewe and allowing her to breathe 12-14% oxygen. Fetal heart rate, blood pressure and amniotic fluid pressure were recorded continuously on a polygraph. Plasma catecholamine, arterial blood gas and biophysical measurements were made in duplicate during a baseline period and after 10 and 20 minutes of each infusion. Plasma catecholamines were measured by radioenzymatic assay as described previously (11). Arterial blood gases were measured at 39°C. All fetal pressures were corrected for amniotic fluid pressure. The fetuses were allowed to recover 2-3 days between studies. All fetuses underwent each of the seven protocols.

In the second series of experiments, an additional group of chronically catheterized fetal sheep were studied at 122-124 days gestation. In this group of experiments plasma catecholamines and plasma enkephalins were measured simultaneously before and at 5, 10, 15 and 20 minutes of hypoxia. Hypoxia was induced similarly. Enkephalins were measured by radioimmunoassay using a commercial met-enkephalin antisera (Immunonuclear Inc., Stillwater, Minn). This antisera cross-reacts 2.8% with leu-ENK. Prior to assay, plasma was acidified with 1/10 volume 5NHCl and then extracted through polystyrene columns (13). This measurement represents therefore free met-ENK immunoreactivity. Recovery of met-ENK standard was greater than 90% at 1000, 500 and 200 pg/ml. Sensitivity of the assay was 2.3±0.3 pg/ml. Inter and intra-assay variability is 13 and 9% respectively. All samples were diluted appropriately prior to assay. For measurement of larger molecular weight forms of ENK, or "total ENK", plasma was first treated to sequential digestion with trypsin and carboxypeptidase B as described by Chaminade et al (8). Gel filtration chromatography was used to separate plasma proteins representing total ENK. Acidified plasma was applied to a 0.9 x 57 cm column equilibrated with 1N acetic acid. The column was eluted at 0.5 ml/min and 0.75 ml fractions were collected. The fractions were then taken to dryness in a Savant speed-vac evaporator and assayed directly for free ENK or digested with trypsin and carboxypeptidase and extracted prior to assay.

All data is expressed as mean ± SEM. All norepinephrine (NE) and epinephrine (E) values were log transformed prior to statistical manipulation. Plasma catecholamine and enkephalin levels and biophysical responses to hypoxia were compared by one-way analysis of variance (ANOVA) followed by Dunnett's test.

RESULTS

There was no significant difference in baseline NE (418±23 pg/ml), E (9±2 pg/ml), pH (7.36±0.03), pO2 (22±0.5 mmHg), HR (157±5 bpm), or BP (77±1) among the animals prior to any of the treatment protocols (p>0.1, ANOVA). Additionally, there was no significant effect of saline alone or naloxone alone on any of these parameters.

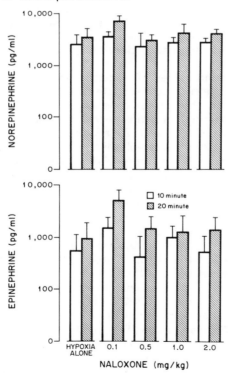

Figure 1. See legend on facing page.

The results of hypoxia alone and hypoxia plus naloxone at each of the four doses on plasma NE and E are shown in Figure 1. Plasma E levels were significantly increased during hypoxia plus 0.1 mg/kg naloxone compared to hypoxia alone (geometric mean E 5400±3144 pg/ml vs 999±981 pg/ml at 20 minutes, ANOVA p<0.05,. There was no significant difference in plasma E during hypoxia at any of the higher naloxone doses. Plasma NE was consistently greater during hypoxia with naloxone than hypoxia alone however these differences were just at the level of significance (0.05<p<0.1).

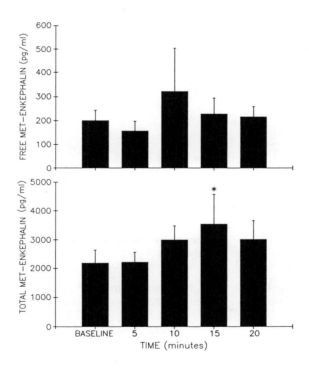

Figure 2: Plasma free and total met-ENK levels during hypoxia in fetal sheep.

Figure 1: Plasma NE and E values during hypoxia alone or hypoxia plus naloxone at the indicated dosages.

The free and total ENK levels during hypoxia in the second series of experiments are shown in figure 2. Baseline free met ENK was 228±72 pg/ml. As can be seen there was no significant change in free met-ENK during hypoxia. Total met-ENK was significantly greater during baseline than free met-ENK (2200 vs 228 p<0.001). During hypoxia total ENK rose significantly (3500±1058 pg/ml at 15 min). The gel filtration results for pooled sheep plasma obtained during hypoxia are shown in Figure 3. Free met-ENK immunoreactivity co-eluted exactly with met-ENK standard. Plasma separated by gel-filtration and then digested with trypsin and carboxypeptidase revealed at least two major peaks of immunoreactivity at molecular weight markers near 67 and 43 kilodaltons.

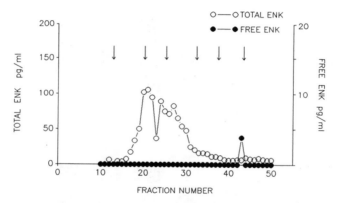

Figure 3: Gel filtration of pooled fetal sheep plasma during hypoxia. Values are for free and total met-ENK.

DISCUSSION

These results confirm and extend our previous observations on the ability of naloxone to augment catecholamine release (11). In the delivery studies we observed an increase in both NE and E with naloxone. During hypoxia only E levels were increased by naloxone administration. It is known that at the gestational ages studied, E is the predominant amine released in response to hypoxia (14). Naloxone is a relatively non-selective opiate receptor antagonist which however has a 10 fold lower Kd for antagonism of mu versus delta receptor mediated effects in adult animals (15,16). We observed an effect on CA release only at the lowest naloxone dose. This is consistent with interpretation the naloxone was antagonizing a mu receptor mediated blockade of catecholamine release. It is possible however that naloxone at the higher dose was blocking a central delta receptor mediated increase in catechol-amine release as suggested by Van Loon (17).

We observed no change in free met-ENK levels during hypoxia but a modest increase in total ENK levels. Co-secretion of catecholamines and ENK peptides has been demonstrated previously in vitro in retrograde perfused bovine (8,9). Both low MW met-ENK peptides and higher molecular weight forms have been observed (8). The species of peptide released appears to depend on the stimulus and strength of depolarization used. Low degrees of depolarization release smaller amounts of all species whereas higher degrees of depolarization release predominantly the larger molecular weight forms (8).

There is relatively little data on release of ENK peptides in vivo. Medbak et al recently reported increased met-ENK immunoreactivity during hypoglycemia in dogs (18). Farrell et al have also reported increased plasma ENK in dog plasma during hemorrhage (19). These are the first data in developing animals of which we are aware.

We observed met-ENK immunoreactivity eluting by gel filtration in the region of MW standards of 40-60 kD. By inference from the primary gene sequence, the MW of the proenkephalin pro-hormone is nearer 30,000 (20). Whether the apparent MW of the plasma substrates we observed represents peptide binding to plasma proteins or multimeric forms of the larger peptides remains to be determined. Singer et al recently reported that pepsin treatment of cat plasma reveals authentic met-ENK immunoreactivity in the near micromolar range (21). Additional clarification of the nature of the plasma substrates and species of circulating ENK peptides in adult and developing animals remains to be determined.

Our data suggests that post-translational processing of the large molecular weight forms of met-ENK immunoreac-tivity takes place post-secretion. Where this processing does take place and where the active peptides exert their physiologi-cal effects are the subjects of exciting future research efforts.

REFERENCES

1. Schultzberg M, Hokfelt T, Lundberg JM, Terenius L, Elfvin L-G, Elde R (1978). Enkephalin-like immunoreactivity in nerve terminals in sympathetic ganglia and adrenal medulla and in adrenal medullary gland cells. Acta Physiol Scand 103:475.

2. Schultzberg M, Lundberg JM, Hokfelt T, Terenius L, Brandt J, Elde RP, Goldstein M (1978). Enkephalin-like immunoreactivity in gland cells and nerve terminals of the adrenal medulla. Neuroscience 3:1169.

3. Holoday JW (1983). Cardiovascular effects of endogenous opiate systems. Ann Rev Pharmacol Toxicol 23:5431.

4. Konishi S, Tsunoo A, Otsuka M (1979). Enkephalins presynaptically inhibit cholinergic transmission in sympathetic ganglia. Nature 282:515.

5. Konishi S, Tsunoo A, Otsuka M (1981). Enkephalin as a transmitter for presynaptic inhibition in sympathetic ganglia. Nature 294:80.

6. Schoffelmeer AMN, Mulder AH (1984). Presynaptic opiate receptor and 2-adrenoceptor mediated inhibition of noradrenaline release in the rat brain: role of hyperpolarization? Eur J Pharmacol 105:129.

7. Kumkura K, Karoum F, Guidotti A, Costa E (1980). Modulation of nicotine receptors by opiate receptor agonists in cultured adrenal chromaffin cells. Nature 283:489.

8. Chaminade M, Foutz AS, Rossier J (1984). Co-release of enkephalins and precursors with catecholamines from the perfused cat adrenal gland in situ. J Physiol 353:157.

9. Viveros OH, Diliberto EJ, Hazum E, Chang KJ (1979). Opiate-like materials in the adrenal medulla: Evidence for storage and secretion with catecholamines. Mol Pharmacol 16:1101.

10. Winkler H, Apps DK, Fischer-Colbrie R (1986). The molecular function of adrenal chromaffin granules: Established facts and unresolved topics. Neuroscience 18:261.

11. Padbury JF, Agata Y, Polk DH, Wang DL, Callegari CC (1987). Neonatal adaptation: Naloxone increases the Neonatal adaptation: Naloxone increases the catecholamine surge at birth. Pediatr Res 21:590.

12. Martinez A, Padbury J, Shames L, Evans C, Humme J (1988). Naloxone potentiates epinephrine release during hypoxia in fetal: Dose response and cardiovascular effects. Pediatr Res 23:343.

13. Vogel Z, Altstein M ((1977). The adsorption of enkephalin to porous polystyrene beads: A simple assay for enkephalin hydrolysis. Febs Letters 80: 332.

14. Comline RS, Silver M (1961). The release of adrenaline and noradrenaline from the adrenal glands of the foetal sheep. J Physiol 156:424.

15. Paterson SJ, Robson LE, Kosterlitz HW (1983). Classification of opioid receptors. Brit Med Bull 39: 31.

16. Gordon FJ (1986). Central opioid receptors and baroreflex control of sympathetic and cardiovascular function. J Pharmacol Exp Ther 237:428.

17. Van Loon GR, Appel NM, Ho D (1981). β-endorphin-induced increases in plasma epinephrine, norepinephrine and dopamine in rats: inhibition of adrenomedullary response by intracerebral somatostatin. Brain Res 212:207.

18. Medbak S, Mason DFJ, Rees LH (1987). Plasma met-enkephalin and catecholamine responses to insulin-induced hypoglycaemia in greyhounds. J Endocrinol 114: 81.

19. Farrell LD, Harrison TS, Demers LM (1983). Immunoreactive met-enkephalin in the canine adrenal: Response to acute hypovolemic stress (41680). Proc Soc Exp Biol Med 173:515.

20. Noda M, Furutani Y, Takahashi H, Toyosato M, Hirose T, Inayama S, Nakanishi S, Numa S (1982). Cloning and sequence analysis of cDNA for bovine adrenal preproenkephalin. Nature 295:202.

21. Singer EA, Mitra SP, Carraway RE (1986). Plasma protein(s) yield met-enkephalin-related peptides in near-micromolar concentrations when treated with pepsin. Endocrinology 119:1527.

Molecular Biology of Stress, pages 153–165
© 1989 Alan R. Liss, Inc.

MECHANISMS OF TRANSSYNAPTIC AND GLUCOCORTICOID REGULATION
OF ADRENAL OPIATE PEPTIDES: A MOLECULAR-DEVELOPMENTAL
APPROACH TO STRESS-RESPONSIVENESS *

Edmund F. La Gamma and Joseph D. DeCristofaro

Pediatrics and Neurobiology & Behavior
School of Medicine
State University of New York at Stony Brook
Stony Brook, New York 11794-8111

ABSTRACT: Multiple lines of evidence indicate that
sympathoadrenal transmitter-gene expression is
regulated by stress-induced changes in transsynaptic
and hormonal environmental signals. The intensity and
duration of these whole animal stimuli can either
augment or suppress enkephalin peptide levels in the
rat adrenal medulla. In contrast, catecholamine
pathways always appear to be induced by these same
stimuli. Early in development transsynaptic impulses
cause transmitter release but fail to alter
biosynthesis of either adrenal medullary
catecholamines or opiate peptides. This suggests that
certain signal-transduction processes are immature.
Moreover, in general, predominant effects appear to
reside at the level of transmitter-gene expression. In
turn, gene read-out is influenced by converging
regulatory signals via calcium, cyclic nucleotide, and
glucocorticoid second-messenger systems. We speculate
that various signal-transduction mechanisms may
influence transmitter-gene expression directly (eg.
glucocorticoids) or indirectly via phosphoprotein
intermediates. Characterization of gene regulatory
proteins and specific molecular mechanisms is the
logical extension of this work.

---

*   This work was supported by grants from the National
Institutes of Health, American Heart Association, March of
Dimes Foundation, Dysautonomia Foundation, and the National
Science Foundation.

INTRODUCTION

Whole animal stress phenomena are manifest as spatial-temporal arrays of biochemical messages which uniquely represent a discrete biological stimulus to individual cells (1). The additional phenomenon of stimulus-secretion-synthesis coupling allows various effector organs to adapt to changing environments by altering effector-receptor molecule number or sensitivity; in many cases, at the genomic level (1,2,34). In this regard, it is generally held that insights into regulated gene expression will have profound implications for understanding neuronal function, differentiation during development, and in defining mechanisms of phenotypic plasticity in maturity (2).

The current report will focus on mechanisms through which stressful enviornmental stimuli are transduced into intracellular messages that regulate catecholamine and opiate peptide transmitter-gene expression. We have chosen a critical stress-organ, the adrenal medulla of the rat, to study transmitter biosynthesis, since this system allows for both in vivo and in vitro studies. The role of release of catecholamines and opiate peptides in mediating stress-responsiveness has been reviewed previously (1,3,4,34).

METHODS

Experimental Animals and Culture Methods

Adrenal medullae were obtained from male Sprague-Dawley rats of various postnatal ages (Hilltop Lab Animals, Scottsdale, PA). Methods of dissection and culture of explanted medullae have been described elsewhere (5-10).

Leu-enkephalin Radioimmunoassay and Measurement of Preproenkephalin mRNA

Leu-enkephalin free peptide and total (prohormone) immunoreactivity was assayed according to methods previously described and validated by high pressure liquid chromatography (5,11).

Preproenkephalin mRNA levels were determined by Northern blot analysis after phenol/chloroform extraction of total nucleic acids from pooled adrenal medullary tissue (6,9).

Transcription "Run-On" Assay

The rate of transmitter gene transcription was
compared using minor modifications of published "run-on"
protocols (12,13) after medullae were obtained from
unmanipulated control rats, or after being grown for 48
hours in standard culture medium with the addition of 50 mM
NaCl (Na $^+$) or 50 mM KCl (K $^+$).

RESULTS AND DISCUSSION

A wealth of evidence indicates that transsynaptic
impulse activity regulates leu-enkephalin peptide,
prohormone, and preproenkephalin mRNA in the rat adrenal
medulla _in vivo_ and _in vitro_ (5-11,14-21). Specifically,
sustained transsynaptic activity and membrane
depolarization appear to suppress enkephalin biosynthetic
pathways (5-11,15-18,25,30), except perhaps during severe
short-term hypoglycemic stress (19-21).

It appears that depolarization prevents the rise in
opiate peptides through the mediation of calcium ion influx
and the activation of a specific second-messenger system.
Chelation of extracellular Ca $^{++}$, blockade of transmembrane
Ca $^{++}$ influx with verapamil or D600, and inhibitors of Ca^{++}
binding to calmodulin or protein kinase C (trifluoperazine)
during KCl-induced depolarization, all attenuate the
inhibitory effects on enkephalin pathways (9). The calcium
ionophore A23187 reproduced the inhibitory effects of
depolarization on enkephalin levels even in the absence of
depolarizing stimuli (9).

Thus, our observations in conjunction with previous
reports suggest that the very same sequence of molecular
events may differentially regulate co-localized adrenal
neurohormones. Increased transsynaptic impulse activity,
nicotinic receptor-induced depolarization, calcium ion
influx, and elevated levels of cAMP all serve to suppress
opiate peptides in the rat adrenal medulla (5-11,14-18,25).
In contrast, these same stimuli induce tyrosine
hydroxylase-mRNA, tyrosine hydroxylase protein, and
tyrosine hydroxylase activity (TH; the rate limiting enzyme
in catecholamine biosynthesis [1,2,22-24,34]). These data
suggest that co-localized opiate peptides and
catecholamines may be independently (differentially ?)
regulated in the rat adrenal medulla and that a
phosphoprotein intermediate may be required (Figure).

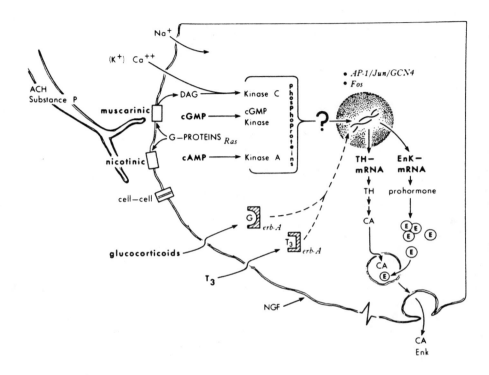

FIGURE: RELATIONSHIPS BETWEEN CHROMAFFIN CELL BIOSYNTHETIC FUNCTIONS AND TRANSMITTER RELEASE. Various extracellular signals converge on multiple interacting receptors and intracellular second-messenger systems to regulate transmitter release and gene expression in the adrenal medulla. Factors important in enkephalin and tyrosine hydroxylase regulation are indicated; see text and cited reviews for details (T3- thyroid hormone, NGF- nerve growth factor, E- enkephalin peptide, CA- catecholamines, TH- tyrosine hydroxylase, italicized words- oncogene proteins that have homologous cellular equivalents or recently characterized transcription factors [1,2,31,32,34,36,38,40, 41]).

Effects of Depolarization on Transmitter Gene Expression

To determine whether membrane depolarization affects the rate of transmitter-gene readout or alternatively, only affected mRNA stability, we exposed medullary explants to elevated levels of potassium ion. Using run-on transcription assays to measure the rate of RNA synthesis, we found that depolarization resulted in a 2.5-fold decrease in enkephalin-gene transcription (25). In contrast, tyrosine hydroxylase-gene readout remained unchanged by KCl-induced membrane depolarization (25). These results are entirely consistent with our previous studies on the effects of depolarization on preproenkephalin mRNA and tyrosine hydroxylase activity in the explant model (5,6,9).
Moreover, these data indicate that depolarizing stimuli may independently alter the transcription of specific transmitter-genes in the rat adrenal medulla. This may not be the case in bovine chromaffin cells where these co-localized transmitter systems appear to be regulated in tandem (27,28) or for the human enkephalin gene where cAMP induces the transfected gene in a tumor cell line (29). Nevertheless, observations in the rat support the contention that mechanisms of differential regulation result from differences in intracellular signal-transduction to the genome. The additional finding of species-specific regulation raises the intriguing question: Are species-specific enkephalin effects the result of the gene's structure or of the cellular environment in which the gene resides ? Future work must address this issue through transfection of human and rat preproenkephalin genes into the same cell line, subsequent in vitro mutagenesis, and further characterization of mechanisms of gene control (see below).

Intensity and Diversity as Control Mechanisms

Regulatory mechanisms in integrated, whole animal stress-responses are unlikely to be restricted to cholinergic-transsynaptic impulses alone (Figure). In fact, it is long recognized that stressful environmental stimuli elicit profound changes in the hormonal milieu as well (see glucocorticoids below [1]). For example, short-term, insulin-induced hypoglycemic shock (2 hours) is a potent stimulus for sympathoadrenal discharge of epinephrine

(1,20,21,31,34,39). This brief stress is associated with a sustained (eg. for several days) _increase_ in preproenkephalin mRNA, prohormone, and peptide which is, at least in part, mediated by cholinergic-nicotinic transsynaptic impulses (19-21) and possibly other hormonal signals as well. How then can the same cholinergic-transsynaptic, depolarizing stimulus both suppress and augment enkephalin levels while simultaneously augmenting catecholamine (ie. tyrosine hydroxylase) pathways under similar conditions (1,20-22,34)?

To begin to answer this question, we used cold-stress (4°C) which has long been recognized as a standard model for augmenting sympathoadrenal impulse activity and for induction of catecholamine pathways (1,22). Cold-stress decreased or had no effect on adrenal medullary opiate peptide levels (30). However, when the severity of cold-stress was increased by wetting the animals twice per day, enkephalin levels also rose to 195% of control animals housed individually at 21°C (30). Wetting in the absence of cold-stress had no effect (30).

Since cold-stress increases catecholamine release and biosynthesis by increasing transsynaptic impulse activity of the splanchnic (cholinergic) nerve, we treated rats with cholinergic-nicotinic and cholinergic-muscarinic receptor agonists. Neither nicotine nor carbechol (preferential muscarinic receptor agonist) alone affected enkephalin levels. However, when administered _simultaneously_, there was a three-fold rise in leu-enkephalin peptide and prohormone (30). Mechanisms of regulation were then examined at the cellular level.

Increased levels of the nicotinic receptor-linked, second-messenger, cAMP, suppressed enkephalin biosynthesis, while elevated levels of the muscarinic receptor-linked, second-messenger, cGMP, had no effect (8,30). Similar to effects using combined receptor agonists, simultaneous administration of forskolin (which increases cAMP; nicotinic receptor pathway [1,32,34]) _plus_ elevated levels of cGMP (ie. db-cGMP; muscarinic receptor pathway [1,32,34]), was associated with a 3-fold rise in enkephalin peptide and prohormone levels (30). These observations suggest there is an interaction between cholinergic-nicotinic and cholinergic-muscarinic, receptor-linked, second-messenger pathways which may begin to explain the differences in effects on enkephalin levels between cell-depolarization and insulin-shock in the rat (5,6,9-11,19-21). We propose that receptor cooperativity can selectively augment or suppress enkephalin levels in proportion to the amount of acetylcholine presynaptically released from the splanchnic nerve.

This hypothesis is tenable since it is already well documented that certain stimuli preferentially yield muscarinic-like, then nicotinic-like responses (1,32,34) or can preferentially release epinephrine (hypoglycemia [1,20,21,31,34,39]) while others release norepinephrine (hypoxia, hypotension [1,31,33, 34]). Other evidence illustrates differential chromaffin vesicle release. Epinephrine-peptide containing transmitter vesicles are released preferentially over norepinephrine (peptide-free) vesicles in response to a specific pattern of nerve stimulation (35,36). Even whole animal analgesic responses (adrenal enkephalin-dependent) are elicited by only certain patterns of electric foot-shock and splanchnic nerve activity, but not by others (37). Together these studies support the contention that selective second-messenger pathway activation is a physiologically relevant transsynaptic-regulatory mechanism governing adrenal transmitter biosynthesis as well as release.

Development of Transsynaptic Regulation

In view of these intriguing observations involving cholinergic receptor pathway interactions, additional insights into regulatory mechanisms may accrue by examining transsynaptic regulation during ontogeny at ages known to be critical for development of the catecholamine system (38,39).

Adrenal leu-enkephalin was first detected at embryonic age 16.5 days (term is 22.5 days) and increased 5 fold from birth to adulthood. Interestingly, the initial appearance of enkephalin occurred significantly later than the appearance of catecholamine markers; similar to studies in human adrenals (10). Distinct ontological schedules for tyrosine hydroxylase and enkephalin supports the thesis that separate regulatory mechanisms govern biosynthesis of these co-localized and co-released transmitters.

Before 10 days postnatal age, adrenal opiate peptide levels fail to increase after removal of transsynaptic influences, (ie. no increase after denervation or explantation [10]), yet these same maturing adrenals require presynaptic terminals to achieve full adult potential (10). Nevertheless, cholinergic-nicotinic receptor stimulation and consequent membrane depolarization result in catecholamine release but only marginal effects on TH induction (10,38). In addition, KCl-induced depolarization is associated with lower enkephalin levels at all ages tested, consistent with either release or inhibition of biosynthesis (10). How can these assorted observations be accounted for ?

Immaturity of transsynaptic regulation of biosynthesis, but apparently not of release mechanisms (10,38,39), may result from limitations of the cellular economy imposed by ongoing cell division (mitosis ceases by 10 days of age [10,38,39]). It is also likely that isolated immaturity of transsynaptic mechanisms of signal-transduction may account for these observations. This latter speculation is reminiscent of arguments levied to explain maturation of transsynaptic regulation of catecholamine pathways (10,38,39). Whether specific cellular processes accounting for opiate peptide regulation in mature medullae are the same as those operative during development is yet to be determined. Nevertheless, transsynaptic processes regulating catecholamine and opiate peptide biosynthetic pathways continue to be independent at all ages examined (10,38,39).

Glucocorticoid Regulation of Adrenal Transmitter Biosysnthesis

Hormonal modulation of adrenal catecholamine metabolism is well recognized (1). We sought to determine whether in addition to transsynaptic factors, adrenal opiate peptides were also subject to hormonal control. Pharmacological destruction of the adrenal cortex lowered enkephalin levels in vivo (7). This effect was further characterized in culture where corticosterone (the predominant glucocorticoid in the rat) was shown to augment enkephalin levels in a dose-dependent fashion, an effect reversible by glucocorticoid antagonists, and reproduced by the synthetic glucocorticoid dexamethasone (7). Other literature exploiting hypophysectomized rats, illustrated that denervation-induced increases in enkephalin levels were also glucocorticoid dependent in vivo (18,19).

Of particular interest is the presence of multiple copies of the glucocorticoid receptor, DNA-binding site in the rat preproenkephalin gene (7). This binding element, in conjunction with steroid-bound glucocorticoid receptors, is believed to function as an enhancer in other genes (40) and may have a similar activity in the enkephalin system. Of interest is that the apparent hierarchy of controls places calcium-dependent membrane depolarization above steroid hormones. Stated otherwise, membrane depolarization can prevent the rise of enkephalin in culture even in the presence of glucocorticoids, suggesting its priority (7).

SUMMARY

Stress-induced cellular signals generated by changes in the whole animal environment influence neuroendocrine responsiveness and neuronal plasticity (2). Moreover, abundant evidence indicates that different neurohumors co-localized to the same cell may be independently regulated by environmental stimuli at the cellular level (1,2,34,40). In the rat, augmented impulse activity and consequent membrane depolarization induces catecholamine biosynthetic enzymes, such as tyrosine hydroxylase, while decreasing leucine-enkephalin peptide and its precursor molecule in the rat (1,2,5-11,14-17,22-25,30). Other effects appear to be mediated by both transsynaptic activity and hormonal interactions (7,18-21,28,30). In turn, these changes are associated with parallel effects on steady-state levels of specific messenger RNA's (mRNA) coding for transmitter-related molecules (2,6,8,9,20-25,27-29). Recent evidence indicates that depolarizing stimuli can differentially regulate tyrosine hydroxylase- and enkephalin-gene readout in adrenomedullary cells (25).

Additional evidence illustrates the presence of cholinergic-nicotinic, and cholinergic-muscarinic, second-messenger pathway interactions which suppress or augment enkephalin levels depending on the intensity of the interaction (30). Moreover, during early postnatal development there is a conspicuous deficiency of transsynaptic regulatory control over either catecholamine or opiate peptide systems (10,38,39). This presumably results from immaturity of signal-transduction mechanisms which regulate transmitter gene expression and biosynthesis independent of release mechanisms (10,38,39).

Finally, glucocorticoid hormones appear to function as enhancer signals (40), augmenting enkephalin levels only when the system is already activated (7,18,19). They do not appear to augment enkephalin pathways in the presence of a depolarizing stimulus or independently (5,6,9-11,25).

Future work in this area requires further elucidation of transsynaptic and hormonal interactions, as well as identification of gene regulatory molecules activated by the various second-messenger phosphorylation mechanisms (see Figure).

ACKNOWLEDGEMENTS

We wish to thank Ms. F. Vatore for secretarial assistance.

REFERENCES

1. Axelrod J, Resine TD (1984). Stress hormones: Their interaction and regulation. Science 224:452.
2. Black IB, Adler JE, Dreyfus CF, Freidman WF, La Gamma EF (1987). Biochemistry of information storage in the nervous system. Science 236:1263.
3. La Gamma EF (1984). Endogenous opiates and cardiopulmonary regulation. Advan Pediatr 31:1.
4. Holaday JW (1983). Cardiovascular effects of endogenous opiate systems. Ann Rev Pharmacol Toxicol 23:541.
5. La Gamma EF, Adler JE, Black IB (1984). Impulse activity differentially regulates leu-enkephalin and catecholamine characters in the adrenal medulla. Science 224:1102.
6. La Gamma EF, White JD, Adler JE, Krause JE, McKelvy JF, Black IB (1985). Depolarization regulates adrenal preproenkephalin mRNA. Proc Natl Acad Sci (USA) 82:8252.
7. La Gamma EF, Adler JE (1987). Glucocorticoids regulation adrenal opiate peptides. Molec Br Res 2:125.
8. La Gamma EF, White JD, McKelvy JF, Black IB (1987). Increased cAMP or Ca^{++} second-messengers reproduce effects of depolarization of adrenal enkephalin pathways. Annals NY Acad Sci 493:270.
9. La Gamma EF, White JD, Mc Kelvy JF, Black IB (1988). Second messenger mechanisms governing opiate peptide transmitter regulation in the rat adrenal medulla. Br Res 441:292.
10. La Gamma EF, Adler JE (1988). Development of transsynaptic regulation of adrenal enkephalin. Develop Br Res 39:177.

11. Inturrisi, EC, La Gamma, EF, O'Franklin SO, Huang T. Nip TJ, Yoburn BC (1988). Characterization of enkephalins in rat adrenal medullary explants. Brain Res (in press).
12. Clayton DF, Darnell JE (1983). Changes in liver specific compared to common gene transcription during primary culture of rat hepatocytes. Molec Cell Biology 3:1552.
13. Clayton DF, Weiss M, Darnell JE (1985). Liver-specific RNA metabolism in hepatoma cells: Variations in transcription rates and mRNA levels. Molec Cell Biology 5:2633.
14. Bohn MC, Kessler JA, Golightly L, Black IB (1983). Appearance of leu-enkephalin immunoreactivity in rat adrenal medulla following treatment with nicotinic antagonist or reserpine. Cell Tissue Res 231:469.
15. Fleminger G, Lahm H–W, Udenfriend S (1984). Changes in rat adrenal catecholamines and proenkephalin metabolism after denervation. Proc Natl Acad Sci (USA) 81:3587.
16. Fleminger G, Howells RD, Kilpatrick DL, Udenfriend S (1986). Intact proenkephalin is the major enkephalin-containing peptide produced in rat adrenal glands after denervation. Proc Natl Acad Sci (USA) 81:7985.
17. Kilpatrick DL, Howells RD, Fleminger G, Udenfriend S (1986). Denervation of rat adrenal glands markedly increases proenkephalin mRNA. Proc Natl Acad Sci (USA) 81:7221.
18. Yoburn BC, Franklin SO, Calvano SE, Inturrisi CE (1987) Regulation of rat adrenal medullary enkephalins by glucocorticoid. Life Sci 40:2495.
19. Sietzen M, Schaber M, Fischer–Colbrie R, Scherman D, Sperk G. and Winkler H (987). Rat adrenal medulla: Levels of chromagranins, enkephalins, dopamine B–hydroxylase and of the amino transporter are changed by nervous activity and hypohophysectomy. Neurosci 22:131.
20. Kanamatsu T, Unsworth CD, Diliberto EJ, Viveros OH, Hong JS (1986). Reflex splanchnic nerve stimulation increases levels of proenkephalin A mRNA and proenkephalin A–related peptides in the rat adrenal medulla. Proc Natl Acad Sci 83:9245.

21. Viveros OH, Diliberto EJ, Hong J-H, Kizer JS, Unsworth CD, Kanamatsu T (1987). The regulation of enkephalin levels in adrenomedullary cells and its relation to chromaffin vesicle biogenesis and functional plasticity. Annals NY Acad Sci 493:324.
22. Stachowiak MK, Fluharty SJ, Stricker EM, Zigmond MJ, Kaplan BB (1986). Molecular adaptations in catecholamine biosynthesis induced by cold stress and sympathectomy. J of Neurosci Res 16:13.
23. Lewis EJ, Harrington CA, Chikaraishi DM (1987). Transcriptional regulation of tyrosine hydroxylase gene by glucocorticoid and cAMP. Proc Natl Acad Sci (USA) 84:3550.
24. Lewis EJ, Tank AW, Weiner N, Chikaraishi DM (1983). Regulation of tyrosine hydroxylase mRNA by glucocorticoid and cAMP in rat pheochromocytoma cell line. J Biol Chem 258:14632.
25. La Gamma EF, Black, IB (1988). Transcriptional control of adrenal catecholamine and opiate peptide transmitter genes. Molec Br Res (in press).
26. La Gamma, EF, Goldstein N, Weisenger G (1988). Characterization of preproenkephalin DNA binding proteins (Abstr). Soc for Neuroscience.
27. Kley N, Loeffler J Ph, Pittius CW, Mollt V (1986). Proenkephalin A gene expression in bovine adrenal chromaffin cells is regulated by changes in electrical activity. EMBO Journal 5:967.
28. Naranjo JR, Mocchetti I, Schwartz JP, Costa E. (1986). Permissive effects of dexamethasone on the increase of proenkephalin mRNA induced by depolarization of chromaffin cells. Proc Natl Acad Sci (USA) 83:1513.
29. Comb M, Birnberg NC, Seasholtz A, Herbert E, Goodman HM (1986). A cyclic AMP- and phorbol ester-inducible DNA element. Nature 323:353.
30. DeCristofaro, JD, La Gamma, EF (1988). Cholinergic-linked, second-messenger interactions biomodally regulate adrenal opiate peptides (Abstr). Soc for Neuro.
31. Brown MR, Fisher, LA (1984). Brain peptide regulation of adrenal epinephrine secretion. Am J Phys 247:E41.
32. Nathanson NM (1987). Molecular properties of the muscarinic acetylcholine receptor. Ann Rev Neurosci 10:195.

33. Johnson TS, Young JB, Landsberg L (1983). Sympathoadrenal responses to acut and chronic hypoxia in the rat. J Clin Invest 71:1263.
34. Unger A, Phillips JH (1983). Regulation of the adrenal medulla. Physiol Rev 63:787.
35. Edwards AV, Jones CT (1987). The effect of splanchnic nerve stimulation on adrenocortical activity in conscious calves. J Physiol 382:385.
36. DeCamilli P, Navone F (1987). Regulated secretory pathways of neurons and their relation to the regulated secretory pathway of endocrine cells. Ann NY Acad Sci 493:461.
37. Lewis JW, Tordoff MG, Sherman JE, Liebeskind JC (1982). Adrenal medullary enkephalin-live peptide may mediate opioid stress analgesia. Science 217:557.
38. Slotkin TA (1985). Development of the sympathoadrenal axis.In "Developmental Neurobiology of the Autonomic Nervous System," Humana Press, p 69.
39. Lau C, Ross, LL, Whitmore WL, Slotkin TA (1987). Regulation of adrenal chromaffin cell development by the central monoaminergic system: Differential control of norepinephrine and epinephrine levels and secretory responses. Neuro Sci 22:1067.
40. Yamamoto KR (1985). Steroid receptor regulated transcription of specific genes and gene networks. Ann Rev Genet 19:209.
41. Jones, NC, Rigby PW, Ziff EB (1988). Trans-acting protein factors and the regulation of eukaryotic transcription: lessons from studies on DNA tumor viruses. Genes & Development 2:267.

Molecular Biology of Stress, pages 167–178
© 1989 Alan R. Liss, Inc.

THE ADRENAL MEDULLA SECRETORY RESPONSE TO STRESS

Oren Zinder[1], Avital Greenberg[1], Hussein Amer[1]
Yael Hiram[2] and Avi Nir[2]

[1]Department of Clinical Biochemistry, Rambam Medical
Center and The Faculty of Medicine The Technion
[2]Faculty of Chemical Engineering, The Technion,
Israel Institute of Technology Haifa, Israel

ABSTRACT   Temperature effects were studied on the
secretory process from isolated adrenal medulla cells
as a model for the physical and mechanical forees
involved in exocytosis. Acetylcholine-stimulated
release was temperature dependent, in two distinct
phases. In the initial phase (1-3 minutes), secretion
was directly correlated to temperature rise. The point
at which desensitization occured and secretion stopped
was found to have a maximum at 28-30°C. This same
transition temperature was also found when release
was stimulated by high potassium concentrations or
calcium ionophore, indicating a control mechanism in
the late stages of the secretion process, perhaps
involving changes in membrane fluidity to allow for
fusion and exocytosis. Preferential secretion of
norepinephrine, at twice the rate of epinephrine
secretion relative to the amounts in the resting cell,
indicate a possible difference in membrane composition
between norepinephrine-and epinephrine-containing cells.

INTRODUCTION

Stimulation of secretion from adrenal medulla cells is initiated by acetylcholine released from the splanchnic nerve followed by depolarization and rise in intracellular calcium ions, and is called "stimulus-secretion coupling" (for reviews, see 1,2). The process has been known and described for many years, however the precise mechanism underlying it has been the subject of much controversy and speculation. While much experimental effort has gone into the study of the biochemical events surrounding exocytosis, little has been done regarding the mechanical forces involved in the process. The final approach of the secretory vesicles to the plasma membrane is dominated by a balance of physical forces which include motion (flow) of the vesicles towards the cell membrane, drainage of cytoplasmic fluid and membrane failure during fusion. The failure and subsequent fusion of the vesicle and plasma membranes has been attributed to changes in membrane fluidity brought about by alterations in the acetylcholine receptor (3,4, others) and by changes in thermotropic properties or phospholipid membranes (5). In previous studies, temperature changes have been used to mimic the changes in the membranes following stimulation by a variety of secretagogues (6,7). Recently, Burgoyne and colleagues (8) have shown that the flow of vesicles to the plasma membrane may be due to failure of the cytoskeletal network, releasing the granules to free movement. These studies do not, however, explain how the granule approaches the plasma membrane or how the fusion process occurs.

In isolated adrenal medulla cells, a distinct differentiation can be determined between those with predominantly epinephrine containing vesicles, and those with a predominance of norepinephrine (9,10). These cells can be partially purified (11,12), yet even in an enriched population of cells, stimulation of secretion results in a preferential secretion of norepinephrine or epinephrine depending on the physiological or pharmacological stimulant (10,13,14). The possibility that preferential secretion in response to the various stimuli is related to physiological needs is enhanced by the fact that peptides which are co-secreted during nicotinic stimulation of catecholamine release from adrenal medulla cells (15), are co-stored in the epinephrine containing cells (16).

The purpose of this study was to investigate the mechanical and physical features of the adrenal medulla cells during secretion, and to identify whether these features could explain the preferential secretion seen following stimulation by a number of secretagogues.

METHODS

Cell preparation

Bovine adrenal medulla cells were isolated from fresh bovine adrenals by our previously published method (17).
Incubation procedures

Adrenal medulla cell suspensions (approx. 10^5 per ml in an incubation vial) were pre-incubated at various temperatures for 10 minutes to adjust to the temperature. Following addition of the stimulatory agents, a further 20 minute incubation followed. The cells were then separated from the medium by centrifugation and the supernatant medium was quantitatively collected. Catecholamine determination was carried out on an aliquot of the supernatant (see below).
Determinations

Catecholamines were determined by the spectrofluorometric method of von Euler and Lishajko (18). Protein was determined by the Bradford assay (19).
Calculations

Results are expressed as nmole catecholamine released per mg protein, or as a percent of the net acetylcholine-induced secretion at 37°C.

RESULTS

Temperature dependence of secretion

Exposure of cells to four different incubation temperatures resulted in two stages of secretion (Fig 1). The initial secretion was very rapid and was usually complete within 1-3 minutes. The second stage reflected saturation levels, and it can be seen that maximum levels of secretion were reached at a temperature 26°C and 30°C, and not at the physiological level of 37°C. The use of three different stimulatory agents, each entering the secretion pathway at a different stage (acetylcholine at the membrane receptor level, high KCl at the depolarization stage, and the calcium ionophore at the level of calcium

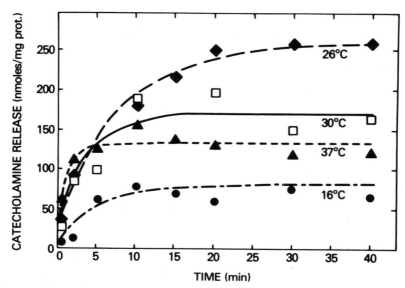

Figure 1   Time curves for acetylcholine-stimulated
(10^{-4}M) secretion of catecholamines at different
incubation temperatures.

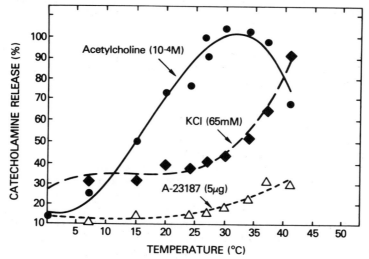

Figure 2   Secretion of catecholamines stimulated by three
different agents as a function of temperature.   Incubation
time was 20 minutes.   Results are as percent of secretion
relative to maximal release with acetylcholine.

influx) produced differing dependencies (Fig 2). Only acetylcholine stimulated secretion had a maximum (at 28°C), while K+ and A23187, albeit at non-steady-state kinetics, had an exponential-like secretory curve.

In Fig 3, the initial velocity rate constant (K_3) of acetylcholine (10^{-4}M)-stimulated catecholamine release is plotted against temperature. This constant is obtained by a series of equations detailed in a previous publication (20), and shows two distinct transition points, at approximately 16°C and especially at 28-30°C. This latter transition point can also be seen in Fig 2 for the release of catecholamines due to depolarization of the plasma membrane by high potassium concentration.

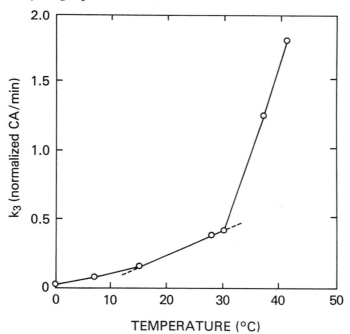

Figure 3   Temperature dependence of the initial velocity rate constant (K_3) of catecholamine secretion on incubation temperature.

Preferential secretion
    Table 1 shows the differential secretion of
epinephrine and norepinephrine due to stimulation of

Table 1: Comparison of the division between epinephrine and norepinephrine
in basal catecholamine release, after stimulation by ACh and
the effect of veratridine and A23187. Incubation time 20 min.
(After 15 min. preincubation) and at 30°C.

	release per mg protein (nmoles)	% of total	
		epinephrine	norepinephrine
Spontaneous	45.7	84	16
+ACh (10^{-4}M)	214.3	61	39
+ Veratridine (10^{-4}M)	364.0	59	41
+ A23187 (20µg/tube	168.0	61	39
Intact cells (Control)	936.4	74	26

Table 2: Comparison between the percent of epinephrine and norepinephrine
released following stimulation by ACh, Veratridine and A23187 in
comparison to their content in the intact cell.

	n	% of content in the cell	
		Epinephrine	Norepinephrine
Spontaneous	12	7±0.4	2±0.4
+ ACh (10^{-4}M)	12	17±2	35±2
+ Veratridine (10^{-4}M)	12	29±5	60±5
+ A23187 20µg/tube)	12	14±2	30±2

secretion by the three secretagogues. It can readily be
seen that preferential secretion of norepinephrine is
achieved by these agents, while spontaneous, non-stimulated,
secretion shows preference for epinephrine.

When comparing the secreted catecholamine to the
amount found initially in the intact cell, it can be seen
that on a relative basis, twice as much norepinephrine
is secreted as compared to epinephrine, with each of the
stimulatory agents (Table 2).

Temperature effects on preferential secretion

When combining the determination of temperature
effects on acetylcholine stimulated secretion with the
differential secretion of epinephrine and norepinephrine,
a significant effect on preferential norepinephrine
secretion is seen (Table 3). The total amount of
catecholamines secreted at the different temperatures
follows the same pattern as that seen before (Fig 2),
however a monotonous increase in the percent of
norepinephrine secreted by the cells is quite evident.

Table 3:   Differential secretion of catecholamines
            at varying incubation temperatures.
            Incubations were for 20' with 10^{-4}M acetylcholine

Incubation Temp	n	Total Release nmole/mg. prot.	% NE
16°C	5	215 ± 34	71 ± 8
24°C	5	247 ± 41	66 ± 7
30°C	5	271 ± 40	64 ± 4
37°C	5	264 ± 31	58 ± 5
41°C	4	227 ± 44	56 ± 3

DISCUSSION

The adrenal medulla plays a major role in the response to stress since it rapidly and effectively releases catecholamine to the circulation, following a stressful event, whether metabolic (e.g. glucose depletion), physical (e.g. shock) or psychological (e.g. fear). Recently, it has become evident that in addition to catecholamines, the secretory vesicles of the adrenal medulla cell also contain a substantial amount of enkephalins (21) and a variety of other peptides in smaller amounts (1,22). These compounds are also implicated in the response to stress, especially the enkephalins, and thus the role of the adrenal medulla has become even more pronounced as the major peripheral responsor to stress stimulus. As such, elucidation of the mechanism(s) underlying secretion from the adrenal gland becomes of great importance in the field.

The key event in the secretory process is the fusion of the chromaffin granules with the plasma membrane. It is this event which is so dependent on physical and mechanical forces. In our study we used external temperature changes to mimic membrane failure, as we have done in our previous publications (7, 20). The results show a most striking acceleration of release at a temperature of 28-30°C, independently corroborating the results of Livett et al (23) and Kao and Westhead (28) with whole cells, and those of Schneeweis et al (4) using isolated plasma membranes. Our study also indicates a possible second transition point at 16-19°C. This has been found by Perlman (24) in chromaffin granule permeability studies, but in our former studies on granule membrane tensile strength (7), this was not evident. Above 16°C, the granule membrane und undrgoes a change in physical properties from a crystaline to a more fluid state (4,5), which is most probably due to the cholesterol to phospholipid ratio and the protein content of the membrane. We have reported (25) that these parameters are significantly different between the granule and plasma membranes of the chromaffin cell, which could account for the two transition points seen in Fig 3. Above 30°C both membranes are in a fluid state, as is the cytoplasma, which will facilitate membrane conductance to ions, depolarization, fusion, secretion and possibly also result in more rapid disruption of the cytoskeletal elements (8). It is interesting to note, that in the initial phase (1-3 mintus) of secretion, the rate and amount secreted is directly related to the rise in temperature, however at a temperature above 30°C there is a more rapid desensitization process, most probably due to high membrane fluidity, and thus total release at the end of the complete incubation period is lower at 37°C than at 30°C. Use of high potassium concentrations or calcium ionophore, do not show a drop in secretion at temperatures above 30°C, probably due to the fact that they cause a continuous elevation in intracellular calcium concentrations and do not allow the cells to desensitize, as happens with receptor mediated secretion.

The preferential secretion of norepinephrine from adrenal medulla cells, following stimulation by nicotinic agonists, has been observed ourselves (17) and others (26). In this study we have shown (Table 1,2) that this preference occurs when secretion is initiated at the level of depolarization (high K^{+}), or calcium influx (A23187) as well and that the norepinephrine released, when calculated as a percent of the amount found in the resting cell, is twice as much as that of epinephrine. This corroborates and elaborates on the studies of Wilson et al (27) and Kao and Westhead (28). Thus it seems that the preferential secretion is determined at a late stage in the secretory process possibly the last one, of fusion and membrane failure. The possibility exists that the epinephrine-containing cells are more susceptible to desensitization, or are more sensitive to the inhibitory effect of the neuropeptides co-secreted by them (29), thus allowing relatively more norepinephrine to be secreted from those cells which contain it. In this study, we have found that there is a slight differential membrane stability and fluidity between the epinephrine and norepinephrine containing cells, since with the rise in temperature a more pronounced preference of norepinephrine secretion is seen (Table 3). This suggests possible chemical differences btween the membranes of the two cell types which could result in different rates of desensitization. This intriguing possibility deserves further study.

In conclusion, we believe that our results point to a key involvement of mechanical and physical properties of the adrenal medulla cell membranes in the process of exocytosis and in the observed differential secretion of epinephrine and norepinephrine in response to stress.

REFERENCES

1. Douglas WW (1968). Stimulus-secretion coupling: The concept and clues from chromaffin and other cells. Br. J. Pharmacol. 34: 451.
2. Livett BG (1984). Adrenal medullary chromaffin cells in vitro. Physiol. Rev. 64: 1103.
3. Axelrod D, Ravoin PM, Podelski TR (1978). Control of acetylcholine receptor mobility and distribution in cultured muscle membranes. Biochem. Biophys. Acta 511: 23.
4. Schneeweis F, Naquira D, Rosenheck K and Schneider AS (1979). Cholinergic stimulants and excess potassium ion increase the fluidity of plasma membranes isolated from adrenal chromaffin cells. Biochem. Biophys. Acta 555: 460.
5. Papahadjopoulos D (1977). Effeets of bivalent cations and protein on thermotropic properties of phospholipid membranes. J. Colloid Interface Sci. 58: 549.
6. Kuight DE (1980). Temperature sensitivity of catecholamine release in response to different secretagogues. J. Physiol. (Lond) 298: 41p.
7. Hiram Y, Nir A, Zinder O (1982). Tensile strength of the chromaffin granule membrane. Biophys. J. 39: 65.
8. Burgoyne RD, Cheek TR, O'Sullivan AJ, Richards RC (1988). Control of cytoskeleton during secretion. In Thoru NA, Trieman M, Petersen OH (eds): "Molecular Mechanisms of Secretion", Alfred Benzon Symposium 25 p. 612.
9. Tomlinson S, Coupland R (1987). Quantitative analysis of rat adrenal medulla tissue. Neurosci 20: 895.
10. Marley PO, Livett BG (1987). Differences between the mechanism of adrenaline and noradrenaline secretion from primary mono-cultures of bovine adrenal chromaffin cells. Neurosci. Lett. 77: 81.
11. Lemaire S, Dumont M, Mercier P, Lemaire I, Calvert R (1983). Biochemical characterization of various populations of isolated bovine adrenal medulla cells. Neurochem. Intl. 5: 193.
12. Wilson SP (1987). Purification of adrenal chromaffin cells on Renograffin gradients. J. Neurosci. Meth. 19:163
13. Worsman J (1984). Adrenomedullary response to maximal stress in humans. Amer. J. Med. 77: 779.

14. Young JB, Rosa RM, Landsberg L (1984). Dissociation of sympathetic nervous system and adrenal medullary responses. Am. J. Physiol. 247: E 35.

15. Manley PD, Livett BG (1985). Neuropeptides in the autonomic nervous system. CRC Crit. Rev. Clin. Neurobiol. 1: 201.

16. Chaminade M, Foutz AS, Rosier J (1984). Co-release of enkephalins and precursors with catecholamines from the perfused cat adrenal. J. Physiol. 353: 157.

17. Greenberg A, Zinder O (1982). α- and β- receptor control of catecholamine secretion from isolated adrenal medulla cells. Cell and Tiss. Pes. 226: 655.

18. von Euler US, Lishajko F (1961). Improved technique for the fluorometric estimation of catecholamines. Acta Physiol. Scand. 51: 348.

19. Bradford MM (1976). A rapid and sensitive method for the quantitation of microgram quantities of protein utilizing the principle of protein dye binding Anal. Biochem. 72: 248.

20. Hiram Y, Nir A, Greenberg A, Zinder O (1984). Temperature effects in the stimulus-secretion process from isolated chromaffin cells. Biophys. J. 45: 651.

21. Livett BG, Day R, Elde RP, Howe PRC (1982). Co-storage of emkephalins and adrenaline in the bovine adrenal medulla. Neuroscience 7: 1323.

22. Fischer-Colbrie R, Diez-Guerra J, Emson PC and Winkler H (1986). Bovine chromaffin granules: Immunological studies with antisera against neuropeptide Y, enkephalin and bombesin. Neuroscience 18: 167.

23. Livett BG, Xin-fu Zhou, Khalil Z, Wan DC, Bunn SJ, Marley PO (1988). Endogenous neuropeptides maintain adrenal catecholamine output during stress. This volume.

24. Perlman PJ (1976). The permeability of chromaffin granules to non-electrolytes. Biochem. Pharmacol. 25: 1035.

25. Zinder O, Hoffman PG, Bonner WH, Pollard HG (1978). Comparison of chemical properties of purified plasma membrane and secretory vesicle membrane from bovine adrenal medulla. Cell and Tissue Res. 188: 153

26. Livett BG, Dean DM, Whelan LG, Udenfriend S, Rossier J (1981). Co-release of enkephalin and catecholamines from cultured adrenal chromaffin cells. Nature 289:317

27. Wilson SP, Chang KJ, Vireros DH (1982). Preportional secretion of opioid peptides and catecholamines from adrenal chromaffin cells in culture. J. Neurochem. 2: 1150.

28. Kao LS, Westhead E (1984). Temperature dependence of catecholamine secretion from cultured bovine chromaffin cells. J. Neurochem 43: 590.

29. Marley PD, Mitchelhill KI, Livett BG (1986). Effects of opioid peptides containing the sequence of met-enkephalin or leu-enkephalin on nicotine induced secretion from bovine adrenal medulla cells. J. Neurochem. 46:1.

Molecular Biology of Stress, pages 179–190

ENDOGENOUS NEUROPEPTIDES MAINTAIN ADRENAL CATECHOLAMINE OUTPUT DURING STRESS[1]

Bruce G. Livett, Xin-fu Zhou, Zeinab Khalil[2],
David C-C. Wan, Stephen J. Bunn[3] and Philip D. Marley

Department of Biochemistry, University of Melbourne,
Parkville, Victoria 3052, Australia.

ABSTRACT   In response to stress, splanchnic nerve activity causes activation of nicotinic acetylcholine receptors and release of catecholamines from the adrenal gland. The neuropeptide, substance P (SP) an endogenous component of the splanchnic nerve, protects against nicotinic desensitization in vitro and is shown to be essential for maintaining adrenal catecholamine secretion in response to stress induced by insulin hypoglycaemia, cold, and histamine. In this action SP acts as a true neuromodulator: it has no action of its own but modulates the efficacy of ACh at the nicotinic receptor. This novel action of SP, to protect against nicotinic desensitization, is shown to be an essential component of the stress response in vivo.

INTRODUCTION

A classical autonomic response to stress is secretion of catecholamines (CA) from the sympathetic nervous system. An essential component of this response is the release of adrenaline from the adrenal medulla. In response to sensory input, a reflex activation of the autonomic nervous system results in increased autonomic outflow via the descending spinal pathways and splanchnic nerve.

[1]This work was supported by grants to BGL and PDM from the NH&MRC (Australia).
[2]Present address: Dept. of Gerontology, Univ. of Melbourne, Mount Royal, Parkville, Victoria, Australia.
[3]Present address: Neuroscience Group, Faculty of Medicine, University of Newcastle, NSW, Australia.

It has been known since the classical studies of Feldberg (1) that the response of the adrenal to splanchnic nerve stimulation is mediated by acetylcholine (ACh). In species such as the cow this is principally, if not exclusively, a nicotinic response whereas in other species such as the cat and chicken CA secretion is mediated by muscarinic receptors on the chromaffin cells. More recently, it has become apparent that in addition to the classical neurotransmitter, ACh, a number of endogenous neuropeptides are present in the splanchnic nerve and/or the adrenal chromaffin cells (Table I) and that some of these modulate the release of CA in response to stress (2). Still other compounds such as dopamine, histamine, 5HT, GABA and glutamate have been reported either to affect adrenal CA secretion or to have high affinity receptors in the adrenal gland (3).

TABLE 1
CATECHOLAMINES AND PEPTIDES IN THE ADRENAL
AND/OR SPLANCHNIC NERVE

Substance	pmol/g	Substance	pmol/g
Adrenaline	10×10^6		
Noradrenaline	3×10^6		
Substance P	1–20	Vasopressin	10
Somatostatin	5–70	Oxytocin	10
VIP	5–20	CGRP	?
Neurotensin	1–400	CRF	10–15
Neuropeptide Y	200–1200	TRH	100–200
Enkephalins	300–2000	ANF	?
B-endorphin	100–300	Galanin	?

Adrenal opioid peptides

The opioid peptides are the most abundant of the endogenous peptides in the adrenal medulla (Table 1). mRNA for proenkephalin A and the transmitter enzyme, phenylethanolamine N-methyltransferase (PNMT), are readily detectable in chromaffin cells (Fig 1). Immunocytochemical and in situ hybridization studies have established that the opioid peptides are colocalized with adrenaline but not noradrenaline in chromaffin cells in the bovine adrenal medulla (4,5). However, in spite of a large body of work over the last 5 years, a clear role for adrenal or splanchnic nerve opioids in adrenal CA secretion in vivo remains to be established.

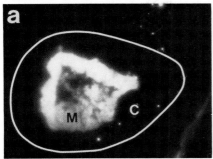 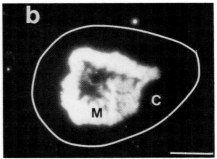

FIGURE 1.   In situ hybridization of (a) ProEnkA-mRNA and (b) PNMT-mRNA in sections of cow adrenal with ^{32}[P]-oligonucleotide probes. C=cortex, M=medulla, Bar=4mm.

The splanchnic nerve contains a number of low molecular weight enkephalin peptides which can be identified by both HPLC and staining with specific antisera (eg., met-enkephalyl-Arg^{6}Phe^7).   In contrast, the chromaffin cells of the adrenal medulla contain principally unprocessed large molecular weight enkephalin precursors (6).   Studies in vitro with isolated cultured bovine adrenal chromaffin cells have shown that relatively high concentrations of the opioid peptides ($>10^{-6}$M) are required to modulate ACh mediated secretion of CA, the most potent being metorphamide (7) with a K_i of 2×10^{-6}M, some 10-fold more potent than met-enkephalyl-Arg^{6}Phe^7 and 100-fold more potent than met- or leu-enkephalin. Moreover, this inhibitory action of the opioids is not reversed by the classical opiate antagonists naloxone, naltrexone or diprenorphine (8).   In part this non-classical behavior of the adrenal opioid receptor may be due to the presence of unique kappa opioid receptor subtypes in the adrenal medulla (k_1 k_2 and k_3) identified by receptor binding studies on membrane preparations (9). A differential distribution of kappa and delta opioid binding sites among the two principal cell types (adrenaline and noradrenaline, respectively) has recently been shown by receptor autoradiography (10, Fig 2) and we have recently shown the presence of K_1 binding sites on splanchnic nerve fibres innervating the bovine adrenal medulla raising the interesting possibility of presynaptic opioid modulation of adrenal CA secretion.

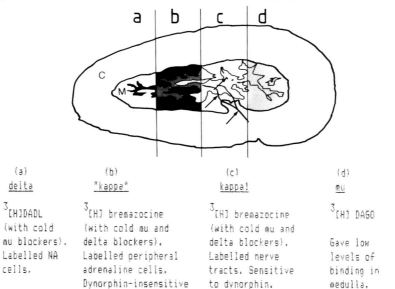

(a) delta	(b) "kappa"	(c) kappa!	(d) mu
^{3}[H]DADL (with cold mu blockers). Labelled NA cells.	^{3}[H] bremazocine (with cold mu and delta blockers). Labelled peripheral adrenaline cells. Dynorphin-insensitive	^{3}[H] bremazocine (with cold mu and delta blockers). Labelled nerve tracts. Sensitive to dynorphin.	^{3}[H] DAGO Gave low levels of binding in medulla.

FIGURE 2. Diagramatic representation of mu, delta and kappa opioid binding sites in the bovine adrenal medulla. Arrows mark high binding to nerve tracts. (from Bunn et al (10) with permission of Pergamon Press, UK).

The lack of effect of endogenous opioids on stimulus-evoked CA secretion is surprising given the presence of most classes of opioid binding sites in the adrenal gland and suggests that opioid function in the adrenal gland is directed to functions other than CA secretion or that adrenal opioids act on processes outside the adrenal gland. The most promising of these studies, indicating a role for adrenal opioids in stress-induced analgesia (11), has to our knowledge not been followed up.

The tachykinin family

The splanchnic nerve contains relatively high concentrations of substance P (SP), the most abundant of the mammalian tachykinins (Table 2).

TABLE 2

COMPARISON OF AMINO ACID SEQUENCES OF MAMMALIAN TACHYKININS

Tachykinin	Primary amino acid sequence
Substance P	ArgProLysProGlnGlnPhePheGlyLeuMet-NH$_2$
Neurokinin A	HisLysThrAspSerPheValGlyLeuMet-NH$_2$
Neurokinin B	AspMetHisAspPhePheValGlyLeuMet-NH$_2$

Early studies by Saria and colleagues (12) identified SP by RIA and HPLC in extracts of the adrenal medulla and splanchnic nerve of the rat and cow. In addition to SP-containing splanchnic nerve terminals in the medulla, studies by Pfister and Gorne (13) have shown in the rat that there are a small number of SP-immunoreactive cells lying between main groups of chromaffin cells in the adrenal medulla. Treatment of rats neonatally with capsaicin, a selective neurotoxin for small diameter sensory afferents, depletes SP from the splanchnic nerve of rats by up to 70% when examined 10 weeks later. These capsaicin-pretreated animals have been particularly valuable for studying the role of endogenous SP in the splanchnic nerve on CA release in-situ (14,15) and in vivo (see below).

In marked contrast to the results obtained with the opioids, pretreatment of chromaffin cells for only 1 min with 10^{-9}-10^{-6} M SP results in a marked attenuation of a subsequent challenge with ACh or nicotine (16). This inhibition of the nicotinic release of CA occurs at low to medium concentrations of agonist (10^{-6}M – 10^{-5}M). At higher concentrations of agonist (eg. 10^{-4}-10^{-3}M nicotine or ACh), SP (10^{-6}M) protects against desensitization of the nicotinic response so permitting the secretory response to be maintained throughout the stimulation period (17, Fig 3).

The ability of SP to protect against nicotinic desensitization accounts for the observation that nicotinic receptor desensitization is not observed in vivo following prolonged periods of stress. Given that the nicotinic response exhibits marked receptor desensitization at high concentrations of agonists in vitro it has always been a puzzle to physiologists that the adrenal gland maintains its secretion of CA throughout a stressful encounter. This is even more surprising considering the marked temperature sensitivity of the nicotinic response between 20° and 37° (18, and Fig 4). It is apparent that at physiological temperatures (37°C) the nicotinic response exhibits only a fraction of its maximum activity due to the temperature sensitivity of receptor desensitization.

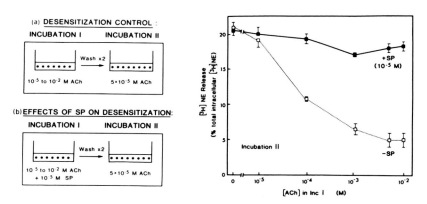

FIGURE 3. (a) Experimental protocol used with monolayer cultures of adrenal chromaffin cells to show in (b) that SP protects against ACh-induced desensitization of [³H]NE release at 37°C. (From Boksa and Livett (17), published with permission of Raven Press).

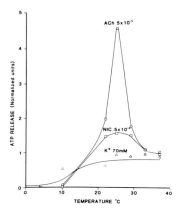

FIGURE 4. Temperature sensitivity of the nicotinic response of isolated bovine chromaffin cells incubated with an EC$_{50}$ concentration (5x10^{-6}M) of nicotine. ATP release was measured on-line by bioluminescence.

We considered the possibility that an endogenous
neuropeptide might be co-released with ACh and act to
provide protection against this desensitization so as to
maintain CA secretion during stress. It is well known
from the literature that agents such as d-tubocurarine
which inhibit the nicotinic response also protect against
nicotinic desensitization (see 17). Our earlier in vitro
studies with isolated bovine adrenal chromaffin cells had
shown that SP could inhibit the nicotinic response. The
question was whether SP could likewise protect against
nicotinic desensitization. Our findings show that SP can
protect against nicotinic desensitization in vitro (17)
and that this is specific to the nicotinic release of CA.
SP did not protect against K^+ induced desensitization
(17). Two other mammalian tachykinins were much less
potent than SP at protecting against nicotinic
desensitization (Fig. 5), requiring 30-fold more on a
molar basis (19,20). It is of interest that both SP and
the two other mammalian tachykinins were more potent at
protecting against desensitization than at inhibiting the
nicotinic response. This suggests that the principal
role of SP in the adrenal might be to maintain CA output
in times of stress.

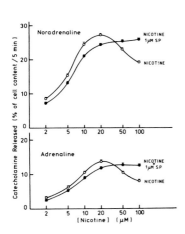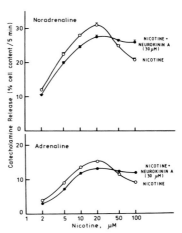

FIGURE 5.   Release of endogenous noradrenaline (upper
panels) and adrenaline (lower panels) from bovine adrenal
chromaffin cells in response to different concentrations
of nicotine in the absence (open circles) and presence
(filled circles) of (a) 1 uM SP, (b) 30 uM neurokinin A.
(From Khalil et al (19), with permission).

Physiological significance.

The concept that SP protects against desensitization of the nicotinic receptor, is supported by studies in situ with anaesthetized rats sampled for adrenal CA output following insulin, cold, or histamine stress (14,15). With all three stressors, the adrenal failed to maintain secretion of adrenal CA in animals that had been depleted of SP at birth by pretreatment with capsaicin (Fig 6). The initial response to insulin produced a small secretion of adrenaline comparable to that in vehicle pretreated controls (Fig 6), but by 10 minutes this nicotinic response to released ACh was markedly attenuated and remained below control levels throughout the first 45 min sampling period (14). Beyond 45 min the combined stress of hypoglycaemia and hypovolemia produced a marked non-neuronal release of CA unaffected by neonatal pretreatment with capsaicin (14).

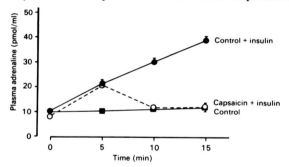

FIGURE 6. Plasma adrenaline levels in ivc blood in vehicle pretreated rats (Control, no insulin), and in vehicle- or capsaicin-pretreated rats injected i.v. with insulin (1 IU/kg). Equithesin anaesthesia (14).
From Khalil et al. (14), published with permission of Cambridge University Press.

In support of our hypothesis that endogenous SP maintains CA secretion during stress by protecting against nicotinic desensitization, the data in Fig. 7 shows that infusion of SP at low concentrations ($<3 \times 10^{-6}$M) facilitates CA secretion from perfused rat adrenal glands evoked by electrical field stimulation, whereas at higher concentrations ($>10^{-5}$M) SP inhibits CA secretion (21). Nicotinic receptor antagonists block the facilitatory action of SP. That SP acts postsynaptically (to protect against nicotinic desensitization) rather than presynaptically (to facilitate ACh release), is indicated by our finding that low concentrations of SP (10^{-7}M) that facilitated CA release by 50% (Fig 7) reduced the overflow of ^{3}[H]-choline by 33% (data not shown).

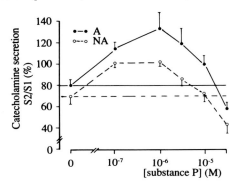

FIGURE 7. Biphasic effect of SP on CA secretion from perfused rat adrenal glands evoked by electrical field stimulation (10 Hz, 60 V, 3ms). The CA released during S_1, 6 min in the absence of SP, is taken as control. SP at the concentrations shown was added to the perfusion stream for 4 min before and 6 min during the second stimulation (S_2). The S_2/S_1 ratio was compared to the control group (no SP).

The tachykinin receptors in the adrenal medulla are unusual. SP is clearly the most potent agonist, suggesting that the receptor may be of the NK_1 class. However, other structure activity studies indicate a unique receptor type similar to that for SP-mediated histamine release from mast cells (22). The finding that SP was 30 fold more active than the two other mammalian tachykinins, (19,20, Fig 5), and that all three share a common C-terminal amino acid sequence (See Table 2) suggests that the these functions are mediated by the N-terminus of SP.

Recent receptor-binding studies from our laboratory (23), have compared the ability of ^{3}[H]-SP and ^{125}[I]-SP (labelled at the C-terminal end by the Bolton-Hunter procedure) to bind to membrane preparations of the adrenal medulla. The results again indicate that it is the N-terminus of SP that is recognized by these adrenal SP receptors and that a unique tachykinin subtype is involved. On the basis of pharmacological studies with SP analogues and an number of non-mammalian tachykinins, Boksa and Livett (22) came to the same conclusion and termed this receptor the SP-S receptor ("S" for SP, the most potent tachykinin). In present day nomenclature (24) it would be better termed the NK_{1N} receptor ("N" for N-terminus of SP). In comparison with some other endogenous neuropeptides known to be present in the adrenal gland and to modulate CA release (Table 3) it is clear that SP is the most potent both at inhibiting the response to low concentrations of agonist (ACh), and in protecting against nicotinic receptor desensitization.

The molecular mechanisms involved in SP's action are not yet understood, but it is possible that SP may exert its actions through nicotinic receptor phosphorylation, the extent of which is related to the degree of receptor

TABLE 3

POTENCY OF SUBSTANCE P, SOMATOSTATIN AND OPIOID PEPTIDES AT INHIBITING THE NICOTINIC RESPONSE AND PROTECTING AGAINST NICOTINIC DESENSITIZATION.

PEPTIDE	Inhibit	Protect
	(relative potency)	
Substance P	100	300
Somatostatin	10	nil
Enkephalins	0.1	nil
Metorphamide	10	1

desensitization (25). SP does not stimulate the breakdown of phosphatidylinositol-4,5,-bisphosphate in chromaffin cells (26), suggesting that SP does not affect phosphorylation through activating protein kinase C in these cells, however SP may affect protein kinases to directly affect nicotinic receptor phosphorylation. Approaches to this question at the molecular level are much needed as they could provide answers to the mechanism by which substance P modulates nicotinic function in the adrenal medulla and at other sites in the nervous system where SP and ACh are known to coexist (2).

The capacity of the autonomic nervous system to maintain homeostasis in the face of stress is well established. The studies described here ascribe a novel and vital role to substance P, as an endogenous peptide whose presence in the splanchnic nerve is essential for maintaining adrenal CA secretion in times of stress.

REFERENCES

1. Feldberg W, Minz B, Tsudzimura H (1934). The mechanism of the nervous discharge of adrenaline. J Physiol (Lond.) 81: 286.
2. Marley PD, Livett BG (1985). Neuropeptides in the autonomic nervous system. CRC Crit Rev Clin Neurobiol 1: 201.
3. Marley PD (1987). New insights into the non-nicotinic regulation of adrenal medullary function. Trends in the Pharmacological Sciences 8: 411.
4. Livett BG, Day R, Elde RP, Howe PRC (1982). Co-storage of enkephalins and adrenaline in the bovine adrenal medulla. Neuroscience 7: 1323.
5. Wan DC-C, Scanlon D, Power B, Choi C-L, Hudson P, Livett BG (1987). Synthesis of a specific oligodeoxy-ribonucleotide probe, and its use for studying pro-enkephalin A gene expression. Neurosci Lett 76: 74.
6. Chaminade M, Foutz AS, Rossier J (1984). Co-release of enkephalins and precursors with catecholamines from the perfused cat adrenal in-situ. J Physiol 353: 157.
7. Marley PD, Mitchelhill KI, Livett BG (1986). Metorphamide: A novel endogenous opioid peptide, inhibits nicotine-induced secretion from bovine adrenal chromaffin cells. Brain Research 363: 10.
8. Marley PD, Livett BG (1987). Effects of opioid compounds on desensitization of the nicotinic response of isolated bovine adrenal chromaffin cells. Biochem. Pharmacol. 36: 2937.
9. Castanas E, Bourhim N, Giraud P, Boudouresque F, Cantau P, Oliver C (1986). Interaction of opiates with opioid binding sites in the bovine adrenal medulla: II Interaction with kappa sites. J Neurochem 45: 688.
10. Bunn SJ, Marley PD, Livett BG (1988). The distribution of opioid binding subtypes in the bovine adrenal medulla. Neuroscience (In Press).
11. Lewis JW, Tordoff MG, Sherman JE, Liebeskind JC (1982). Adrenal medullary enkephalin-like peptides may mediate opioid stress analgesia. Science 217:557.
12. Saria A, Wilson SP, Molnar A, Viveros OH, Lembeck F (1980). Substance P and opiate-like peptides in human adrenal medulla. Neurosci Lett 20: 194.
13. Pfister VC, Gorne RC (1983). Substance-P-like immunofluorescence in the adrenal medulla of the rat. Acta Histochem 72: 127.

14. Khalil Z, Livett BG, Marley, PD (1986). The role of sensory fibres in the rat splanchnic nerve in the regulation of adrenal medullary secretion during stress. J Physiol (Lond.) 370: 201.
15. Khalil Z, Livett BG, Marley PD (1987). Sensory fibres modulate histamine-induced catecholamine secretion from the rat adrenal medulla and sympathetic nerves. J Physiol (Lond.) 391: 511.
16. Mizobe F, Kozousek V, Dean DM, Livett BG (1979). Pharmacological characterization of adrenal paraneurons: Substance P and somatostatin as inhibitory modulators of the nicotinic response. Brain Research 178: 555.
17. Boksa P, Livett BG (1984) Substance P protects against desensitization of the nicotinic response in isolated adrenal chromaffin cells. J Neurochem 42: 618.
18. Knight DE (1980). Temperature sensitivity of catecholamine release in response to different secretagogues. J Physiol (Lond.) 298: 41P.
19. Khalil Z, Marley PD, Livett BG (1988a). Mammalian tachykinins modulate the nicotinic secretory response of cultured bovine adrenal chromaffin cells. Brain Research (In Press).
20. Khalil Z, Marley PD, Livett BG (1988b). Effect of substance P on nicotine-induced desensitization of cultured bovine adrenal chromaffin cells: Possible receptor subtypes. Brain Research (In Press).
21. Zhou X-f, Livett BG (1987). Biphasic effects of substance P on catecholamine secretion from perfused rat adrenal glands. Proc 4th Int Symp Chromaffin Cell Biology, Alice Springs, P20.
22. Boksa P, Livett BG (1985) The substance P receptor subtype modulating catecholamine release from adrenal chromaffin cells. Brain Research 332: 29.
23. Geraghty DP, Livett BG, Burcher E (1988). N-terminal specificity of binding sites for substance P in bovine adrenal medulla. Proc. Int. Symposium on Tachykinins, Graz, Austria, 16-18 July 1988 (In Press).
24. Burcher E, Chahl LA (1988). Tools for tachykinin and neuropeptide research. Neurosci Lett 86: 38.
25. Miles K, Anthony, DT, Rubin LL, Greengard P, Huganir RL (1987) Regulation of nicotinic acetylcholine receptor phosphorylation in rat myotubes by forskolin and cAMP. Proc Natl Acad Sci USA 84: 6591.
26. Bunn SJ, Livett BG (1988). Inositol phospholipid metabolism in cultured bovine adrenal chromaffin cells. Neurosci Lett Suppl 30: S51.

Molecular Biology of Stress, pages 191–201

ASCORBIC ACID REGULATION OF NOREPINEPHRINE BIOSYNTHESIS IN SITU

Mark Levine, William Hartzell, Kuldeep Dhariwal, Philip Washko, and Peter Bergsten

Laboratory of Cell Biology and Genetics
NIDDK, NIH
Bethesda, Maryland 20892

ABSTRACT   Ascorbic acid was found to regulate biosynthesis in situ of the stress hormone norepinephrine from the substrate dopamine, in isolated adrenal medullary chromaffin cells and chromaffin granules. The mechanism of action of ascorbic acid in situ was found to be much more complex than for the isolated enzyme dopamine beta-monooxygenase. These data provide strong support for the essential role of in situ enzyme kinetics in determining optimal vitamin requirements.

INTRODUCTION

The optimal requirements of ascorbic acid (vitamin C) in humans are unknown. While methods exist to determine how much ascorbic acid can prevent the vitamin C deficiency disease scurvy, there has been no way to determine optimal requirements (1,2).

We have proposed that the concentrations of ascorbic acid required in situ for specific reactions may provide critical information for determining optimal vitamin requirements (1,2). Vitamin C is required for maximal activity of 8 isolated enzymes. However, the behavior of these isolated enzymes with repsect to vitamin C may not be at all similar to behavior of the enzymes in organelles, cells, and animals. If the activities of these enzymes are measured in situ as a function of ascorbic acid concentration in situ, we can determine precisely how much ascorbic acid is required for a specific biochemical effect. Furthermore, similar information can be determined for reactions which are specifically vitamin C dependent but not enzymatically mediated. Thus, the information that is needed for both enzymatic and non-enzymatic reactions is similar to dose response curves. Using this information, it will be feasible to measure how these concentrations of ascorbic acid can be achieved and maintained in cells, animals, and humans.

To validate the hypothesis of in situ enzyme kinetics for ascorbic acid, it is of fundamental importance to characterize a dose response curve for one enzyme which is vitamin C dependent when isolated (1,2). To determine this curve, the enzyme selected should be found in cells known to contain vitamin C, and it must be possible to adjust the concentration of ascorbic acid in the cells across a wide range (3). The vitamin should then be shown to effect the specific enzymatic reaction in cells and/or organelles as a function of vitamin concentration, and it should be determined whether the vitamin stimulates only one reaction or several related reactions (4). The specificity in situ for ascorbic acid must be measured, and the effect of the vitamin on reaction rate should be found under a wide variety of cell conditions. Perhaps most important, we must understand the mechanism of vitamin C action in situ. Indeed, it is only through insight into this mechanism that we can predict reaction conditions for maximal vitamin C activity in situ.

The vitamin C dependent enzyme dopamine beta-monooxygenase is found in adrenal medulla in chromaffin cells and their secretory vesicles, chromaffin granules (5). For the isolated enzyme, ascorbic acid is required for synthesis of the stress hormone norepinprhine from the substrate dopamine (6) in the catecholamine biosynthesis pathway (figure 1). To test the hypothesis of in situ kinetics for ascorbic acid, we studied biosynthesis of norepinphrine in chromaffin cells and chromaffin granules of bovine adrenal medulla.

METHODS

Chromaffin cells and chromaffin granules were isolated from bovine adrenal medullae by standard techniques (3,4,7). Incubation conditions, experimental procedures, and HPLC assays for catecholamines and ascorbic acid have been described elsewhere (3,4,7,8).

RESULTS AND DISCUSSION

Isolated dopamine beta-monooxygenase requires vitamin C for maximal activity (6). However, the requirement for ascorbic

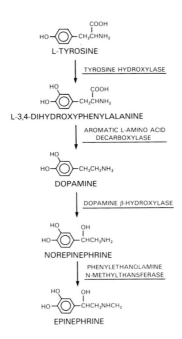

Figure 1.   Catecholamine biosynthesis pathway.

acid in chromaffin tissue of the adrenal medulla did not
appear as straightforward as for the isolated enzyme. The
enzymes required for catecholamine synthesis are cytosolic
except for dopamine beta-monooxygenase, which is localized
exclusively to the inner aspect of chromaffin granules (9).
However, while some ascorbic acid is found within chromaffin
granules, most cellular ascorbic acid is cytosolic (10,11).
Furthermore, ascorbic acid is unable to enter isolated
chromaffin granules, which are functional as measured by Mg-
ATP dependent catecholamine uptake (3,12). Thus, if ascorbic
acid is not freely available to the intragranular enzyme
dopamine beta-monooxygenase in situ, the need for ascorbic
acid in situ for enzyme activity is uncertain.
     To test whether ascorbic acid regulated norepinephrine
biosynthesis in situ, it was first necessary to be able to
adjust the intracellular concentration of ascorbic acid across
a wide range. We found that chromaffin cells when isolated

contain 2-6 mM ascorbic acid (3,13). When the cells are
cultured for 3-6 days, they lose more than 90% of their ascorbic acid (3). If the cells are then incubated with 200 uM
ascorbic acid for 3 hours they can re-accumulate and concentrate the vitamin more than 10 fold (figure 2), similar to
the amounts found originally in the cells. Thus, low
concentrations of intracellular ascorbic acid can be achieved
by cell culture, and high intracellular concentrations of
ascorbic acid are restored by addition of vitamin to the
culture medium (3).

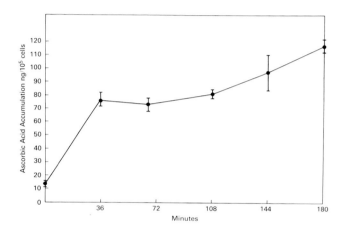

FIGURE 2.   Ascorbic acid accumulation into 3 day old
cultured chromaffin cells: cells were incubated at time 0
with 200 uM ascorbic acid and accumulation determined over
time by HPLC.

Using these conditions, we were able to test the ability
of ascorbic acid to regulate norepinephrine biosynthesis in
situ, in chromaffin cells (4).   Chromaffin cells were depleted
of ascorbic acid by cell culture for several days. The cells
were then incubated with and without 250 uM ascorbic acid for
3 hours, after which radiolabelled tyrosine was added.   When
uptake of tyrosine and biosynthesis of dopamine and norepinephrine were measured, only norepinephrine biosynthesis was
stimulated by ascorbic acid (figure 3). By contrast, tyrosine
uptake and dopamine content were unaffected by ascorbic acid.
We also found that ascorbic acid did not influence synthesis
of the precursor DOPA (3), nor was there an effect on

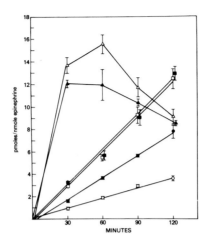

FIGURE 3. Ascorbic acid enhancement of norepinephrine biosynthesis in resting chromaffin cells. Chromaffin cells were pre-incubated with or without 250 uM ascorbic acid for 3 hours (see fig. 2). Cells were then incubated with [14C] tyrosine 10 uM for varying times with (closed symbols) and without (open symbols) ascorbic acid (4). [14C]Tyrosine content (▲,△); [14C]dopamine content (■,□); [14C]norepinephrine biosynthesis (●,○). See (4) for details.

epinephrine synthesis under these conditions (3). When the dopamine beta-monooxygenase inhibitor diethyl-dithiocarbamate was added to the cells, the effect of ascorbic acid on norepinephrine biosynthesis was lost, but no other effects of ascorbic acid were apparent on dopamine biosynthesis and tyrosine uptake (4). The effect of ascorbic acid also could not be explained by changes in catecholamine catabolism in these cells (4). These data all indicate that vitamin C stimulates only the enzyme dopamine beta-monooxygenase in the catecholamine biosynthesis pathway.

The effect of ascorbic acid in cells on increasing norepinephrine biosynthesis was found to be specific for ascorbic acid, as other endogenous reducing agents were ineffective (4). These data could also not be explained by lack of uptake of these reducing agents into the cells (7).

Since ascorbic acid specifically stimulated only nor-epinephrine biosynthesis in situ, we predicted that the effect should occur under a wide variety of conditions. Ascorbic acid was effective in resting cells (figure 3). We therefore

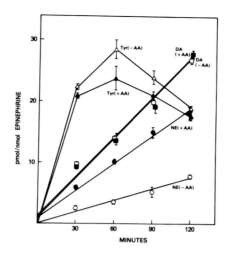

FIGURE 4.   Ascorbic acid enhancement of norepinephrine biosynthesis in stimulated chromaffin cells. Cells were treated as in figure 3 except 300uM carbachol was added with 10 uM [^{14}C]tyrosine. Symbols are as in figure 3.

tested the effect of ascorbic acid on norepinephrine bio-synthesis using stressed cells, or chromaffin cells stimulated to secrete. Chromaffin cells were incubated with and without ascorbic acid as above, and the secretagogue carbachol was added concurrently with [^{14}C]tyrosine. As shown in figure 4, ascorbic acid again stimulated only norepinephrine biosynthesis (4). This effect was also found with the secretagogues acetylcholine, veratridine, and KCl (4). Thus, ascorbic acid stimulates norepinephrine biosynthesis under a wide variety of conditions. Furthermore, all of these data with resting and stimulated cells satisfy the conditions outlined in the introduction for determining in situ enzyme kinetics.

     Although ascorbic acid stimulated norepinephrine bio-synthesis in cells, the mechanism of action was not clear. Since ascorbic acid does not enter isolated chromaffin granules (3,12), and since most ascorbic acid is found out-side chromaffin granules in intact chromaffin cells (10,11,13), we predicted that ascorbic acid might regulate norepinephrine biosynthesis by transfering reducing equivalents to an intragranular electron acceptor (7). To test this hypothesis we used isolated chromaffin granules. Since isolated chrom-affin granules are functionally intact and contain all of

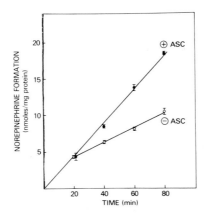

FIGURE 5. Ascorbic acid regulation of norepinephrine biosynthesis in isolated chromaffin granules. [^{3}H]Norepine-phrine biosynthesis was measured in chromaffin granules incubated with 50 uM [^{3}H]dopamine and 2.5 mM Mg-ATP in the presence (●) or absence (0) of 1 mM ascorbic acid.

the chromaffin cells' dopamine beta-monooxygenase, these vesicles are an ideal system for studying in situ enzyme kinetics for ascorbic acid (5,7).

Isolated chromaffin granules were incubated with 50 uM dopamine and 2.5 mM Mg-ATP, in the presence and absence of ascorbic acid (figure 5). While ascorbic acid itself did not enter the granules, norepinephrine biosynthesis from dopamine was stimulated by extragranular ascorbic acid (7). Thus, electron transfer must occur from extragranular ascorbic acid (7,14).

To characterize the mechanism of extragranular ascorbic acid regulation of intragranular norepinephrine biosynthesis, we tested the requirement for Mg-ATP. In figure 5, Mg-ATP was essential for dopamine uptake when external dopamine concentration was 50 uM. To determine if Mg-ATP was necessary for norepinephrine biosynthesis independent of substrate entry, we incubated granules with higher dopamine concentrations. At 10 mM external dopamine, dopamine uptake occured by diffusion independent of Mg-ATP and without granule lysis (8). We also determined that at 10 mM external dopamine, norepine-phrine biosynthesis was maximal (8).

We therefore incubated chromaffin granules with 10 mM dopamine in the presence and absence of ascorbic acid and Mg-ATP and measured norepinephrine biosynthesis (8).

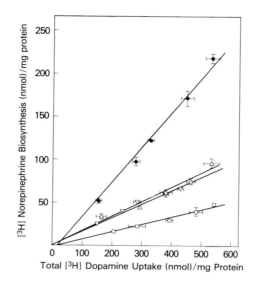

FIGURE 6. [3H]Norepinephrine biosynthesis as a function of [3H]dopamine uptake in isolated chromaffin granules incubated with and without Mg-ATP and ascorbic acid. Chromaffin granules plus 10 mM [3H]dopamine were incubated 15–60 minutes with ascorbic acid 2.0 mM and Mg-ATP 2.5 mM (●), ascorbic acid alone (▽), Mg-ATP alone (△), or neither (□).

Norepinephrine biosynthesis was maximal only in the presence of both Mg-ATP and ascorbic acid. This effect of Mg-ATP and ascorbate was independent of substrate uptake and occured at every intragranular concentration of dopamine (figure 6). Thus, Mg-ATP is required for maximal norepinephrine biosynthesis, independent of substrate entry.

Having characterized conditions at which norepinephrine biosynthesis was maximal, we were then able to determine the extragranular requirements for ascorbic acid. We incubated chromaffin granules with Mg-ATP and 10 mM dopamine in the presence of 25–1000 uM ascorbic acid (8). Norepinephrine biosynthesis was measured as a function of external ascorbic acid concentration (figure 7). Indeed, this represents a dose response cuve as required for determination of in situ kinetics. The apparent K_m of intragranular norepinephrine biosynthesis for extragranular ascorbic acid was approximately 300 uM (7,8), which is several fold lower than the cytosolic concentration of ascorbic acid in chromaffin cells (3,13). Thus, ascorbic acid concentration found in chromaffin cells

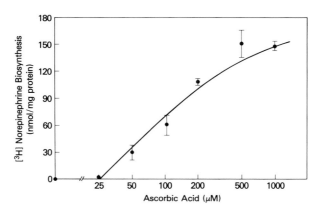

FIGURE 7. Effect of ascorbic acid on [³H]norepinephrine biosynthesis is concentration dependent. Isolated chromaffin granules were incubated for 60 minutes with 10 mM [³H]dopamine, 1 mM Mg–ATP, and 0.025-1.0 mM ascorbic acid.

<u>in situ</u> may encourage maximal norepinephrine biosynthesis.

The mechanism of action of Mg–ATP and ascorbic acid to stimulate norepinephrine biosynthesis is under investigation in our laboratory. We have recently determined that intragranular ascorbic acid is essential for norepinephrine biosynthesis (15). Furthermore, extragranular ascorbic acid is required to maintain intragranular ascorbic acid in the presence of external dopamine (15). Since isolated dopamine beta-monooxygenase appears to accept single electrons from ascorbic acid (16), our recent data support the concept that the intragranular electron acceptor might be the ascorbic acid free radical, semidehydroascorbate. Thus, extragranular ascorbic acid might transfer electrons to intragranular semidehydroascorbate (figure 8). Intragranular semidehydro-ascorbate may be formed as intragranular ascorbate reduces dopamine beta-monooxygenase with single electron transfer; extragranular ascorbate could reduce intragranular semidehydroascorbate back to ascorbic acid, which could be oxidized again.

The role of Mg–ATP with ascorbic acid in norepinephrine biosynthesis is also under investigation. While the mechanism is not known, our preliminary observations indicate that Mg–ATP is not required for maintaining membrane potential nor Δ pH (8). Furthermore, Mg–ATP is not required for electron transfer from extragranular to intragranular ascorbic acid.

ASCORBIC ACID AND NOREPINEPHRINE BIOSYNTHESIS

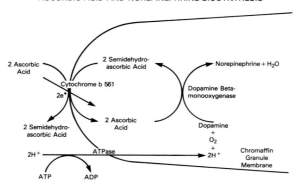

FIGURE 8. A model for ascorbic acid and Mg–ATP action in norepinephrine biosynthesis in chromaffin granules.

The action of Mg–ATP appears to be mediated, however, by the chromaffin granule Mg–ATP proton ATPase. These preliminary observations all imply that Mg–ATP, via the proton ATPase, provides protons which are required for norepinephrine biosynthesis (8)(figure 8). Some of these protons might also come from the intragranular core, which has a large buffering capacity, and may be replaced by action of the proton Mg–ATPase. In the presence of extragranular ascorbate and electron transfer, protons may also be required for norepinephrine biosynthesis to maintain electroneutrality (14).

SUMMARY

Ascorbic acid in situ specifically stimulates norepinephrine biosynthesis by increasing only dopamine beta-monooxygenase activity in chromaffin cells. Ascorbic acid also specifically increases norepinephrine biosynthesis in a concentration dependent fashion in isolated chromaffin granules. However, the mechanism of action of ascorbic acid in situ is very different than for the isolated enzyme. Mg–ATP also is required with ascorbic acid for maximal norepinephrine biosynthesis in chromaffin granules, independent of dopamine uptake. These data validate the hypothesis and demonstrate the importance of in situ kinetics for vitamin C.

REFERENCES

1. Levine M (1986) N Engl J Med 314:892.
2. Levine M, Hartzell W (1987) Ann N Y Acad Sci 498:424.
3. Levine M, Morita K, Pollard H (1985) J Biol Chem 260:12942.
4. Levine M (1986) J Biol Chem 261:7347.
5. Kirshner N (1957) J Biol Chem 226:821.
6. Friedman S, Kaufman S (1965) J Biol Chem 240:4763.
7. Levine M, Morita K, Heldman E, Pollard H (1985) J Biol Chem 260:15598.
8. Levine M, Hartzell W, Bdollah A (1988) Manuscript submitted.
9. Laduron P (1975) FEBS Lett 52:132.
10. Levine M, Asher A, Pollard H, Zinder O (1983) J Biol Chem 258:13111.
11. Morita K, Levine M, Pollard H (1985) J Biol Chem 260:15112.
12. Tirrell J, Westhead E (1977) Neuroscience 4:181.
13. Levine M, Pollard H (1983) FEBS Lett 158:134.
14. Wakefield L, Cass A, Radda G (1986) J Biol Chem 261:9739.
15. Dhariwal K, Washko P, Hartzell W, Levine M (1988) Endocrinology 122(Suppl):104. Manuscript also in preparation.
16. Skotland T, Ljones T (1980) Biochim Biophys Acta 630:30.

III. IMMUNOBIOLOGY OF STRESS

Molecular Biology of Stress, pages 205-214
© 1989 Alan R. Liss, Inc.

SHOCK INDUCED IMMUNOSUPPRESSION:
NALTREXONE SENSITIVE AND INSENSITIVE PARAMETERS

Joan E. Cunnick, Donald T. Lysle,
Ada Armfield, and Bruce S. Rabin.

Division of Clinical Immunopathology, Department of
Pathology, University of Pittsburgh, PA, 15217-3417, USA

ABSTRACT   The present research shows that signalled
footshock induces suppression of splenic NK activity and
T-cell response to the mitogens concanavalin A (Con A)
and phytohemagglutinin (PHA). The suppression of
mitogenic responsiveness habituated after 5 daily
sessions of shock, while NK activity remained
suppressed. Administration of naltrexone but not
diazepam prior to a session of shock prevented the
suppression of NK function indicating mediation via
opiate receptors. However, neither naltrexone nor
diazepam were able to prevent the shock induced
suppression of mitogenic responsiveness to Con A or PHA.
Collectively, these results indicate that the shock
induced immune alterations are mediated by different
mechanisms.

INTRODUCTION

Recent research has demonstrated that the physical
stress of electric shock can suppress immune function. Rats
which have experienced presentations of shock have
decreased lymphocyte responsiveness to stimulation by plant
lectins (1), decreased natural killer (NK) cell activity
(2), and increased susceptibility to tumor challenge (3,4).
However, few of the reports have attempted to assess more
than one shock parameter or identify the mechanisms
mediating the suppression of the immunologic measures.
The research in our laboratory (5) indicates that the
aversive experience of foot-shock differentially affects
immunologic compartments. For example, one session of foot-

shock produces a suppression of the mitogenic response of splenic and blood lymphocytes to concanavalin A (Con A). However, the suppressive effect of shock on the splenic response to mitogens diminishes over 5 daily shock sessions, whereas the response of the blood lymphocytes remains suppressed. This demonstrates that the number of shock sessions has a significant influence on immunosuppression. Our findings indicate that initial exposure to shock induces suppression of both blood and spleen mitogenic response and continued exposure will result in habituation of that suppression, but only for the spleen lymphocytes.

Those studies that have investigated mechanisms mediating the immunosuppressive effects of foot-shock have found that endogenous production of opiates is important. Shavit and colleagues (2) have demonstrated that intermittent foot-shock produces an opioid analgesia and is associated with supppressed NK activity in rat splenocytes. The suppression of NK activity can be prevented by administration of the opiate receptor antagonist naltrexone, prior to foot-shock. Administration of the exogenous opiate, morphine, can induce a similar suppression of NK activity. Although it has been suggested that the suppression of T-lymphocyte responsiveness to mitogens is also mediated via endogenously produced opiates, those studies involving the mechanisms of splenic immune suppression have only examined NK function.

Other mechanisms of stress induced immunosuppression have been suggested. Several investigators have implicated the benzodiazepine receptor in the physiological control of stress and anxiety (6-9). The benzodiazepine receptor inverse antagonist, FG 7142 (a B-carboline) has been used as a model of anxiety (8) and is capable of suppressing immune function (10) Diazepam, a common anxiolytic drug, is an effective blocker of FG 7142 (8) and has been effective in attenuating several stress induced changes in rats, such as an increased turnover of noradrenalin in several brain regions, and the behavioral changes of increased defecation and vocalization (7,9).

This study was designed to compare the parameters of shock induced suppression of splenic NK activity and mitogenic responsiveness, as well as possible mechanisms mediating both types of suppression. The first experiment examined the parameters of NK activity over one and 5 daily sessions of foot-shock and compared them to the parameters of the mitogenic response of T-lymphocytes. The second set of experiments examined the effects of administration of naltrexone or diazepam on the observed splenic suppression of NK activity and mitogenic responsiveness.

METHODS

Animals. Male, Lewis rats, 250-300 grams in weight, (Charles-River Laboratories) were individually caged in a colony room where a reversed day-night (12-hour) cycle was maintained through artificial illumination. The rats were acclimated for two weeks prior to the experimental manipulations.

Shock Apparatus. Standard Coulbourn conditioning chambers (Coulbourn Instruments Model E10-10), measuring 25 x 30 x 33 cm, served as the shock apparatuses. The output of a shock generator and scrambler (BRS/LVE Models 903 and SC 902) provided a 5.0-second, 1.6-mA, footshock. An audio generator (BRS/LVE Model AU-902) provided an auditory signal: a 78-dB clicking signal (15 sec). The shocks were delivered on a 4 min variable time basis (range 2-6 min). Each shock was always preceded by and coterminated with the 15-second clicker signal.

Parameters of Shock-Induced Suppression. The experimental subjects were presented with 16 signaled-shocks per session for 1, or 5 daily sessions. Control subjects remained undisturbed in their home cages.

Immediately following the last shock experience, each experimental subject was rapidly sacrificed by cervical dislocation. The control subjects were removed from their home cages and sacrificed in the same manner and at the same time as the experimental subjects.

Mitogen Assay. A mitogenic stimulation assay was performed with whole spleen lymphocytes, using the non-specific, T-cell mitogen, Con A (Difco) and PHA type HA-16 (Wellcome) as described previously (11). Preliminary investigations showed that Con A at a final concentration of 2.5-5.0 ug/ml provided optimal lymphocyte stimulation, while PHA was optimal at a final concentration of 5 ug/ml.

Natural Killer (NK) Cell Assay. Whole spleen lymphocytes were tested for their ability to lyse chromium-51 labeled YAC-1 tumor cells in a standard 4 hr cytotoxicity assay. Effector:target ratios of 100:1, 50:1, and 25:1 were tested in triplicate.

Lytic units per 10^7 were calculated using a computer program in the Pittsburgh Cancer Institute based on the equations of Pross and Maroun (12). The percent cytotoxicity at all effector:target ratios were utilized to determine LU, which are based on the number of leukocytes necessary to lyse 20% of the targets. The mean LU for non-treated controls was 13.1.

Naltrexone Treatment. Fifteen minutes prior to a single session of signalled shock, experimental animals received an intraperitoneal (i.p.) injection of naltrexone (10 mg/kg body weight) in phosphate buffered saline (PBS) or an equal volume of PBS. Injection control rats received either an injection of naltrexone or PBS but remained in their cages for 80 min, a time equal to the shock session plus the fifteen min post injection period. After the shock session or 80 min time period the injected rats, as well as non-treated control rats, were sacrificed.

Diazepam Treatment. Diazepam (2.5 mg/kg) or an equal volume of PBS was administered, i.p.,15 min prior to one session of signalled shock. The injection controls were given diazepam or saline 80 min prior to sacrifice. A fifth group of non-treated control subjects were also sacrificed.

Statistical Treatment of Data. To afford comparisons among the experiments that were unaffected by variations in assay conditions, the means of the triplicate background, Con A and PHA stimulated scintillation counts and LU for each experimental subject were transformed into percentage scores based on the means for its respective untreated control group. For each of the experiments, the total leukocytes per spleen were also analyzed. A computerized program for one-way analysis of variance (Statistix, NH Analytical Software) was used to assess differences among experimental and control groups. The significance level was set at a probability of less than or equal to 0.05.

RESULTS

Splenic Leukocytes.

In all experiments, total splenic leukocytes were 6-8 x 10^8 leukocytes/spleen. There were no significant differences between experimental and control rats in any of the manipulations.

Parameters of Shock-Induced Suppression.

The immune function of rats, that received presentations
of signaled-shocks for 1 session or 5 consecutive daily
sessions, were compared to a non-treated control group
(n=9). Table 1 presents the mean mitogenic response to the
optimal concentrations of Con A and PHA of the two shocked
groups and non-treated control group, expressed as the
percent of non-treated control response. Analysis of
variance of all concentrations of Con A and PHA showed
similar results. The subjects that received signaled-shocks
were significantly suppressed relative to the non-treated
control group, $p < .0001$. Those animals which received 5
daily sessions of shock had a significantly higher
mitogenic response than those animals receiving only one
session of shock, $p < .025$. Therefore this data demonstrated
a suppression of the mitogenic response after one shock
session and an habituation of that suppression after 5
consecutive days of shock.

TABLE 1

THE EFFECT OF NUMBER OF SHOCK SESSIONS ON IMMUNE
FUNCTION (MEAN±SE).

| TREATMENT | PERCENT OF NON-TREATED CONTROL | | |
	CON A	PHA	LU
1 SHOCK SESSION	20±2	19±4	73±5
5 SHOCK SESSIONS	49±14	51±13	68±9
NO TREATMENT	100±2	100±6	100±4

Table 1 also presents the mean LU for animals shocked 1
or 5 days, expressed as the percent of untreated control
response. The subjects that received signaled-shocks were
significantly suppressed relative to the non-treated control
group, $p < .001$. There was no statistical difference between
the two shocked groups. Thus, the signaled-shocks suppressed
splenic NK activity and this suppression showed no evidence
of habituation after 5 daily sessions of shock. These
findings suggest that the parameters of shock-induced immune
suppression of mitogen responsiveness and NK activity were

differentially affected, even though the leukocytes were derived from the same spleens.

Naltrexone Treatment.

As one session of signaled-shock was capable of inducing significant suppression of NK activity and mitogenic responsiveness, we used one session to test the effects of naltrexone on the observed immunosuppression. Table 2 presents the mean LU of all five groups as percent of the non-treated control group (n=6). The experimental (shocked) and injection (inj.) control subjects that received injections of either naltrexone or PBS were significantly suppressed relative to the non-treated control group, $p <$ .015. The injection control groups were not significantly different from each other; nor were they significantly different from the experimental/naltrexone group. However, the experimental/PBS group was significantly suppressed relative to those three groups, $p < .025$. This data demonstrates that suppressed NK function can be attenuated by naltrexone and indicates that the NK suppression is mediated via an opiate receptor. Furthermore, the stress of the injection of PBS or naltrexone is sufficient to induce suppression of NK activity.

TABLE 2

THE EFFECT OF NALTREXONE ON SHOCK INDUCED
IMMUNOSUPPRESSION (MEAN±SE)

TREATMENT	PERCENT OF NON-TREATED CONTROL		
	CON A	PHA	LU
EXPERIMENTAL			
NALTREXONE	52±16	31±2	82±5
PBS	59±15	45±13	63±7
INJ. CONTROL			
NALTREXONE	119±9	112±14	82±7
PBS	118±6	92±8	86±10
NO TREATMENT	100±3	100±8	100±5

Table 2 also presents the mean mitogenic response of splenic lymphocytes to the optimum concentrations of Con A and PHA expressed as percent of untreated controls. Analysis of variance of all concentrations of Con A and PHA showed similar results. The injection control groups were not significantly different from each other; nor were they significantly different from the non-treated control group. Also, the experimental groups were not significantly different from each other. However, the two experimental groups were significantly different from all three control groups, $\underline{p}$ < .003. These analysis confirm our findings of a significantly suppressed mitogenic response due to a single shock session. However, there was no effect of naltrexone on this suppression.

Diazepam Treatment.

We examined the effects of diazepam, an anxiolytic drug, on the stress induced immunosuppression. Table 3 presents the mean LU of all five groups as percent of the non-treated controls (n=8). The injection control groups were not significantly different from each other; nor were they significantly different from the non-treated control group. Also, the two experimental groups were not significantly different from each other. However, the two experimental groups were significantly suppressed relative to the three control groups, $\underline{p}$ < .002. These results indicated that diazepam had no attenuating effect on the suppression of NK activity by signaled-shock.

Table 3 also presents the mean mitogenic response of splenic lymphocytes to the optimum concentrations of Con A and PHA, expressed   as percent of untreated controls. Analysis of variance of all concentrations of Con A and PHA showed similar results. The injection control groups were not significantly different from each other. Also, the two injection control groups were not significantly different from the non-treated control. Furhtermore, the two experimental groups were not statistically different from each other. However, the two experimental groups were significantly different from the three control groups, $\underline{p}$ < .0001. These data show that diazepam has no attenuating effect on the suppression of the mitogenic response induced by signaled-shock.

TABLE 3
THE EFFECT OF DIAZEPAM ON SHOCK INDUCED
IMMUNOSUPPRESSION (MEAN±SE)

TREATMENT	PERCENT OF NON-TREATED CONTROL		
	CON A	PHA	LU
EXPERIMENTAL			
DIAZEPAM	51±11	29±9	75±9
PBS	50±12	46±12	64±3
INJ. CONTROL			
DIAZEPAM	101±7	80±15	97±11
PBS	94±3	95±8	94±8
NO TREATMENT	100±2	100±6	100±8

DISCUSSION

The present results demonstrated that different types of mononuclear cells in the spleen are differentially affected by the same stressor. The T-cell mitogenic response to Con A and PHA was suppressed by one shock session, but the suppression diminishes with repeated sessions of shock. The NK cell activity was also suppressed after a single shock session. However, repeated sessions of shock did not result in the reduction of the suppression. These results indicate that the T-cells habituate to the immunosuppressive effect of shock whereas the NK cells do not habituate.

Although the NK cells did not exhibit habituation, the suppression of NK activity could be attenuated by administration of naltrexone prior to the presentation of the shock, indicating that the suppression of the NK cell activity was mediated via an opiate receptor. The suppression of the mitogenic response was not prevented by the prior administration of naltrexone, and therefore does not appear to be mediated via an opiate receptor. Furthermore, the suppression of NK activity and the suppression of the T-cell mitogenic response were not affected by the administration of diazepam. This suggested that immunological suppression induced by the physical stressor does not involve the benzodiazepine receptor.

Collectively, these results show that the parameters of the responses of the T-cells and NK cells to stressors were different. The splenic mitogenic response confirms our previous findings of habituation (5), but extends this work by demonstrating that splenic NK cells, do not show habituation. Also the response of the T-cells and NK cells to the stress of the injections differed. These differences suggest that stress-induced immunosuppression of these two cell types was mediated by different mechanisms.

The data obtained in the naltrexone experiment corroborates the findings of Shavit et al. (2) which show that NK activity is suppressed by stress and the suppression is prevented by prior treatment with an opiate receptor antagonist. Thus, the suppression of NK activity appears to be mediated via endogenous opiates. However, the lack of an effect of naltrexone on the mitogenic response indicates that the suppression of T-cell responsiveness is mediated by a different mechanism.

Thus, this study indicates that not all cell types are equally affected by presentation of a physical stressor such as shock. There are many possible direct and indirect pathways by which stress induced immune suppression may be mediated. Further testing is necessary to determine if similar pathways mediate immune suppression induced by a a psychological stressor.

ACKNOWLEDGEMENTS

This research was supported in part by a grant from the Office of Naval Research (N00014-86-K-0500) and from the National Institute of Mental Health (MH43411). The authors wish to express their appreciation to Ellen Hamill, Barbara Kucinski, and Paul Wood for their technical assistance. The authors thank E. I. Du Pont De Nemours & Co., Glenolden Laboratory, Glenolden, PA for there generous gift of naltrexone.

REFERENCES

1.   Keller SE, Weiss JM, Schleifer SJ, Miller NE, Stein M (1981). Suppression of immunity by stress: Effect of a graded series of stressors on lymphocyte stimulation in the rat. Science 213:1397.

2.   Shavit Y, Lewis JW, Terman GW, Gale RP, Liebeskind JC (1984). Opioid peptides mediate the suppressive effect of stress on natural killer cell cytotoxicity. Science 223:188.

3.   Lewis JW, Shavit Y, Terman GW, Gale RP, Liebeskind JC. (1983/84). Stress and morphine affect survival of rats challenged with a mammary ascites tumor (MAT 13762B). Nat Immun Cell Growth Regul 3:43.

4.   Lewis JW, Shavit Y, Terman GW, Nelson LR, Gale RP, Liebeskind JC (1983). Apparent involvement of opioid peptides in stress-induced enhancement of tumor growth. Peptides 4:635.

5.   Lysle DT, Lyte M, Fowler H, Rabin BS (1987). Shock-induced modulation of lymphocyte reactivity: Suppression, habituation, and recovery. Life Sci 41:1805.

6.   Dadhich AP, Sharma VN, Godhwani JL (1980). Effect of restraint stress on immune response and its modification by chlorpromazine, diazepam and pentobarbitone. Indian J Exp Biol 18:756.

7.   Ida Y, Tanaka M, Tsuda A, Tsujimaru S, Nagasaki N (1985). Attenuating effect of diazepam on stress-induced increases in noradrenaline turnover in specific brain regions of rats: Antagonism by Ro 15-1788. Life Sci 37:2491.

8.   Insel TR, Ninan PT, Aloe J, Jimerson DC, Skolnick P, Paul SM (1984). A benzodiazepine receptor-mediated model of anxiety. Arch Gen Psychiatry 41:741.

9.   Skolnick P, Ninan P, Insel T, Crawley J, Paul S (1984). A novel chemically induced animal model of human anxiety. Psychopathology 17(sl):25.

10. Arora PK, Hanna EE, Paul SM, Skolnick P (1987). Suppression of the immune response by benzodiazepine receptor inverse agonists. J Neuroimmunol 15:1.

11. Lysle DT, Cunnick JE, Fowler H, Rabin BS (1988). Pavlovian conditioning of shock-induced suppresion of lymphocyte reactivity: Acquistion, extinction, and preexposure effects. Life Sci 42:2185.

12. Pross HF, Maroun JA (1984). The standardization of NK cell assays for use in studies of biological response modifiers. J Immunol Methods 68:235.

Molecular Biology of Stress, pages 215–224
© **1989 Alan R. Liss, Inc.**

REGULATION OF INTERLEUKIN-2 EXPRESSION BY DEXAMETHASONE
IN A MOUSE T CELL LINE[1]

Barbara A. Sorg,[2] Nancy S. Magnuson,[*]
and Raymond Reeves

Department of Genetics and Cell Biology,
and [*]Department of Microbiology,
Washington State University,
Pullman, Washington 99164

ABSTRACT   We examined the effects of the synthetic
glucocorticoid, dexamethasone (dex), on the
production of interleukin-2 (IL-2) and its
corresponding mRNA in the mouse T cell line, LBRM-
33.4A2. Treatment of Concanavalin A (Con A)-
stimulated cells with 10 nM dex inhibited IL-2
activity by approximately 70%, which corresponded
with the reduction in steady-state levels of IL-2
mRNA. Dex inhibited the accumulation of IL-2 mRNA
in a dose-dependent manner, with maximal inhibition
by treatment with > 0.1 μM dex. Actinomycin D
experiments suggest that dex does not mediate its
suppression of IL-2 mRNA by decreasing the stability
of this message. The effect of dex on another Con
A- inducible gene, c-myc, showed that in contrast to
IL-2 mRNA, much higher concentrations of dex (up to
10 μm) only partially inhibited c-myc mRNA levels
(by 30%). Dex did not inhibit c-myc mRNA levels
early after induction, as was found for IL-2 mRNA.
The levels of β- tubulin mRNA were unaffected by
treatment with dex concentrations as high as 10 μM.
These data suggest that dex specifically inhibits
IL-2 mRNA, and that this inhibition is not mediated
by a decrease in mRNA stability.

---

[1]This work was supported by NIH AI-07025, USDA CRCR-
1-1730 and NSF DCB-8602622.
[2]Present Address: Department of Psychology,
Washington State University, Pullman, Washington
99164.

INTRODUCTION

Glucocorticoids elicit a wide range of effects on the immune system, resulting in an overall inhibition of the inflammatory and immune responses (1). Some of these effects are mediated by the inhibitory action of glucocorticoids on the production of lymphokines, including interleukins-1,-2, and-3 (IL-1, IL-2, and IL-3, respectively) (2-5). IL-2 has several biological activities which promote the growth and differentiation of lymphocytes (6). The mechanism by which glucocorticoid-mediated suppression of IL-2 production occurs is not known. Studies with IL-1- and IL-3-producing cell lines suggest that glucocorticoids act by suppressing the transcription of these genes (3,5).

The present work was undertaken to determine the effects of the synthetic glucocorticoid, dexamethasone (dex) on the production of IL-2 in the mouse T lymphoma cell line, LBRM- 33, clone 4A2. We also examined the effects of dex on c-myc and β-tubulin mRNA accumulation. The constitutively expressed β-tubulin gene was chosen to determine if the effects of dex were specific for IL-2 mRNA or if dex reduced expression of all mRNAs. The levels of c-myc mRNA were measured for several reasons. 1) IL-2 and c-myc mRNAs both are induced by mitogens and are transiently expressed in T lymphocytes (7,8), suggesting that these genes may be regulated by similar processes, and 2) It was of interest to test whether dex suppressed mRNAs that have a short $t_{1/2}$ in cultured cell lines (c-myc, IL-2) to a greater extent than it suppressed longer-lived mRNAs (β-tubulin). Thus, we wanted to examine the possibility that IL-2 and c-myc were affected by dex via a mechanism acting at the same level of their gene expression.

METHODS

Cell lines

The T cell lymphoma line, LBRM-33 cells (clone 4A2)(9) was obtained from the American Type Culture Collection (Rockville, MD). Cells were grown in the medium recommendedby the ATCC. The IL-2-dependent mouse cell line, HT-2 (10), was maintained in RPMI 1640 supplemented with 10% fetal calf serum, 165 U/ml penicillin, 75 U/ml streptomycin and 30 U/ml human recombinant IL-2 (Chiron Corporation, Emeryville, CA).

IL-2 assay

LBRM-33 cells (7×10^5/ml) were treated with 20 μg/ml
Concanavalin A (Con A) (Sigma) in the presence or absence
of various concentrations of dex (Sigma). In all
experiments, "control" cells refer to ethanol-treated
cells. At the end of the time periods, supernatants were
harvested and IL-2 activity was determined by a
modification of a standard microassay (11). One unit of
activity is defined as the amount of IL-2 that induced 50%
of maximal ^{3}H-TdR incorporation of a 48 h culture medium
conditioned by Con A stimulation of LBRM-33 cells.

RNA isolation

LBRM-33 cells (7×10^5cells/ml) were incubated in the
presence of Con A (20 μg/ml) for various times in the
presence or absence of dex or 5 μg/ml actinomycin D (AD)
(Sigma). At the end of the time periods, total cellular
RNA from 100 ml cells was isolated by a modification of
the procedure by Cathala et al. (12).

Northern blot analysis

The RNA samples were separated in a 1.2% agarose, 6%
formaldehyde gel and transferred to a nylon membrane in
20xSSC. The blot was exposed to ultraviolet light for 3
min and treated as described by Sorg et al. (13). The 18S
and 28S ribosomal RNAs served as RNA size standards.
Quantitative estimates of mRNA levels were obtained by
either cutting out the bands and determining radioactivity
by liquid scintillation counting or by scanning
autoradiographs with an LKB UltroScan XL densitometer.

Probes

A mouse IL-2 cDNA (M-pIL2.1) was a generous gift from
Dr. Verner Paetkau, (University of Alberta, Edmonton)
(14). A mouse c-myc cDNA (pSVc-myc) was kindly provided
by Dr. Robert Weinberg (Massachusetts Institute of
Technology) (15). The chicken B-tubulin cDNA (pT2) was a
kind gift from Dr. Donald Cleveland (Johns Hopkins
University School of Medicine) (16).

RESULTS

Effect of dexamethasone on IL-2 production

Preliminary experiments with Con A and dex indicated that concentrations >$1x10^{-7}$M dex inhibited IL-2 production to <1% of control levels by 24 h. Therefore, $1x10^{-8}$M dex was chosen for all subsequent experiments. Figure 1 shows the time course of induction of IL-2 in LBRM-33 cells incubated with Con A in the presence or absence of $1x10^{-8}$M dex. IL-2 was induced rapidly to high levels by 20 h, but in the presence of dex, inhibition of IL-2 accumulation occurred from the first time point of 4 h and reached a maximal inhibition (18 % of control levels) by 20 h.

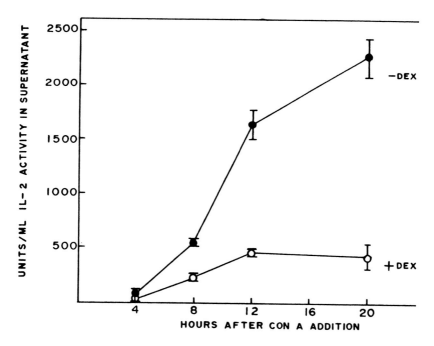

FIGURE 1. Time course of IL-2 production by LBRM-33 cells in the presence or absence of $1x10^{-8}$M dex added simultaneously with 20 µg/ml Con A. At the indicated times after Con A stimulation, the supernatants were collected and assayed for IL-2 activity as described in Methods. Each value represents duplicate assays of duplicate cultures.

Measurement of IL-2 mRNA

    To investigate whether dex treatment caused a
corresponding decrease in the level of IL-2 mRNA as was
observed for IL-2 activity (Fig. 1), total RNA was
isolated and Northern blot analysis was performed. Figure
2 shows a Northern blot of total RNA isolated from cells
incubated for various times with Con A in the presence or
absence of 1×10^{-8}M dex. No detectable levels of IL-2 mRNA
were present in uninduced cells, and IL-2 mRNA was
expressed as early as 2 h after Con A stimulation, with
peak levels occurring between 8-13 h. For all subsequent
studies, total RNA was isolated from cells incubated for 8
h or less, a time during which cellular viability remained
high ($\sim 80\%$, not shown). Treatment of cells with dex
severely inhibited IL-2 mRNA accumulation from the
earliest time point (4 h) throughout the incubation. The
levels of IL-2 mRNA in dex-treated cells were reduced by
approximately 70% of their time-matched controls, which
correlated with the level of suppression observed for IL-2
activity in cell supernatants.

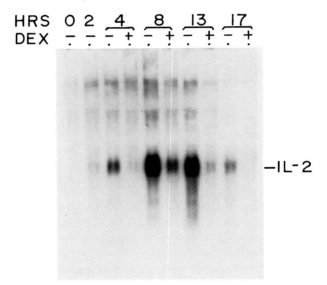

    FIGURE 2. Time course of IL-2 mRNA levels in Con A-
stimulated cells in the presence or absence of 1×10^{-8}M
dex. Total RNA (20 μg) was analyzed using a mouse IL-2
cDNA probe. RNA was isolated as described in Methods from
cells treated as indicated above.

Dosage effect of dex

    Figure 3 shows a Northern blot of total RNA isolated
from cells treated with dex concentrations ranging from
$1x10^{-5}$M to $1x10^{-10}$M dex added simultaneously with Con A
and hybridized to IL-2, c-myc, or β-tubulin cDNAs.   The
level of IL-2 mRNA was affected in a dose-dependent
manner. IL-2 mRNA was reduced to negligible levels by
concentrations >$1x10^{-7}$M dex while c-myc was reduced by
only about 30% at these dosages, and β-tubulin mRNA levels
were not affected by dex treatment as high as $1x10^{-5}$M.
These data suggest that dex-mediated inhibition is
specific for IL-2 mRNA.

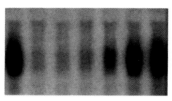

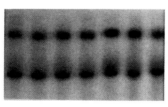

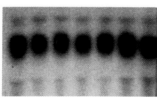

    FIGURE 3.   Effect of various dex concentrations on
steady-state levels of IL-2, c-myc, and β-tubulin mRNA
isolated from Con A-stimulated 8 h cultures.   Dex was
either absent (lane 1) or added at the same time as Con A
to a final concentration of $1x10^{-5}$M (lane 2), $1x10^{-6}$M
(lane 3), $1x10^{-7}$M (lane 4), $1x10^{-8}$M (lane 5), $1x10^{-9}$M (lane
6), or $1x10^{-10}$M(lane 7), and incubated for 8 h.   Total RNA
(20 μg/lane) was analyzed as described in Methods.

Actinomycin D treatment and mRNA $t_{1/2}$

To determine whether the suppression of IL-2 mRNA by dex was mediated by changes in IL-2 mRNA $t_{1/2}$, AD was added to cultures to inhibit transcription at various times following Con A induction. Addition of AD at the same time as Con A did not allow expression of any detectable levels of IL-2 mRNA. Figure 4 shows a Northern blot of IL-2 mRNA isolated from cells treated with AD 6 h after Con A induction. After 1 h incubation with AD, dex was added to half the cultures and incubation was continued for 30 min or 4 h to determine if dex decreased the $t_{1/2}$ of IL-2 mRNA. The Northern blot shows that the addition of dex did not decrease the $t_{1/2}$ of IL-2 mRNA by 0.5 h or 4 h after dex treatment. Also observed in the Northern blot in Figure 4 was the disappearance of a faint band migrating at 3.3 kilobases (kb) (arrow 1), which may be a stable nuclear precursor of IL-2 mRNA, and the appearance of a 3.0 kb mRNA (arrow 2) in AD-treated cultures. This suggests that some processing of an IL-2 nuclear precursor may occur in AD-treated cells.

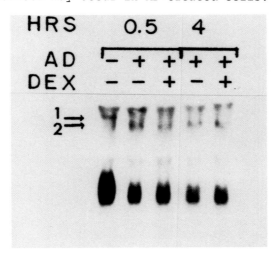

FIGURE 4. Effect of dex on IL-2 mRNA stability in Con A- plus AD-treated LBRM-33 cells. AD (5 μg/ml) was added to the cultures as indicated above following a 6 h incubation in the presence of Con A. Cells were incubated for 1h, 1×10^{-8}M dex was added to half of the cultures as indicated, and total RNA was isolated 0.5 h and 4 h later. Total RNA (20 μg/lane) was analyzed as described in Methods.

DISCUSSION

We examined the effects of dex treatment on the synthesis of IL-2 in a Con A-stimulated mouse T-cell lymphoma line, LBRM-33, clone 4A2. Treatment of the cells with 1×10^{-8}M dex resulted in a marked inhibition of IL-2 in the supernatant from the earliest time point throughout the 20 h incubation. Analysis of total RNA on Northern blots indicated that no IL-2 mRNA was present in unstimulated cells, and the appearance of IL-2 required synthesis of new RNA molecules. This is consistent with the results of Efrat and Kaempfer (17), who showed that induction of IL-2 mRNA requires de novo transcription. Northern blot analysis of IL-2 mRNA levels in Con A- plus 1×10^{-8}M dex-treated cells indicated that dex-mediated suppression of IL-2 activity in the supernatants was due to reduced levels of IL-2 mRNA accumulation in these cells. A 70% reduction of IL-2 mRNA levels in dex-treated cells was present at both early (4 h) and late (13h) time points. The dose-dependence of IL-2 mRNA levels on dex indicated that the effects of dex on IL-2 may occur by a receptor-mediated process.

The suppression of IL-2 mRNA levels by dex treatment results from a block in one or more steps of IL-2 mRNA biosynthesis. We did not detect any accumulation of stable RNA processing intermediates in dex-treated cells, as determined by Northern blot analysis. The stability of mature IL-2 mRNA in the presence of dex was examined. When AD was added to LBRM-33 cells to block transcription, the addition of dex did not decrease the stability of IL-2 mRNA. These results suggest that transcription of the IL-2 gene may be inhibited in the presence of dex. Transcription of other genes has been shown to be blocked by glucocorticoids (18, 19). Glucocorticoid receptors bind to specific DNA sequences to regulate the expression of several genes (20). These canonical DNA sequences are also present in the 5' flanking region of the mouse IL-2 gene, 26 bp upstream from a unique DNA sequence in IL-2 that has been shown to be involved in the induction of IL-2 expression and other T-cell-specific genes (21). It is also possible that dex-mediated suppression of IL-2 mRNA requires ongoing transcription. The immediate decrease in IL-2 mRNA levels after AD treatment followed by only slight decreases several hours later suggests that AD may inhibit transcription of factors which contribute to the reduction of IL-2 mRNA levels.

The effects of dex on c-myc mRNA did not mimic what was observed for IL-2 mRNA. Unlike for IL-2 mRNA, no differences were detected in dex-treated and control cells at 4 h (not shown), and by 8 h, only a small decrease in c-myc mRNA levels occurred. In addition, levels of c-myc mRNA were maximally inhibited by about 30% over a wide range of dex concentrations. Thus, dex does not appear to cause a preferential turnover of short-lived mRNAs. β-tubulin mRNA was constitutively expressed during all treatments; their levels remained unaffected by dex at all concentrations of dex tested. These studies suggest that inhibition by dex appears to be specific for IL-2 mRNA, and that dexamethasone suppresses accumulation of IL-2 mRNA levels by regulation at the transcriptional level.

REFERENCES

1. Fauci AS (1979). Immunosuppressive and anti-inflammatory effects of glucocorticoids. In Baxter JD, Rousseau GG (eds): "Glucocorticoid Hormone Action", New York: Springer-Verlag Press, p. 449.
2. Snyder DS, Unanue ER (1982). Corticosteroids inhibit murine macrophage Ia expression and interleukin 1 production. J Immunol 129:1803.
3. Knudsen PJ, Dinarello CA, Strom TV (1987). Glucocorticoids inhibit transcriptional and post-transcriptional expression of interleukin 1 in U937 cells. J Immunol 139:4129.
4. Gillis S, Crabtree GR, Smith KA (1979). Glucocorticoid-induced inhibition of T cell growth factor production I. The effect on mitogen-induced lymphocyte proliferation. J. Immunol 123:1624.
5. Culpepper JA, Lee F (1985). Regulation of IL-3 expression by glucocorticoids in cloned murine T lymhocytes. J Immunol 135:3191.
6. Smith KA (1980). T cell growth factor. Immunol Rev 51:337.
7. Kelley K, Cochran BH, Stiles CD, Leder P (1983). Cell-specific regulation of the c-myc gene by lymphocyte mitogens and platelet-derived growth factor. Cell 35:603.
8. Reed JC, Alpers JD, Nowell PC, Hoover RG (1986). Sequential expression of protooncogenes during lectin-stimulated mitogenesis of normal human lymphocytes. Proc Natl Acad Sci USA 83:3982.
9. Gillis S, Scheid M, Watson J (1980). Biochemical and biologic characterization of lymphocyte regulatory molecules. III. The isolation and phenotypic characterization of interleukin-2 producing T cell lymphomas. J Immunol 125:2570.

10. Watson J (1979). Continuous proliferation of murine antigen specific helper T lymphocytes in culture. J Exp Med 150:1510.
11. Gillis S, Ferm MM, Ou W, Smith KA (1978). T cell growth factor: parameters of production and a quantitative microassay for activity. J Immunol 120:2027.
12. Cathala G, Savouret J-F, Mendex B, West BL, Karin M, Marial JA, Baxter JD (1983). A method for isolation of intact, translationally active ribonucleic acid. DNA 2:329.
13. Sorg BA, Smith MM, Campagnoni AT (1987). Developmental expression of the myelin proteolipid protein and basic protein mRNAs in normal and dysmyelinating mutant mice. J Neurochem 49:1146.
14. Shaw J, Meerovitch K, Elliott JF, Bleackley RC, Paetkau V (1987). Induction, suppression, and superinduction of lymphokine mRNA in T lymphocytes. Mol Immunol 24:409.
15. Land H, Parada LF, Weinberg RA (1983). Tumorigenic conversion of primary embryo fibroblasts requires at least two cooperating oncogenes. Nature 304:596.
16. Cleveland DW, Lopata MA, MacDonald RJ, Cowan NJ, Rutter WJ, Kirschner MW (1980). Number and evolutionary conservation of α- and β-tubulin and cytoplasmic β- and γ-actin genes using specific cloned cDNA probes. Cell 20:95.
17. Efrat S, Kaempfer R (1984). Control of biologically active interleukin 2 messenger RNA formation in induced human lymphocytes. Proc Natl Acad Sci USA 81:2601.
18. Nakanishi S, Kita T, Taii S, Imura H, Numa S (1977). Glucocorticoid effect on the level of corticotropin messenger RNA activity in rat pituitary. Proc Natl Acad Sci USA 74:3283.
19. Guertin M, Baril P, Bartkowiak J, Anderson AA, Belanger L (1983). Rapid suppression of alpha 1-fetoprotein gene transcription by dexamethasone in developing rat liver. Biochemistry 22:4296.
20. Beato M (1987). Induction of transcription by steroid hormones. Biochim Biophys Acta 910:95.
21. Fujita T, Shibuya H, Ohashi T, Yamanishi K, Taniguchi T (1986). Regulation of human interleukin-2 gene: functional DNA sequences in the 5' flanking region for the gene expression in activated T lymphocytes. Cell 46:401.

Molecular Biology of Stress, pages 225–230

CHARACTERIZATION OF HISTAMINE H_1 RECEPTORS ON HUMAN T LYMPHOCYTES

Françoise Villemain[1], Lucienne Chatenoud[1], M. Garbarg[2], J.C. Schwartz[2] and J.F. Bach[1]

[1]. INSERM U 25 - CNRS LA 122 - Hôpital Necker, 161 rue de Sèvres
75015 Paris, France
[2]. INSERM U 109 - Centre Paul Broca, 2 ter rue d'Alésia
75014 Paris, France

ABSTRACT [^{125}I] Iodobolpyramine, a recently described radioiodinated ligand, that specifically binds to H_1 histamine receptors, has been used to detect H_1 receptors on human peripheral blood lymphocytes. Data obtained in kinetic and saturation experiments showed the presence on human T cells of a single high affinity binding site for [^{125}I] Iodobolpyramine. Scatchard analysis of data recovered from saturation binding experiments showed that the number of H_1 receptors/T lymphocyte averaged 2835 ± 1500 sites exhibiting a K_D for [^{125}I] Iodobolpyramine of 0.12 to 0.28 nM. Preliminary results obtained when analyzing the number of H_1 receptors expressed by the two main functionally distinct T lymphocyte subsets, namely helper/inducer $CD4^+$ and suppressor/cytotoxic $CD8^+$ T cells, showed that a significantly higher number of specific [^{125}I] Iodobolpyramine binding sites is present on $CD8^+$ T cells than on $CD4^+$ T cell.

Correspondence to :Dr. F. Villemain - INSERM U 25 - CNRS LA 122 -Hôpital Necker - 161 rue de Sèvres 75015 Paris, France.

INTRODUCTION

Histamine is an autacoid, playing a central role both as a neuromediator and immunomodulator. Concerning immune reactions, histamine has been shown to be involved not only in immediate hypersensitivity reactions but also in various lymphocyte cooperation mechanisms that mediate delayed type hypersensitivity reactions (for example allograft rejection) (1). Three different histamine receptors, namely H_1, H_2, and H_3 (2,3) have been described so far. The study of histamine receptors has met some difficulties due to the lack of specific ligands to be used in binding experiments allowing reliable identification of the receptors. To get further insight into the basis of histamine induced immunomodulation, one of the histamine targets that are lymphocytic cells expressing specific receptors for the hormone, have been characterized. Thus by using a new H_1 histamine receptor ligand, $[^{125}I]$ Iodobolpyramine, the number of H_1 receptors expressed by human T lymphocytes has been determined and in parallel their pharmacological behaviour has been analyzed.

MATERIALS AND METHODS

Chemicals

$[^{125}I]$ Iodobolpyramine (2125 Ci/mmole) was from Amersham (United Kingdom), SK&F 94461 from Smith Kline and French (England), d- and l- chlorpheniramine from Burrough-Wellcome, mepyramine from Specia. Histamine, histidine and bovine serum albumin fraction V (BSA) were from Sigma Chemical Company (St. louis. Mo).

Cell preparations

Fourty milliliters of heparinized peripheral venous blood were collected and centrifugated (30 min at 400 g) on a Ficoll Paque gradient (Pharmacia, Uppsula Sweden).
Mononuclear cells were recovered at the interface, washed twice in RPMI 1640 medium (Gibco, Paisley, Scotland) and diluted to 10 x 10^6 cells/ml. T lymphocytes were purified by means of E-rosetting using neuraminidase treated sheep red blood cells (for formation of E-rosettes) according to an already described technique (4).

[^{125}I] Iodobolpyramine binding assays

The binding of [^{125}I] Iodobolpyramine on freshly collected human peripheral T lymphocytes was studied using the following experimental procedure : [^{125}I] Iodobolpyramine (0.03 to 0.65 nM) was incubated at 27°C with the T cell suspension   (1 x 10^6 cells/ml resuspended in 400 µl total volume of Tris 100 mM/ Cl$_2$ 20 mM/Histidine 5 mM buffer, pH 7.4) (5). Nonspecific binding was defined as the amount of [^{125}I] Iodobolpyramine bound in the presence of 10^{-6}M d-chlorphe-niramine.Incubation was stopped by adding 3 x 3 ml of fresh phosphate buffer containing 0.1% BSA and followed by rapid filtration (20 ml) under reduced pressure through glass fibre filters (GF/C Whatman) which had been previously treated by 0.1% BSA to reduce the binding of the ligand in the filters. The radioactivity trapped on the filters was mesured using an LKB gammer counter, with an efficiency of 82%.

RESULTS

Kinetics of [^{125}I] Iodobolpyramine binding

At 27°C, binding of [^{125}I] Iodobolpyramine (0.12 nM, 1 x 10^6 cells/ml) occured within 30 min of incubation. Saturation experiments were performed by incubating different concentrations of [^{125}I] Iodobolpyramine (0.03 nM to 0.65 nM) in the presence or absence of 10^{-6} M d-chlorpheniramine used as the cold ligand. Specific binding averaged 60% of total bound [^{125}I] Iodobolpyramine. Scatchard analysis of specific binding gave a straigh line thus defining a single high affinity binding site : K$_D$ = 0.12 to0.28 nM for [^{125}I] Iodobolpyramine on human T cells. B max values were deduced showing that the number of H$_1$ receptors/cell ranged 2835 ± 1500.

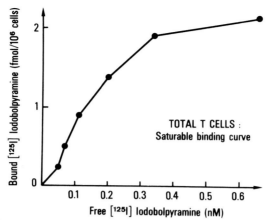

Figure 1 : Saturable binding curve on human T cells.

Kinetics of $[^{125}I]$ Iodobolpyramine binding to intact human T lymphocytes were analysed as follows :

    - Association kinetics : cell suspensions were incubated with $[^{125}I]$ Iodobolpyramine (0.20 nM final concentration) and specific binding was determined at different ti me intervals. A K_{obs} (bimolecular association constant) value of 0.038 min^{-1} was determined by analysis of pseudo-first order association curve.

    - Dissociation kinetics : cell suspension were incubated with $[^{125}I]$ Iodobolpyramine (0.20 nM final concentration) for 30 min at 27°C. At time zero, 10^{-6} M d-chlorpheniramine was added to each sample and specific binding was determined at various time intervals. A single dissociation phase (K_2 (equilibrium dissociation constant) = 0.016 min^{-1}) was observed by analysis of first order dissociation curve.

    The K_D-calculated by using the experimental K_{obs} and K_2 values was 0.14 nM thus confirming the data obtained by Scatchard analysis of saturation curves.

Pharmacology of [125I] Iodobolpyramine binding

    The specific binding of 0.12 nM $[^{125}I]$ Iodobolpyramine was completely inhibited by a series of H_1-receptor antagonists and histamine itself as agonist. The K_i values were calculated from the analysis of the various competitive curves by means of the following formula :

$$K_i = \frac{IC50}{L + 1/K_D}$$

L=[^{125}I] Iodobolpyramine concentration

K_D=[^{125}I]Iodobolpyramine equilibrium dissociation constant

Thus the following values were found : mepyramine : K_i = 3.46 ± 2.8 nM ; SK&F 94461 : K_i = 5.03 ± 0.32 nM ; d-chlorpheniramine : K_i = 0.025 ± 0.014 nM ; l-chlorpheniramine : K_i = 2.08 ± 0.41 nM ; histamine : K_i > 100 000 nM.

These K_i were closely related to the ones describes for H_1 receptors present on guinea-pig cerebellum (6).

DISCUSSION

The aim of the present study was to document the presence of H_1 histamine receptors on lymphocytic cells by using a new H_1 receptor antagonist, [^{125}I] Iodobolpyramine . The demonstration of the presence of H_1 histamine receptor on human T cells is brought by Scatchard analysis and pharmacological competition experiments using a panel of various H_1 receptor antagonists and as an agonist histamine itself. The binding of [^{125}I] Iodobolpyramine to intact T cells reached the equilibrium in 30 min at 27°C; the binding was saturable when using a 0.65 nM concentration of radioligand and reversible in presence of an excess of cold H_1 antagonist d-chlorpheniramine. Calculation of the mean dissociation constants (K_D) showed that a single high affinity binding site for [^{125}I] Iodobolpyramine is demonstrated on human T cells. Thus, 2835 ± 1500 binding sites/cell were defined with a K_D ranging from 0.12 to 0.28 nM. Preliminary analysis of H_1 receptor expression on different T cell subsets namely CD4+ helper/inducer T cells and CD8+ suppressor/cytotoxic T cells showed that higher proportions of H_1 histamine receptors were present on suppressor/cytotoxic lymphocytes as compared to helper/inducer lymphocytes. This quantitative dissociation would provide a molecular basis to explain the immunomodulatory role of histamine. Moreover, it stimulates interest for analyzing the H_1 receptor expression on lymphocytes in different pathological situations. Our findings are at variance with those reported by Cameron et al (7), who described the presence of a single, specific [^{3}H] pyrilamine binding site on human lymphocytes that was equally distributed among the various human peripheral T lymphocyte subsets. The discrepancy between these results and the ones reported in the present study are probably limited to the fact that two different H_1 receptor ligands were used. In fact,

$[^{125}I]$ Iodobolpyramine as compared to tritiated ligands like $[^3H]$ pyrilamine allows detection of H_1 receptors with a higher sensitivity. Studies are currently in progress to further define whether lymphocyte H_1 receptor expression is modulated during immune responses (i.e., mitogenic or antigenic stimulation).

REFERENCES

1.   Dy M, Lebel B, Kamoun P, Hamburger J (1981). Histamine production during the anti-allograft response. Demonstration of a new lymphokine enhancing histamine synthesis. J Exp Med 153 : 293.

2.   Ganellin CR, Person ME (1982)"Pharmacology of histamine receptors" Wright PSG.

3.   Arrang JM, Garbarg M, Schwartz JC (1987). Auto-inhibition of brain histamine release mediated by a novel class H_3 of histamine receptor. Nature 302 : 832.

4.   Chatenoud L, Dugas B, Beaurain G., Touam M, Drueke T, Vasquez A, Galanaud P, Bach JF, Delfraissy JF (1986). Presence of preactivated T cells in hemodialysed patients : their possible role in altered immunity. Proc Natl Acad Sci USA 93 : 7457.

5.   Casale TB, Kaliner M (1982).A rapid method for isolation of human mononuclear cells free of significant platelet contamination . J Immunol Methods 55 : 347.

6.   Korner M, Bouthenet ML, Ganellin CR, Garbarg M, Gros C, Ife RJ, Sales N, Schwartz JC (1986). $[^{125}I]$ Iodobolpyramine, a highly sensitive probe for histamine H_1-receptors in guinea-pig brain. Eur J Pharmacol 12 : 151.

7.   Cameron W, Doyle K, Rocklin RE (1986). Histamine type 1 (H_1) receptor radioligand binding studies on normal T cell subsets, B cells, and monocytes. J Immunol 136 : 2116.

IV. PHYSICAL CONSEQUENCES
OF STRESS

Molecular Biology of Stress, pages 233–240
© 1989 Alan R. Liss, Inc.

ENZYMATIC AND MORPHOLOGICAL ADAPTATION TO PHYSICAL EXERCISE IN YOUNG, MIDDLE AGED AND OLD MICE: A MODEL FOR PHYSICAL STRESS[1]

A.Z. Reznick[2], E. Steinhagen-Thiessen[3], D. Gershon[4] and M. Silbermann[2]

[2]The Rappaport Institute for Research in the Medical Sciences and Faculty of Medicine, Technion, Haifa. [3]Medical Clinic, The Max Burger Hospital Berlin, W.Germany and [4]Department of Biology, Technion — Israel Institute of Technology, Haifa, Israel.

ABSTRACT. Old age has been shown to be involved in reduced enzyme activity. Enzymes such as Aldolase (Ald), creatine phosphokinase (CPK) and superoxide-dismutase (SOD) were shown to have reduced activities in muscles of old mice (1-4). The response of muscular and bone tissues to physical exercise was studied in CFW-1 and C-57BL/6J mice ranging from young to old age. Short periods of enforced training for 5 to 10 weeks resulted in an increase of enzyme activities in muscles of young mice by 20-50%, while muscles of old mice revealed a reduction of 10-40% in enzyme activities. Morphological studies on muscles and bones of old trained mice showed indications of muscle atrophy and signs of severe osteopenia. When mice were trained for longer periods of time (12-14 months) beginning at young or middle age, the levels of the above enzymes were elevated in a fashion similar to that obtained in young mice trained for short and or long periods. These results indicate that if training as a model for physical stress is started prior to a critical physiological threshold, it may encompass beneficial effects on muscles and bones of old animals.

---

[1] This work was supported in part by the United States-Israel Binational Science Foundation,#84-00371.

INTRODUCTION

A simplified model for the main categories of the causes of the aging process is illustrated in Figure 1.

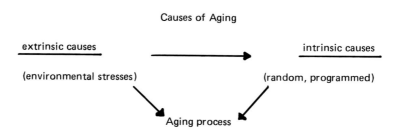

Figure 1. Causes of the aging process

Fig. 1 demonstrates that the main causes of aging can be divided into two categories; extrinsic causes and intrinsic causes. The extrinsic causes which are basically various environmental stresses and insults, may affect the aging process directly or indirectly by influencing intrinsic processes. The latter are subdivided into random causes and programmed causes which are dictated by the genetic machinery of cells. Physical exercise which involves the recruit of physiological, biochemical and energetic resources of the body may be considered as an environmental stress which is imposed upon the intrinsic biological systems. Therefore, the application of such a stress and the response of the aging organism may shed some light on the importance and influence of extrinsic causes on basic processes that take place in muscles and bones of aging animals.

The choice of the above enzymes (Ald, CPK and SOD) were for two reasons. First, all these enzymes were shown to have reduced specific activities in muscles of old mice. Second, Ald and CPK are important in the energy providing systems of muscles while SOD has been shown to act as a protective enzyme against damaging superoxide free radicals.

METHODS

The training paradigms for the short and long periods of physical exercises have been described previously in detail (1-5). In essence two different strains of mice were used for these studies. 1. CFW-1 white outbred female mice and 2. C-57BL/6J black female strain of mice. Both strains of mice underwent similar training regimens. But while in the CFW-1 strain, enzyme studies were done on homogenates of whole hind leg muscles, in the C-57BL/6J strain, specific hind leg muscles were examined after exercise. The procedure for the preparation of the muscles' extracts for enzyme studies have been described previously (1-5). Also, the procedures used for histological studies have been elaborated in previous works (6).

RESULTS

Figure 2 shows the specific activities of Ald, SOD and CPK in striated muscles of nontrained control (C) and trained (T) CFW-1 mice that were exercised for five weeks (30 min/day at 3.5 meters/min).

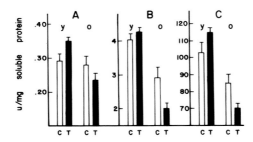

Figure 2. Specific activities (units μ/mg protein) of an aldolase (A), SOD (B) and CPK (C) in hind leg striated muscles of control (c) and trained (T) young (y) and old (o) mice. Values are average of 3 measurements of activities in pooled muscles of 10 animals.

In young animals (6 months old), in all cases, the activities were higher in trained animals compared to control untrained animals. However, in old animals, exercise caused a further reduction of activities of these enzymes which already had lower activities at the onset of the training period.

Figure 3 shows similar data with reference to the activity of Ald in specific muscles of young and old trained and control C-57BL/6J mice.

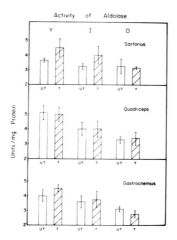

Figure 3. The activity of aldolase in sartorius gastrocnemius and quadriceps muscles of young (Y), intermediate (I) and old animals (O). UT — untrained, T — trained.

Here again in aging animals there was a reduction or no change of Ald activity while in young trained animals at least in the gastrocnemius there was again an increase of activity by 20%.

Figure 4 shows cross section of gastrocnemius muscle of old nontrained animal. Note a marked penetration of connective tissues into muscle tissue, a phenomenon which was not observed in young animals.

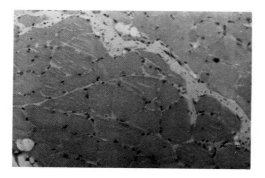

Figure 4. Cross section of gastrocnemius muscle of old non trained animal. H & E, x 288.

Figures 5 and 6 show similar cross section of old trained muscles. H & E, × 288.

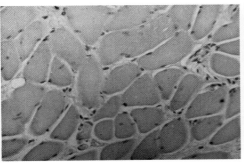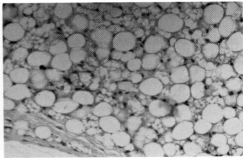

Figure 5. Cross section through the gastrocnemius muscle of an old animal that was trained for a short period of 10 weeks. H & E, × 288.

Figure 6. A similar section to that shown in Figure 5 showing a severe damage to the muscle in the form of lipidons accumulation within the tissue.

In Figure 5 single muscle fibers are surrounded by invading connective tissue while in Fig. 6 multiple adipocytes are observed within the muscle tissue of old trained animals.

Figure 7. Cross section of cortical area of femur of young nontrained animals. H & E, × 480.

Figure 7 shows cross section of a femur bone of young non-trained animal. Multiple layer of perieosteal cells can be observed at the outer surface of the bone (arrow). Also osteocytes are present and fill up all the lacunae within the cortical bone.

In contrast to young bones, bones of old nontrained animals showed a decrease in the number of osteocytes along with many empty lacunae. Also, in some areas multiple longitudinal cracks could be observed along with "cavitations" within the cortical bone (Fig. 8). These observations were further enhanced in bones of old mice trained for short periods of time (Fig. 9).

In Figure 10 as well as in Figure 11 where specific hind leg muscles were examined, CPK activity of muscles of animals trained for long periods remined at higher levels even if training started at 15 months of age.

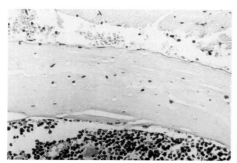 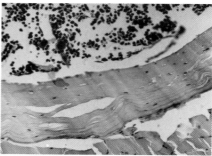

Figure 8. Cross section of portion of femur of old animal. H & E, X 240.

Figure 9. Cross section of portion of femur of old trained animal. H & E, X240.

Figures 10 and 11 show the activities of CPK in hind leg muscles of mice trained for long periods of time (12-14 m).

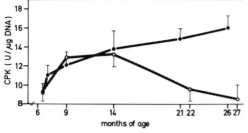

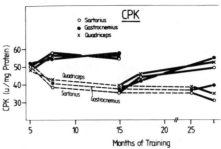

Figure 10. CPK activity in hind leg muscles of straited muscles of CFW-1 mice. Solid line - trained animals. Published from Ref. 4 with permission of S. Karger   AG, Basel.

Figure 11. CPK activity in muscles of C-57BL/6J mice of control and long trained animals. Solid lines - trained animals. Published from Ref. 4 with permission of S. Karger   AG, Basel.

DISCUSSION

The results presented in this work show that already with age there is a marked reduction of enzymes specific activity. Using the rationale elaborated in Fig. 1, the essential question is whether old animals can respond to the same physical exercise as do young animals. Indeed, muscles of young mice responded with hypertrophy and increase in enzyme levels after training for short durations of 5-10 weeks. Under the same training conditions, muscles of old mice showed—inability to adapt to stress. It was manifested in a general reduction of enzyme activities and in morphological changes which were indicative for muscle atrophy and myopathy of muscle fibers (Figs. 5, 6).

Similar observations were observed in bones of old trained animals. Again, the sudden imposition of exercise has caused severe damage to femur bones of old trained mice (Fig. 9). However, training for long periods of time (Figs. 10, 11) clearly demonstrated that the levels of enzyme activities remained elevated and did not show the age related decrease as observed in old animals. Morphological observation supported these biochemical studies. These results indicate that if training is started prior to a critical stage in life it may have a beneficial effect on enzyme activity. This concept of age-related threshold was first put forward by Edington and his co-workers (7, 8). They showed that rats trained throughout life had longer life-spans than their sedentary counterparts. Similar observations were also reported by Goodrick (9). The latter workers also showed that old animals trained intensively died more rapidly than the control group (7, 8). The results reported in this work support the idea of Edington et al (7, 8) that for a certain type of exercise there is a "threshold of age" beyond which exercise may become detrimental to aging animals.

REFERENCES

1. Steinhagen-Thiessen E, Reznick A, Hilz H (1981). Positive and negative adaptation of muscle enzymes in aging mice subjected to physical exercise. Mech Ang Dev 16:363.

2. Reznick AZ, Steinhagen-Thiessen E, Gershon D (1982). The effect of exercise on enzyme activities in cardiac muscles of mice of various ages. Biochem Med 28:347.

3. Reznick AZ, Steinhagen-Thiessen E, Gellerssen B, Gershon D (1983). The effect of short and long term exercise on aldolase activity in muscles of CW-1 and C-57/BL mice of various ages. Mech Age & Dev 23:253.

4. Steinhagen-Thiessen E, Reznick AZ (1987). Effect of short and long term endurance training on creatine phosphokinase activity in skeletal and cardiac muscles of CW-1 and C-57/BL mice. Gerontology 33:14.

5. Steinhagen-Thiessen L, Reznick A, Hilz H (1980). Negative adaptation to physical training in senile mice. Mech Age & Dev 12:231.

6. Silbermann M, Weiss A, Reznick AZ, Eilam Y, Szydel N, Gershon D (1987). Age-related trend for osteopenia in femurs of female C-57/BL/6 mice. Comp Gerontol 1:45.

7. Edington UW, Cosmas AC, McCafferty WB (1972). Exercise and longevity: Evidence for a threshold of age. J Geron 27:341.

8. McCafferty WB and Edington DW (1974). Skeletal muscle and organ weights of aged and trained male rats. Gerontologia 20:44.

9. Goodrick CL (1980). Effects of long term voluntary wheel exercise on male and female Wistar rats. Gerontology 26:22.

Molecular Biology of Stress, pages 241–249
© 1989 Alan R. Liss, Inc.

GASTRIC EROSION FORMATION BY STRESS:
BRAIN STEM MECHANISMS

Herbert Weiner, M.D.[1] Robert L.
Stephens, Ph.D[1,2] Thomas Garrick, M.D.[1,2]
and Yvette Taché, Ph.D[2]

[1]Department of Psychiatry and Biobehavioral
Sciences, University of California
Los Angeles, 90024 and [2]Center for Ulcer
Research and Education, West Los Angeles
Veterans Administration Medical Center
Los Angeles, CA 90073

ABSTRACT The literature relating cold-
restraint stress, and restraining
prematurely separated rats to gastric
erosions is reviewed. Both forms of stress
are mediated by a fall in body temperature.
The results of testing the hypothesis that
hypothermia releases thyrotropin releasing
hormone (TRH) to induce increased gastric
contractility, acid secretion and promote
gastric erosions are reviewed. Recent work
showing that TRH injected into specific
medullary nuclei promotes the first two
effects is reported. Intracisternal TRH
also causes increased serotonin secretion
into the gastric lumen which modulates acid
secretion. Corticotrophin releasing factor
injected into the cisterna magna
counteracts TRH and 2-deoxy-d-glucose
increases in gastric contractions.

INTRODUCTION

Many experimental techniques have been devised to produce gastric erosions in rats since Selye's (1) demonstration that restraint would do so; some of them (e.g., drugs) are designed to enhance gastric acid secretion (e.g., cholinergic agonists, histamine, etc.), inhibit prostaglandin synthesis (e.g., aspirin, etc.) or reduce the protective mucosal barrier. Lateral hypothalamic lesions, unavoidable electric shocks to the tails or feet of rats, cooling and restraining rats, pyloric ligation, all induce gastric erosions. Although these experimental methods do have their intended effect, they are quite artificial. Other and more naturalistic techniques, such as restricting the number of feedings (to increase activity), or the more drastic one of starving rats (especially if they were previously prematurely weaned) are also effective in inducing gastric erosions (2, 3).

Nonetheless, the question still remains whether the gastric erosions produced in this manner in rats are good models of human (gastric) ulceration: They usually only afflict the mucosa! Leaving this vexing issue aside, the models used having heuristic value in attempting to understand, for example, how prior experience interacts with later restraint or starvation to produce gastric erosions with an incidence of about 90%. This experimental model (for review see 4) lead to two conclusions that:

1. A fall in body temperature is a critical intervening variable: When averted no gastric erosions occurred.

2. Although cooling animals is highly correlated with acid secretion, prematurely separated animals evidence no greater secretory response to cold or secretogogues than do normal rats.

Therefore, factors other than (or additional to) acid secretion play a role in erosion formation. These could include diminutions in mucosal resistance, including bicarbonate secretion, and/or blood flow, and altered gastric motility.

Role of Increased Gastric Contractions with Stress.

Garrick et al. (5), by using miniature pressure transducers has shown that in cold-restrained, restrained prematurely separated rats, and under conditions of unavoidable shock slow (1 per 2 min.), high amplitude gastric contractions are produced.

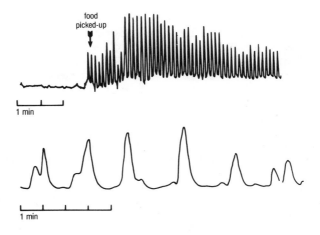

FIGURE 1. The top graph shows the gastric contractile activity when a rat that has fasted for 24 hours starts to eat. The bottom reading shows gastric contractile activity when a 24-hour fasted rat is subjected to 3 hours of cold restraint at 20° C. (From: Garrick T et al. Western J Med, 143:219, 1985).

Papaverine pretreatment averts the increased gastric contractions and erosion formation in the cold-restrained rat. Yet, gastric acid secretion, which actually diminishes initially in these animals, plays a permissive role in erosion formation; only by completely suppressing it with cimetidine are erosions prevented from occurring.

Mechanism of Ulcer Formation

The experimental models that were initially listed (above) may be divided into two main categories:
1.   Those that induce or promote a fall in body temperature: e.g., cold-restraint, continuous activity induced by feeding the rat once daily, premature separation followed by restraint;
2.   Those that produce an increase in body temperature: e.g., lateral hypothalamic lesions, and prolonged unavoidable shock (?), intracisternal injection of TRH.
The fact that a fall in body temperature is a critical intervening variable inevitably has led a number of investigators to examine the role of the thyrotropin releasing hormone (TRH) in altering gastric secretion, motility and erosion formation. This hypothesis was supported by the demonstration that exposing rats to $4^{\circ}C$ increases the TRH content of the median eminence, and of third ventricular fluid (6). Furthermore, 12% of the total TRH content of the brain is contained in the brain stem, particularly in the dorsomotor nucleus of the vagus (DMV), N. ambiguus and tractus solitarius (7).
Tache et al. (8) first showed that intracisternal (IC) or intracerebroventricular (ICV) TRH or its stable analog (RX 77368) increased gastric acid and pepsin secretion, and vagal efferent discharge (9). They also enhance gastric contractions in a dose-

dependent manner; an effect that is
averted by atropine or vagotomy (10). They
also produce gastric erosions in the gastric
corpus and antrum (11).

Site of Action of TRH

     The site of action of IC or ICV injections
of TRH or its analog have been determined.
Both Rogers et al. (12) and Okuma et al. (13)
demonstrated that dorsal motor nucleus
injection of TRH elicited a gastric secretory
response whereas injections into the area
postrema or various hypothalamic nuclei had no
effect.
     Our studies demonstrate (14) that 10-100 ng
RX 77368 produces a dose-dependent acid
secretory response which peaks at 40 min when
injected into the DMV and NTS but not N.
reticularis or cuneatus.

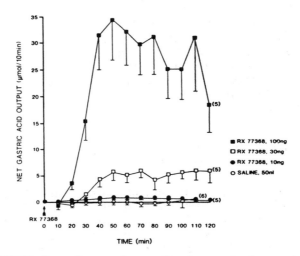

     FIGURE 2.   Dose-dependent gastric output
when the TRH-analog, RX 77368 is injected into
the left dorsal vagal complex of a rat.   Note
that peak response occurs at 40-50 min. after
injection. (From: Stephens RL, et al: Am J
Physiology, 254:G, July 1988).

This secretory response to TRH micro-
injected into the dorsal vagal complex is
abolished by vagotomy, and is not mimicked by
the TRH metabolites, TRH free acid, and
diketopiperazine.

Effect of TRH-Analog on Serotonin Release.

While increasing gastric acid secretion RX
77368 (100 ng) IC also markedly increases the
content of serotonin (5-HT) in the gastric
lumen -- an effect that peaks at 45 min. The
secretion of 5-HT is also abolished by
atropine. When the gastric content of 5-HT is
reduced by 66% following pretreatment with
para-chlorphenylalanine (PCPA) (300 mg/kg) a
reduction (57%) of gastric 5-HT secretion also
occurs when RX 77368 is injected IC.
However, pretreatment with PCPA markedly
increases the gastric acid secretory response
($p < 0.05$) to RX 77368. Once may, therefore,
conclude that TRH or its analog releases 5-HT
which counter-regulates maximal, gastric acid
secretion (15). At the same time, intravenous
(IV) or intra-arterial (IA) 5-HT (3-10 mg/kg)
produces a biphasic change in intragastric
pressure and increases the amplitude of gastric
contractions.

Effects of Corticotrophin Releasing Factor
(CRF) on Gastric Function.

Taché (9, 16) had shown that CRF by itself
delays gastric emptying and acid secretion, and
prevents gastric erosion formation induced by
cold-restraint. We have examined the role of
IC and IV CRF and gastric contractions
stimulated by IC RX 77368, IC 2-deoxy-D-glucose
(2-DG), and IV carbachol. Intracisternal CRF
(6-210 pmol) reduces significantly the
contractions induced by the two former but not
those promoted by IV carbachol (200 mg/kg/hr).

Intravenous CRF in very large doses (10 x above) inhibits increased contractions produced by RX 77368 but not those by 2-DG or IV carbachol (17).

We have as yet no idea where in the brain (stem?) CRF functions to inhibit TRH (analog)- or 2-DG-induced contractions or acid secretion, promoted by these secretogogues.

SUMMARY

Evidence has been presented that in some models of stress-induced gastric erosions, a fall in body temperature is the critical intervening variable. This has lead us to examine the role of TRH in promoting gastric acid secretion, increasing contractility and producing erosions. This peptide is a powerful inducer of the two former when injected into the DMV and NTS but not neighboring medullary nuclei. At the same time, TRH releases 5-HT into the gastric lumen which reduces the acid secretory response to the peptide, while raising the amplitude of gastric contractions (when given IV and IA). Another peptide, CRF, when administered IC, markedly reduces gastric contractions stimulated by IC TRH-analog and 2-DG but not those produced by IV carbachol.

These data do not directly prove or disprove the roles of TRH, 5-HT or CRF in gastric erosion formation when body temperature falls on cold-restraining, or restraining a prematurely separated rat.

REFERENCES

1. Selye HA (1936). A syndrome produced by diverse nocuous agents. Nature 138:32.
2. Ackerman SH, Hofer MA, Weiner H (1975). Age at maternal separation and gastric erosion susceptibility in the rat. Psychsom Med 37:180.

3. Paré WP (1980). Psychological studies
    of stress ulcer in the rat. Brain Res
    Bull 5(suppl 1):19.
4. Ackerman SH ((1981). Premature weaning,
    thermoregulation, and the occurrence of
    gastric pathology. In Weiner H, Hofer MA,
    Stunkard AJ (eds): "Brain, Behavior and
    Bodily Disease," New York: Raven Press,
    p 67.
5. Garrick T, Buack S, Bass P (1986). Gastric
    motility is a major factor in cold
    restraint-induced lesion formation in rats.
    Am J Physiol 250:G191.
6. Arancibia S, Tapia-Arancibia L, Assenmacher
    I, Astier H (1983). Direct evidence of
    short-term cold-induced TRH release in the
    median eminence of unanesthetized rats.
    Neuroendocrinol 37:225.
7. Kubek M, Rea MA, Hodes ZI, Aprison MH
    (1983). Quantitation and characterization
    of thyrotropin-releasing hormone in vagal
    nuclei and other regions of the medulla
    oblongata of the rat. J Neurochem 40:1307.
8. Taché Y, Vale W, Brown M (1980). Thyro-
    tropin-releasing hormone - Central nervous
    system action to stimulate gastric acid
    secretion. Nature 287:149.
9. Taché Y (1985). Role of brain neuro-
    peptides in the regulation of gastric
    secretion. In Weiner HW (moderator):
    "Specialty Conference: Neurobiologic and
    Psychobiologic Mechanisms in Gastric
    Function and Ulceration," Western J Med
    143:207.
10. Garrick T, Buack S, Veiseh A, Taché Y
    (1987). Thyrotropin-releasing hormone
    (TRH) acts centrally to stimulate gastric
    contractility in rats. Life Sci 40:649.
11. Goto Y, Taché Y (1985). Gastric erosions
    induced by intracisternal thyrotropin-
    releasing hormone (TRH) in rats. Peptides
    6:153.

12. Rogers RC, Hermann GE (1985). Dorsal medullary oxytocin, vasopressin, oxytocin antagonist, and TRH effects on gastric acid secretion and heart rate. Peptides 6:1143.

13. Okuma Y, Osumi Y, Ishigawa T, Mitsuma T (1987). Enhancement of gastric acid output and mucosal blood flow by tripeptide thyrotropin releasing hormone microinjected into the dorsal motor nucleus of the vagus in rats. Jnp J Pharmacol 43:173.

14. Stephens RL, Ishikawa T, Weiner H, Novin D, Tache´Y (1988). TRH and TRH analog micro-injected into the dorsal vagal complex stimulated gastric acid secretion in the rat. Am J Physiol 254:G, July.

15. Stephens RL, Raybould H, Garrick T, Weiner H, Tache´Y (1988). Inhibitory role of endogenous serotonin on gastric acid secretion and contractility stimulated by intracisternal injection of TRH analogue RX 7736 8 in rats. Gastroenterol (submitted).

16. Tache´Y, Maeda-Hagiwara M, Turkelson CM (1987). Central nervous system action of corticotropin-releasing factor to inhibit gastric emptying in rats. Am J Physiol 253:G241.

17. Garrick T, Veiseh A, Sierra A, Weiner H Tache´Y (1988). Corticotropin-releasing factor (CRF) acts centrally to suppress stimulated gastric contractility in the rat. Regulatory Peptides, in press.

V. STRESS AND BEHAVIOR

Molecular Biology of Stress, pages 253–264
© 1989 Alan R. Liss, Inc.

INFORMATION-INDUCED STRESS IN HUMANS

Shlomo Breznitz

Ray D. Wolfe Centre for
Study of Psychological Stress
University of Haifa
Haifa, Israel

ABSTRACT Although there is now a growing body of
knowledge about anticipatory stress instigated by
threatening information, surprisingly little is known
about the effects of information concerning the termination of the stressful experience. The present study
utilizes the "tour of duty" phenomenon as the main
research paradigm. Specifically, subjects are given
differential information about the duration of the
stressful task, using the following four conditions:
full information, no information, false short information with subsequent discouragement, and false long
information with subsequent encouragement. The stressors
were an arduous march by soldiers on active duty, as
well as the Cold Pressor Test and a Dynamometer Task
within the controlled laboratory environment. The
results indicate the importance of veridical information
on coping with stress. In addition, information about
stress duration has significant impact on the timing
of a crisis and its eventual resolution.

The central feature distinguishing psychological from physical stress is that it is caused primarily by information. Whereas physical stress denotes some agent presently acting against the homeostatic requirements of the organism, psychological stress indicates that the organism will be exposed to stressors sometime in the future. (1,2) The concept of threat is, therefore, central to understanding psychological stress. Its two components, namely, indication of a negative event and the fact that it will be forthcoming in the future, suggest the importance of anticipatory factors. The human mind has a great capacity for anticipating the future, a fact which often prolongs the duration of stress. There are several severe threats which operate long before the actual impact of the event itself.

Studies attempting to specify the parameters of threat which have systematic influence on the stress reaction in humans suggest that temporal factors are of primary importance. (3,4) Thus, the fear reaction to information about impending pain is largely determined by the question whether the person knows the exact onset of the pain itself. If he is provided with such "temporal certainty" the fear reaction to the threat follows a reliable U-shaped curve. Upon receiving the threatening information there is a clear rise in fear reaction, followed by some recovery and then as the expected onset of pain approaches there is a dramatic second increase in fear. (3) Furthermore, the duration of anticipation is yet another temporal factor with clear influence on the stress reaction. It has been documented that in situations of objective helplessness, the longer the duration of anticipation of a frightening event, the higher the anticipated fear reaction prior to its occurrence. This phenomenon has been labelled as "incubation of threat". (5,6)

In case of "temporal uncertainty", the reaction is entirely different. When there are discrete warning signals indicating the growing proximity of the danger, they produce brief changes in level of fear, followed by recovery. Thus, the inter-warnings interval, as well as the anticipated number of such warnings, exert significant control over the pattern of fear reaction during the anticipatory phase. (3) These, as well as other related findings have been documented to be quite robust and reliable, and are now part of an expanding data base concerning anticipatory stress.

There is, however, yet another logical counterpart to the issues of anticipation of stress onset, namely, anticipation of stress termination. In other words, humans can be given information about the anticipated duration of the stress itself. Such information will tell them when the difficulty will be over. The main thrust of a research program, part of which is reported here, consists of mapping the impact of such information. There is some anecdotal evidence that knowing when the stress will be over may be a major factor in the ability of people to endure it in the first place.

The impact of information which alters expectations about the future is best seen in situations where it has no direct effect on ongoing stressors. In such a case, any change in behavior is due to expectations alone. There is hardly a more dramatic illustration of the power of information than the "tour of duty" phenomenon. Its potency to affect both physical and psychological level of functioning was first appreciated in World War II:

In an important chapter in The American Soldier (7), Janis describes the intense stress to which crews of American bombers were exposed during their nightly missions over Germany in World War II. Planes and crews were lost each night, and had to be replaced by new ones. At some point, many members of these crews developed major symptoms of stress, and often could not continue to fly.

The psychological analysis of these soldiers indicated that they felt caught in a no hope situation. Each night brought new casualties, and from their point of view it was only a matter of time until their turn would come.

The U.S. Air Corps dealt with this situation in a very elegant and effective way, psychologically. The crews were informed that their tour of duty consisted of forty missions, after which they would be relocated to a safer theatre of operation. Although forty missions were not fewer than they were flying before, and although planes were still being downed by enemy action just as before, psychologically the situation altered dramatically, with excellent results in terms of symptom reduction and prevention. Instead of counting forward (e.g.: "today it was this friend, tomorrow it can be me"), the airmen started to count backwards (e.g.: "thirty nine to go, thirty eight to go, etc."). Thus, with each new mission their subjective probability of coming out of the experience alive was augmented. Stated differently, by telling the airmen when the danger would be over, their expectations became much more positive, and hope was introduced into the situation.

In spite of the success of the "tour of duty" intervention, and in spite of its subsequent usage as standard policy in many areas of conflict, the underlying psychological mechanisms of this phenomenon were never systematically studied. This is particularly surprising in view of the high cost-effectiveness of increasing endurance and performance level by information management. The main objective of the present research is to analyze this paradigm in a laboratory setting. An experimental program controlling the relevant features of the information will make it possible to map its potential enhancement of effective functioning under stressful conditions.

The power of information is such, that if mismanaged, its impact can be psychologically detrimental. It is thus necessary to test the typical pitfalls and constraints of this paradigm, as well as its opportunities. The experimental program contains, therefore, specific attempts to understand how certain types of information, and/or its timing, can lead to psychological discouragement.

Pilot Study

In suggesting an experimental analog of the "tour of duty" paradigm we are encouraged by the results obtained in a pilot field experiment involving Israeli soldiers on a difficult march. They had to cover 20 kilometers at a very fast pace, carrying heavy loads. We divided them randomly into four experimental conditions:

A. Full information: Soldiers were told that the distance is 20 kilometers, and as they were marching they were told 15, 10, 5, etc.

B. No information: Soldiers were told that this was the difficult march they heard about. No additional information was given either before or during the march.

C. False short: Soldiers were told that the distance is 15 kilometers, and as they were marching they were told 15, 10, 5. At the 14th kilometer, just one before the end, they were told the distance was 20, i.e., 5 kilometers more than expected.

D. False long: Soldiers were told the distance was 25 kilometers, and at the 14th kilometer that was reduced to 20.

Thus, all marched the same distance, on the same day, but with different information. Each group was subdivided into several small units of 10-12 soldiers, with two officers observing each unit. The march was one of the final tests at the end of a training course for a highly selected unit,

and the soldiers were highly motivated. The rules of the
march did not permit slowing down, and if a soldier could not
keep up the pace, he had to give up.

At the 14th kilometer all soldiers gave blood samples for
measurement of cortisol and prolactin. Exactly 24 hours later,
long after the march itself, another blood sample was taken,
to measure rest levels.

Results: The findings were unequivocal in supporting the
"tour of duty" phenomenon. Thus, the number of soldiers who
successfully completed the march was significantly different
between groups. The order of performance was: Group A best
(6.2% failed), Group B worst (21% failed), with Group C somewhat better than Group D (8.2% and 11.4% respectively). This
order was found also in the two independent evaluations by the
officers, who rated each soldier on many scales, such as:
physical stress, morale, helping behavior, etc. Furthermore,
both cortisol levels and prolactin levels were significantly
higher in Group B than in Group A. Thus, like in the case
of the U.S. air crews, knowing exactly when the ordeal will
be over helped the soldiers both physically and mentally.

Field experiments, such as the pilot study described
above, have many advantages considering their high relevance
to the military. At the same time, however, a more precise
explication of the critical parameters involved in this
paradigm cannot be adequately accomplished without the advantages of the controlled laboratory.

Cold Pressor Test. The cold pressor test (CPT) is a frequently used experimental paradigm of stress research. It provides
an opportunity to study reactions to pain within a controlled
setting. Typically, the subject is required to immerse one
hand in water mixed with ice, maintained at 1-2 degrees
centigrade. With the possible exception of patients with
advanced coronary heart disease, this procedure, although
very painful, is totally harmless. Since the most frequently
tested outcome using the CPT is duration of pain tolerance,
it is particularly well suited for the purposes of the present
research program.

It is interesting to note, that in spite of virtually
hundreds of experiments using this method, only one attempted
recently to manipulate information about duration of the
pain. (8) The rest are predominantly interested in a host of
mediating factors, coping strategies and individual differences
variables, that may affect tolerance levels.

METHOD

The Stressors. The above analysis suggests the usefulness of the cold pressor test (CPT) as the basic stressor to be used in this research program. There is extensive evidence that pain tolerance is sufficiently sensitive to experimental interventions. At the same time, in order to increase both the generalizability and the applicability of our results, it is important to use other stressors as well. The obvious relevance of physical exertion to a variety of military tasks made the task of pressing a dynamometer an appealing candidate. All subjects were thus exposed to two stressors: the dynamometer test (DT) and the CPT, in that order.

Independent variables. The target for the DT was set at 70 seconds, at 60% of subject's maximal press, with the dominant hand. The target for the CPT was set at 4 minutes, with the non-dominant hand. Using a between subjects design, 80 subjects were randomly divided into four different conditions:

In the no information condition, subjects were asked to perform both tasks until the experimenter tells them that the test was over. There was no clock in the subjects' room, and their watches were removed prior to the beginning of the DT.

In the exact information condition, subjects were asked to perform the DT for 70 seconds, and subsequently to keep their hand in the ice cold water for 4 minutes. A digital clock in front of their eyes indicated the passage of time precisely.

In the false long condition, subjects were asked to press the dynamometer for 120 seconds, and after 30 seconds heard that the duration was shortened to 70 seconds. Next, they were asked to endure the CPT for 5 minutes. However, after 2:45 they were told that the duration was only 4 rather than 5 minutes.

Lastly, in the false short condition, subjects were asked to press the dynamometer for 45 seconds. After 30 seconds this was prolonged to 70 seconds. In the second task they were asked to endure the pain for 3 minutes, but after 2:45 this was prolonged to 4 minutes.

Dependent variables. The present experiment focussed primarily on the behavioral measures of endurance. Thus the frequency of subjects carrying out the task to its successful completion, as well as the exact time of 'giving up' was measured. Heart-rate was measured continuously throughout the entire experimental sequence. Subjective reports of stress, as well as responses to direct questions pertaining to the various features of the experiment, were secured shortly after termination of the CPT.

Subjects and procedure. All subjects were male students at the University of Haifa. They were recruited from the entire body of students on a voluntary basis. A fee of IS20.00 (about $12.00) was offered for participation. All subjects were tested individually.

The 'Baseline Instructions' were the same for all subjects, irrespective of their subsequent experimental treatment: "For your participation in the experiment you will receive a basic sum of IS20.00. We are interested to read your lowest heart-rate, so please sit quietly for a few minutes, and try to relax as much as possible."

Next followed two minutes of 'baseline' recording, followed by the first task, i.e., pressing the dynamometer. This task presents two methodological difficulties: Firstly, it is unreasonable to expect subjects to keep the dynamometer pressed to the maximum for any significant duration. In fact, the maximal press can be maintained for a few seconds only. Secondly, it was important to reduce the effects of individual differences in muscular strength as much as possible. In order to resolve both problems, we asked each subject, using his dominant hand, to briefly press the dynamometer once to the maximum, and read his own score. The actual task then consisted in pressing the dynamometer again, and keeping it pressed above 60% of their own maximum. The dynamometer was connected to the polygraph, providing full information about subject's performance.

The DT instructions were: "When you will be told to start, press the handle in front of you once, as strongly as you can. Now!...Release."

And after five seconds, depending upon the experimental variation: "Don't do anything before the start signal. Now we shall test your ability to sustain a prolonged effort. You will be asked to press the handle in front of you as strongly as possible, and keep it pressed

until we tell you.	(No Information)
for 70 seconds.	(Exact Information)
for 120 seconds.	(False Long)
for 45 seconds.	(False Short)

If you could finish the task without releasing the handle below 60% of your short previous press, you will receive

IS10.00 in addition to your basic remuneration. Take care, releasing the handle below 60% of your short press will be considered as termination of the task. The intensity of the press is continuously recorded, and you will be able to check our decision, if you so desire. Remember, your previous press was....units, therefore, 60% are....units. START!"

After 30 seconds, subjects in the last two groups were given the correction: "Pay attention! The time was
          shortened from 120 to 70 seconds.   (False Long)
          prolonged from 45 to 70 seconds.   (False Short)
          All other conditions remain the same."

Following the termination of DT (either by the subject himself, or after 70 seconds), the 'Between Tasks Relaxation' Instructions, similar for all subjects, were given: "The pressing task is now over. Relax and rest for a few minutes."

The 'Between Tasks Relaxation' period was of 2 minutes duration, followed by the 'CPT Instructions': "We are now going to test your ability to cope with prolonged pain. You will be asked to insert your left hand in a bucket full with ice water. You have to keep your hand in the water
          until we tell you. (No Information)
          for 4 minutes.   (Exact Information)
          for 5 minutes   (False Long)
          for 3 minutes   (False Short)
If you are able to finish the task, you will receive IS10.00 in addition to your previous earnings. START!"

After 2 minutes and 45 seconds, subjects in the last two groups were given the correction: "Pay attention! The time
          was shortened from 5 to 4 minutes. (False Long)
          was prolonged from 3 to 4 minutes. (False Short)
          All other conditions remain the same."

Following the termination of the CPT (either by the subject or after 4 minutes), the 'Final Relaxation' Instructions were given: "Now try to relax for a few minutes."

This took 2 minutes, after which time one of the experimenters entered the subject's room, removed the heart-rate electrode, and presented the subject with the Post Experimental Questionnaire.

RESULTS AND DISCUSSION

The total sample consisted of 80 male subjects that were randomly allocated to the four experimental groups. Due to some technical difficulties, such as occasional noise in the recording of heart-rate, not all subjects produced the entire spectrum of data collected.

Effectiveness of the stressors. The first analysis tested
two important issues at the same time: the fairness of the
allocation procedure, and the validity of the stress manipulation. This was accomplished by comparing the heart-rate
between groups during the last 30 seconds of the pre-stress
relaxation, and during the first 30 seconds of stress. This
was done twice, for each stressor separately. A Repeated
Measures Manova was carried out. The analysis indicates that
there are no significant Group effects either before the
stressor, or during stress onset. The random allocation to
the different groups was, therefore, fair.

More important, however, are the dramatic changes in
heart-rate as a consequence of the dynamometer task. Whereas
the pre-stress mean for the entire sample was 76.8 beats per
minute, the stressor raised this to the mean level of 110.2.
Moreover, the comparisons of the respective means for each of
the groups separately, suggests that the size of this effect
is highly reliable.

The CPT data presents essentially the same picture. Once
again, there are no significant Group effects, whereas the
impact of the stressor on heart-rate is highly significant.
The pre-stressor mean for the entire sample was 78.8 beats per
minute, which the stressor raised to 95.3. The within groups
comparisons are highly consistent. Comparing the impact of
the two stressors, it is obvious that the dynamometer task
has a greater impact on heart-rate than the cold pressor task.
This is consistent with the different nature of these two
stressors: whereas the dynamometer requires expenditure of
effort, the CPT is essentially a passive task.

Effect of Information/No Information on endurance. The central
hypothesis of this research is that absence of information
concerning the duration of a stressful task increases the
deleterious effects of stress, and reduces its endurance. Our
study makes it possible to test this hypothesis utilizing the
obviously valid criterion of task completion. This is done by
comparing the first two groups, i.e., the No Information group
(Group 1) with the Exact Information group (Group 2).

Starting with the Dynamometer task, in Group 1, 31.6%
of subjects were able to successfully complete the task, as
compared with 76.5% in Group 2! The analysis of variance
yields F(1,36)=8.581, which is significant (P .01).

Moving now to the Cold Pressor Test, in the No Information
condition 30% of subjects were able to keep their hand in the
ice water for the entire 4 minutes, whereas in the Exact Infor-

mation group there were 60% that endured the stressful task
to the end! The Anova showed F(1,38)=3.8 (P=.05). While the
relatively small number of subjects used, necessarily reduced
the significance level of these results, the chances of endurance until completion is doubled by procuring exact information
about the duration of the task!

And what about those subjects who were unable to finish
the task given to them? Starting with the Dynamometer Task,
we find that if subjects were unable to go all the 70 seconds,
there were no major differences between the two groups. Thus,
in the No Information group the mean duration was 43.6 seconds,
whereas in the Exact Information group it was 50 seconds.
Moving now to the CPT, the means are 67.3 and 67.8 seconds
respectively. This negligible advantage of information is not
significant, and suggests that there may be a qualitative
difference between finishing the task and the duration of
perseverance without finishing it. When there is a clear goal
to be achieved, it is conceivable that the main difference is
between conditions which facilitate the achievement of the
goal and those that are detrimental to its completion. If the
goal is not attained, it is, perhaps, of lesser import how
long a person kept up the activity before breaking down under
the strain.

Effects of information change. Our design allows us to test
the potential impact of information change during the stressful tasks themselves. Whereas one of the groups started with
essentially discouraging information with subsequent encouraging correction (Group 3), the other one (Group 4) received
an exactly opposite treatment, i.e., encouraging information
at start, with discouraging correction later.

Our first analysis is concerned with the chances of
successful completion of the two tasks in these different
groups. Results indicate that there are no significant
differences between these two groups in either of the tasks.
Furthermore, their rate of success falls halfway between the
No Information and the Exact Information groups (Group 3 had
65% success with the first task as compared with 50% for
Group 4). In the CPT the numbers are 53% and 56% respectively.

The fact that successful completion rates fall in between
the two extreme groups of No Information and Exact Information,
makes, of course, psychological sense. Whatever the psychological disadvantage of Group 3 at start, it is subsequently
alleviated when the subjects hear the good news about the
duration of the task. At the same time, however, the advantages and disadvantages, while cancelling each other, do not

do so entirely. The detrimental effects of the disadvantages appear to be more potent than the beneficial effects of the advantages, leading to a net result which is below the success rate of the Exact Information condition. Due to the paucity of experimental evidence at this stage of our enquiry, this conclusion is necessarily a tentative one. Further research, as planned in our experimental program, can throw additional light on this important issue.

When endurance breaks down: Search for indicators. There is no need to dwell upon the practical importance of having access to signs which precede the point when a persons' endurance breaks down. The variety of potential uses of such information encompasses both corrective and preventive measures. Not less important, however, are the potential theoretical payooffs of such indicators. By providing a better clue to our understanding of endurance on the one hand, and the transition from effective performance to the point of breaking down under the strain, such understanding opens a whole variety of new, potentially very important issues.

In each segment of the experiment, the exact time when subjects' heart-rate was at its peak, or maximum was measured. The mean timing of maximal heart-rate for the CPT according to groups were: Group 1: 67.2 seconds, Group 2: 42.4 seconds, Group 3: 29.8 seconds, and Group 4: 62.8 seconds after the start. Group 1, i.e., the No Information condition, is a special case, since subjects have no idea about the expected duration of the stress. Thus, for them, the crisis can actually signal the breaking point of endurance. Computing the average timing of CPT for those subjects who did not finish the task, we find that it was 67.3 seconds after its onset. This corresponds almost exactly to the timing of the maximal heart-rate in this group! This finding raises the possibility that in the absence of information about duration of a stressful task, the maximal heart-rate can be a potentially useful predictor of breakdown.

Looking at the results of the remaining three groups, we observe a highly systematic pattern: Group 3, which anticipates a 5 minute duration of CPT reaches the maximum first, then comes Group s, which anticipates 4 minutes, and finally Group 4, which believes that the task will last 3 minutes only. In other words, the longer the anticipated duration of the stressful task, the sooner the maximal heart-rate. Such a clear relationship between the two adds some validity to the notion that maximal heart-rate is associated with a crisis.

REFERENCES

1. Lazarus RS, Folkman S (1984). "Stress, Appraisal, and Coping." New York: Springer.
2. Lazarus RS, Launier R (1978). Stress-related transactions between pwesons and environment. In Pervin LA, Lewis M (eds.): "Perspective in Interactional Psychology." New York: Plenum.
3. Breznitz S (1984). "Cry Wolf: The Psychology of False Alarms." New Jersey: Lawrence Erlbaum Associates.
4. Breznitz S, Goldberger L (1982). Stress at crossroads. In Goldberger L, Breznitz S (eds): "Handbook of Stress." New York: Free Press.
5. Breznitz S (1967). Incubation of threat: Duration of anticipation and false alarm as determinants of fear reaction to an unavoidable frightening event. J Exp Res in Personality 2:173-180.
6. Breznitz S (1968). Incubation of threat in a situation of conflicting expectations. Psych Reports 22:755-756.
7. Janis IL (1949). In Stouffer SA, et al (eds): "The American Soldier: Combat and its Aftermath. Vol 2." Manhattan, KS, MA-AH PUB.

ACKNOWLEDGMENTS

Part of this research was sponsored by the U.S. Army Research Institute for Behavioral and Social Sciences Contract No. DAERO-75-G-055 and DAJA45-86-C-0048. The opinions expressed are those of the author and do not necessarily represent those of the U.S. Army.

Molecular Biology of Stress, pages 265–275
© 1989 Alan R. Liss, Inc.

HORMONAL AND PSYCHOLOGICAL PROFILES IN RESPONSE TO A WRITTEN EXAMINATION

Gerald A. Hudgens,[1] Robert T. Chatterton, Jr.,[2]
James Torre, Jr.,[1] Sue E. Slager,[2]
Linda T. Fatkin,[1] Louis G. Keith,[2]
Robert W. Rebar,[2] Frank A. DeLeon-Jones,[3]
and James M. King,[1]

[1]U.S. Army Human Engineering Laboratory, Aberdeen
Proving Ground, Maryland 21005-5001; [2]Department
of OB/GYN, Northwestern University Medical
School, Chicago, Illinois 60611; [3]Westside VA
Hospital, Chicago, Illinois 60612

ABSTRACT Profiles of psychological and
hormonal responses were obtained from male
medical students on the day they took an
important written exam and, subsequently, on
a day during a period of no exams. Control
data were also obtained for an independent
non-student group. A battery of standardized psychological questionnaires was administered before and after the exam to assess
anxiety, mood, and subjective stress. Both
before and after the exam, the students
displayed greater anxiety and rated their
experience as more stressful than did they
or the non-students under control conditions. Post-exam depression and hostility
were also significantly elevated over control conditions. Hormone levels were
measured before and after the exam. Before
the exam, prolactin for the exam group was
significantly elevated over levels for
both control groups, while, after the exam,
it was significantly elevated only relative
to the independent control. Cortisol,
however, was elevated in both the pre- and
post-exam periods for the students under

both exam and control conditions relative to independent controls. For the exam group, pre-exam anxiety and stress measures correlated significantly and negatively with both pre- and post-exam levels of luteinizing hormone and prolactin. Post-exam anxiety and stress measures correlated negatively with luteinizing hormone but not prolactin. Performance on the exam was predicted by both pre-exam MAACL-R anxiety and post-exam stress scores but not by hormone levels.

INTRODUCTION

Both stress theory and research have been under the dominant influence of notions and directions proposed by Hans Selye since he first described stress as "a syndrome produced by diverse nocuous agents" in 1936 (1). In subsequent publications he has defined stress as "...the nonspecific response of the body to any demand made upon it" (2, p. 692) and emphasized the role of the pituitary-adrenal-cortical system in expression of the nonspecific response. In 1971, Mason (3), criticized Selye's emphasis on stress as a physiological concept and presented evidence that stress is better regarded as a behavioral concept. He argued that consideration of psychological factors and higher-order central nervous involvement in responses to a broad range of environmental stimuli would implicate a number of endocrine systems. Mason's work led to the development of his notion of profiles of hormonal response patterns associated with different kinds and intensities of stimuli (4).

Others have contributed to the developing view of stress as a multifacited, dynamic, interactive process involving a number of physiological and psychological factors. Lazarus and Folkman (5) emphasized the relationship between state characteristics of the person and characteristics of the environment as determinants of stress reaction when the environmental situation is perceived as taxing the person's resources. They viewed the stress process as being dynamic wherein the person-environment interaction involves a repeating series of appraisals and attempts to cope. Frankenhaeuser (6) has chosen to incorporate approaches of both Mason and Lazarus and to relate neuroendocrine, state perception, and coping measures to more enduring trait characteristics.

The combined impact of these investigators has been to outline the elements of a much more complex formulation for the concept of stress and to suggest new research approaches. However, few investigators have attempted to pursue the elaborate and systematic investigations called for. Frankenhaeuser (6) has investigated many different stressors, and different levels of stress, and included extensive batteries of physiological and psychological measures, but the measures have not been consistent across studies. Vingerhoets (7) also made use of batteries of measures across levels of stress, but limited himself to film stress. No one has yet put together a comprehensive program to evaluate the relative importance of the various proposed physiological and psychological factors and determine profiles of responses associated with various kinds and intensities of stress.

The present work represents one portion of a program initiated to validate the notion of unique physiological and psychological response profiles associated with different kinds and intensities of stress. This report presents data relating to the hormonal and psychological stress perception profiles generated in an important written medical examination.

METHODS

Subjects

Male, third- and fourth-year (N=26) medical students in a clinical clerkship program, taking a 3-hour final written examination for a required course, were recruited for study (Exam group). Of those, 18 volunteered to return during a rela-

tively non-stress (non-exam) control period to
repeat the protocol (Self C group). An independent, age-matched, group of male non-students
(N=8) was also evaluated under control conditions
(Indep C group).

Procedures

     The written exam was administered to the
students in a classroom setting from 0900 hrs to
1200 hrs. An indwelling catheter, with heparin
lock, was established on the exam day and control
days at 0700 hrs. Blood samples, obtained at 60,
45, 30, and 15 mins before the start of the exam
period and at 90, 120, 180, and 240 mins after
the exam period, were assayed by radio-immunoassay for cortisol, prolactin, luteinizing hormone (LH), testosterone, and growth hormone (GH).
     A 5-min battery of state anxiety and stress-
perception measures was administered to the subjects 15 mins before and after the exam. The
battery included the Multiple Affect Adjective
Checklist-Revised (MAACL-R) (8), which contains
subscales for anxiety, depression, and hostility,
the State-Trait Anxiety Inventory (STAI Form Y)
(9), the Subjective Stress Scale (SSS) (10), and
a post-exam Rating of Events (ROE), a measure
designed for this program wherein the subjects
rated, on a scale of 0-100, how stressful the
event was to them.
     Data for the 4 pre-exam collections and for
the 4 post-exam collections were each pooled to
yield single values for the anticipatory and recovery periods. Group comparisons were made by
analysis of variance or paired t-test.

RESULTS

Psychological State Measures

     As shown in Figure 1, the MAACL-R anxiety
scores for the Exam group before the exam were
significantly elevated over their Self C scores
(p<.01) and the Indep C scores (p<.05). After

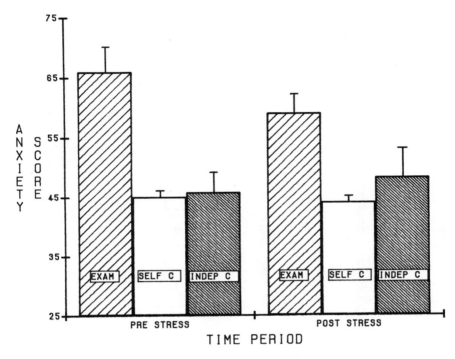

FIGURE 1.   Mean MAACL-R anxiety scores
(+SEM) measured before and after exam stress
period.

the exam their anxiety scores remained elevated
over Self C (p<.01) and Indep C scores (p<.10).
The other state anxiety measure (STAI) and measures of stress perception (SSS and ROE) yielded
patterns of scores virtually identical with
MAACL-R anxiety.

As shown in Figure 2, the Exam group did not
differ sigificantly from controls on depression
expressed before the exam.   However, depression
expressed by the Exam group increased significantly (p<.01) from the pre-exam to the post-exam
period, and was significantly greater (p<.05)
than by either control group after the exam.

As was the case for the depression measure,
the Exam group did not differ significantly from
controls on hostility expressed before the exam

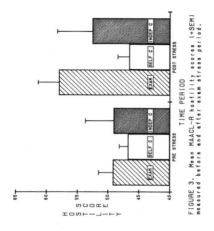

FIGURE 2. Mean MAACL-R depression scores (+SEM) measured before and after exam stress period.

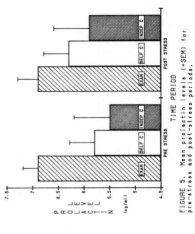

FIGURE 3. Mean MAACL-R hostility scores (+SEM) measured before and after exam stress period.

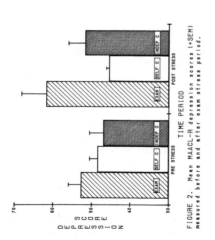

FIGURE 4. Mean cortisol levels (+SEM) for pre-stress and post-stress periods.

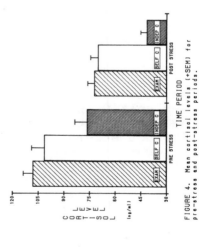

FIGURE 5. Mean prolactin levels (+SEM) for pre-stress and post-stress periods.

(Figure 3). However, Exam group hostility increased significantly (p<.05) from -15 mins to +15 mins and was significantly greater (p<.01) than that for the Self C group at +15 mins.

Hormone Measures

All three groups showed significant (p<.01) drops in plasma cortisol from the pre-stress period (early morning) to the post-stress period (late afternoon), following the unusual circadian variation (Figure 4). Cortisol levels for the Exam and Self C groups were significantly elevated (p<.01) over those for the Indep C group for both time periods.

As shown in Figure 5, the mean prolactin level for the Exam group was significantly elevated (p<.05) over those for both control groups prior to the exam. After the exam, the Exam group prolactin was elevated significantly (p<.05) relative only to that for the Indep C group.

No significant differences between groups were obtained for testosterone, LH or GH.

Correlational Relationships Among Psychological, Hormonal and Performance Variables

The most consistent finding was that pre- and post-exam LH levels correlated significantly, and negatively, with most measures of state anxiety and perceived stress obtained both before and after the exam. Lower LH levels were associated with higher levels of perceived anxiety and stress. Similarly, lower levels of prolactin were associated with higher levels of perceived anxiety but only as measured by the MAACL-R before the exam.

Significant negative correlations were obtained between performance on the exam and state anxiety scores on the MAACL-R before the exam (r=-.40, p<.05) and perceived stress on the ROE (r=-.44, p<.05) after the exam.

DISCUSSION

Clearly, the students perceived conditions on the exam day as being more anxiety-provoking and stressful than the conditions of merely being in the study on a day with no exam. The consistency of the between-group differences across the 2 anxiety and the 2 stress-perception measures strongly suggests they were measuring the same construct under the conditions of this investigation.

Whereas anxiety was affected both before and after the exam, the mood states of depression and hostility, as measured by the MAACL-R, were significantly increased over control values only for the post-exam assessment.

In an early validation effort, Zuckerman, Lubin, Vogel and Valerius (11) looked at anxiety, depression, and hostility scores under 4 conditions: baseline, immediately following the threat of an unannounced exam, immediately before a scheduled written exam, and immediately after receiving artificially-lowered exam grade reports. All 3 measures were significantly increased under test conditions relative to baseline with the exceptions that depression and hostility were not increased prior to the scheduled exam. Watts, Herbert, Moore and Levy (12) also found MAACL-R anxiety, but not depression or hostility, was increased before an oral exam. The above findings, along with those of the present study, suggest that state anxiety is more generally affected than are state depression and hostility relative to the events of an examination. State depression and hostility increases do not appear to be part of the anticipatory response, but do appear to occur afterward in response to more well-defined, negatively-perceived aspects of the exam situation.

That the students taking the exam were stressed was corroborated by the elevated levels of cortisol and prolactin relative to Indep C levels. Both cortisol and prolactin remained elevated in the Exam group into the 1.5-4 hr post-exam period. The finding that cortisol was elevated in the Self-C group, suggests that the students were experiencing chronic stress. Hellhammer, Heib, Hubert and Rolf (13) also found elevated cortisol level during anticipation of an exam and noted, further, that "...cortisol levels were abnormally high even in control samples," suggesting "...a period of chronic stress," in the student subjects. Prolactin levels in the present study were not elevated in the Self C group, suggesting that it may not be as affected as cortisol by chronic stress as experienced by the students. It is noteworthy, furthermore, that Herbert, Moore, de la Riva and Watts (14) investigated cortisol, prolactin, LH and testosterone levels in medical students 4 weeks and 30 mins before an important written exam, and that, as in the present study, they found elevated levels of both cortisol and prolactin just before the exam relative to the base period, and that they, too, found no effects on testosterone or LH levels.

The significant correlational associations obtained strongly suggest that both hormonal responses and performance may be influenced by individuals' perceptions and resulting mood states.

The consistency of the findings from this study, along with those from a number of similar studies, indicate the emergence of a reliable profile of psychological and hormonal responses related to medical students taking an important exam. Those students report higher levels of anxiety and perceived stress than non-students or students during non-exam periods. They score higher on both depression and hostility scales for the exam period, as measured shortly post exam, than prior to the exam. Their cortisol levels are chronically high. They exhibit elevated levels of both cortisol and prolactin, both shortly before and 1.5-4 hr after the exam, but their levels of GH, LH and testosterone are not affected.

We have demonstrated a reliable profile of psychological and physiological responses to an important written examination. Further validation of the notion of unique response profiles to different kinds and intensities of stress will depend on comparison with profiles obtained for other stressors and intensities in our continuing program.

REFERENCES

1. Selye H (1936). A syndrome produced by diverse nocuous agents. Nature (Lond) 118:32.
2. Selye H (1973). The evolution of the stress concept. Am Sci 61:692.
3. Mason JW (1971). A re-evaluation of the concept of 'non-specificity' in stress theory. J Psychiat Res 8:323.
4. Mason JW (1975). Emotion as reflected in patterns of endocrine integration. In Levi L (ed): "Emotions: Their Parameters and Measurement," New York: Raven Press, p 143.
5. Lazarus RS, Folkman S (1984). "Stress, Appraisal, and Coping," New York: Springer Publ Co, p 1.
6. Frankenhaeuser M (1978). Psychoneuroendocrine approaches to the study of emotion as related to stress and coping. In Howe HE, Dienstbier RA (eds): "Nebraska Symposium on Motivation 1978," Lincoln: Univ Nebr Press, p 123.
7. Vingerhoets A (1985). "Psychosocial Stress: An Experimental Approach: Life Events, Coping, and Psychobiological Functioning," Lisse, The Netherlands: Swets & Zeitlinger.
8. Zuckerman M, Lubin B (1985). "Manual for the MAACL-R: The Multiple Affect Adjective Checklist Revised," San Diego: EdITS.
9. Spielberger CD, Gorsuch RL, Lushene R, Vagg PR, Jacobs GA (1983). "Manual for the State-Trait Anxiety Inventory: STAI (Form Y)," Palo Alto, CA: Consl Psychol Press.
10. Kerle RH, Bialek HM (1958). "The Construction, Validation and Application of a Subjective Stress Scale," Presidio of Monterey, CA: US Army Leadership Hum Res Unit.

11. Zuckerman M, Lubin B, Vogel L, Valerius E (1964). Measurement of experimentally induced affects. J Consl Psy 28:418.
12. Watts FN, Herbert J, Moore GF, Levey A (1986). Approaches to studying, personality and examination anxiety. Pers Indiv Diff 7:243.
13. Hellhammer DH, Heib C, Hubert W, Rolf L (1985). Relationships between salivary cortisol release and behavioral coping under examination stress. IRCS Med Sci 13:1179.
14. Herbert J, Moore GF, de la Riva C, Watts FN (1986). Endocrine responses and examination anxiety. Biol Psy 22:215.

Molecular Biology of Stress, pages 277–284

AFFECT SPECIFIC RETRIEVAL FROM ARCHIVAL MEMORY

H. Weingartner[1,2],
M.Eckardt[2],R. Lister[2]

[1]Department of Psychology, The George Washington
University, Washington, DC 20052
[2]Laboratory of Clinical Studies, DICBR, NIAAA,
Bethesda, MD 20892

ABSTRACT Affective states, like many psychoactive
drugs, serve as discriminative stimuli, which serve
as a context biasing the types of events that are
likely to be retrieved from long term memory or
knowledge. Consequently, affect state dependent
retrieval from knowledge memory determines how we
perceive, encode and organize and represent our
experience in episodic memory.

Changes in affect, such as in states of depression
and anxiety, induce alterations in several psychologically
distinct types of cognitive operations. Some of these
cognitive changes are expressed as alterations in
attention, encoding, storage and retrieval processes that
require cognitive capacity and effort (Weingartner and
Silverman, 1984; Roy-Byrne, et. al., 1986; Tariot and
Weingartner, 1986). Other changes in cognition are
qualitative in nature.

---

[1]Department of Psychology, George Washington
University
[2]Laboratory of Clinical Studies, DICBR, NIAAA,
Bethesda, MD 20892

MOOD AND MEMORY

Information acquired in one mood state is frequently
more effectively retrieved from memory in that same mood
state (Bower, 1981). This phenomena which is often
referred to as mood state-dependent learning or more
correctly state-dependent retrievel (SDR) that occurs in
response to many types of psychoactive drugs.
A number of strategies have been used to study mood
SDL-SDR. These strategies differ in terms of the nature
of the treatment variable (e.g. how mood states are
altered) and the type of "learning" and "memory" methods
used in access mood SDL-SDR. Most studies designed to
investigate mood SDL-SDR have used behavioral methods to
induce changes in affect in "normal" subjects. Behavioral
manipulations of mood have included asking subjects to
process emotion relevant information, that subjects are
asked to process, manipulations of set, expectations (e.g.
experience of success, or failure), task demands (solvable
vs. insolvable problems). Such manipulations of mood
precede both the learning and memory retrieval phase of an
experiment. Relatively few studies exploring mood SDL-SDR
have used clinically significant "experiments of nature",
such as those that appear in changes in mood, in affective
disorder patients. There have also been few studies using
drugs as tools for altering mood, acutely, in normal
volunteers, in order to test for mood SDL-SDR effects.
The pattern of findings obtained in affect related
SDL-SDR are similar to those findings, that have emerged
from studies of drug related SDL-SDR. Mood states appear
to be discriminative stimuli that, much like drugs, have
cuing functions, eliciting at least partially unique
response hierarchies associated with a given stimulus.
Changes in mood are associated with alterations in central
and peripheral nervous system activity, which would serve
as the neurobiological bases for the stimulus properties
of mood. Such a notion is quite consistent with a
behavioral analysis view of drug-stimulus specific
response hierarchies as a framework for defining the
discriminative properties of drugs (Overton, 1978, 1984).
Three types of factors account for the likelihood of
demonstrating state dependent dissociations in memory.
The most important factor is the robustness of the
treatment variable. Most investigators have observed that
drug related SDL-SDR effects are fragile and subtle

phenomena not easily or reliably demonstrated under "weak"
treatment conditions (e.g. low doses of drugs, small
changes in affect). The kind of treatment used as a
manipulation and its "intensity" such as dose of drug, or
rate of administration, is important in determining the
likelihood of demonstrating dissociative effects (Overton,
1984). This issue of intensity of treatment variable may
be particularly important in studies of mood SDL-SDR.
Subtle, weak, alleviation of mood may not suffice as a
manipulation of state sufficient for demonstrating
dissociative effects (Bower, 1981; Bower and Mayer, 1985).
     A second class of variables that influences the
expression of SDL-SDR effects involves the characteristics
of the stimuli subjects are asked to process and how
subjects are asked to remember previously attended events,
e.g. the manner in which memory is tested. The types of
events that are dissociated ("lost") in memory when
retrieval is attempted in a state different from that of
the acquisition state is highly dependent upon the nature
of the events that have been processed, i.e., how well
they have been encoded. Well processed events are less
likely to be lost in recall than poorly processed
information when retrieval is tested under disparate
memory state test conditions (Weingartner, et al., 1976;
Eich & Birnbaum, 1982). The manner in which memory for
those events is tested also is a crucial factor in whether
subjects demonstrate dissociations in memory. For
example, SDR effects are apparent when subjects are asked
to freely recall information. Such a memory test
condition requires subjects to generate their own
retrieval strategy for searching memory. However, if
subjects are provided with cues or prompts that bias and
presumably help them search memory such as in tests of
recognition memory, then SDL-SDR effects are unlikely to
be apparent. The appearance of SDL-SDR is highly
dependent upon the learning, processing methods used,
modality of stimulus presentations, characteristics of
subjects, and retrieval test methods (Eich, et al., 1975;
Weingartner, 1978; Eich, 1980).
     A third class of variables that is just beginning to
be considered important in studies of SDL-SDR effects
concerns the types of memory representations that subjects
are asked to remember under congruent vs. disparate

acquisition-retrieval test conditions. In the past, most SDL-SDR studies have been concerned with the class of memory representations that involve episodic memory, that is, memory for events that are tied to a unique context and sequence of biographical experience. Another class of memory representations, memory for previously acquired knowledge which is part of long term memory, has generally not been studied in SDL-SDR experiments. Knowledge memory, or what is sometime also called archival memory, is information that represents a knowledge base no longer linked to the context in which the learning occurred. This includes memory representations for information about words, facts, logical routines, characteristics of people, places, things, etc. It is this type of information that is necessary for encoding, organizing and understanding our experiences. There is good reason to hypothesize that this system of memory representations is particularly likely to be accessed in a state dependent manner. Furthermore, it is because information in knowledge memory is accessed in a state dependent manner that we are likely to observe SDL-SDR in episodic memory. A number of published studies can be interpreted in support of such a notion (Fogarty & Hemsley, 1983; Laird, et al., 1982; Mathews & Bradley, 1983; Natale & Hantas, 1982; Siegel, et al. 1979; Snyder & White, 1982; Teasdale, et al, 1980; 1983). The hypothesis that knowledge in long term is, in fact, mood state specific for at least some classes of stimuli seem to be supported by the findings from those studies.

The study described below provides one example of how mood states can serve to bias how previously acquired knowledge is accessed in a mood state specific manner. In this clinical-demonstration study, we directly compared the types of responses subjects would self-generate from knowledge memory in one state with responses generated in either the same or altered mood state condition.

A small group of bipolar patients (N=8) were asked to generate a single word response in association to 20 standard noun stimuli (for which normative data were available (N=500). This task is one that could be done even when patients were either quite depressed or manic. Patients were tested using different sets of equivalent stimuli over a period of months, including periods of normal mood and mania. Associative word responses were scored on the basis of their frequency or probability of occurrence in normal controls. During mania, as defined by standardized and validated NIMH affective rating scale, 33% of patients' responses would usually occur less than once in 500 responses elicited from normal controls (p < .001, Fisher exact probability test). These same patients usually produced well under 5% such unusual responses when tested in a "normal" mood state. It would appear different sets of associated responses (part of archival memory or knowledge) are elicited in response to common stimuli during the manic phase of bipolar affective illness. This is in fact a salient feature of the altered thought process that is part of affective disorders (Weingartner & Silberman, 1984).

The issue of the state specific stability or consistency with which these responses are elicited during mania in contrast to normal mood state was also addressed in another study. Here 8 hospitalized patients with bipolar affective disorders were repeatedly studied for 4-9 weeks. During this time, these rapidly cycling patients exhibited periods of mania, depression and normal mood. Instead of a single response, patients were asked to self-generate 20 single word responses to standard stimuli and then reproduce these associations four days later. During this time changes in mood were determined by the clinical staff using pretested and validated, behaviorally defined, standardized rating instruments. Over 150 pairs of observations were collected from these eight patients. These paired events of generation and four days later regeneration of associations included a broad range of altered mood states.

The probability that a patient would reproduce their responses was related to the absolute measure of change in mood state that occurred between the time they generated their associative response and when they were asked to regenerate them. The extent to which there appeared a change in mood state for each four day period was significantly related to the number of associations that could be reproduced (r = - .48 p < .002). That is, responses were far less reliably reproduced when large differences in mood differentiated the generation and regeneration phase of this association task. That is,

when there was a relatively large change in mood between
the time when associations were generated and when they
were reproduced, four days later then the reproduction of
those associations was less complete than under conditions
of congruent mood state at the time of generation and
regeneration of associations.

The finding that responses come to mind are different
in different mood states is just one example of mood state
specific access to archival memory. The types of life
events that subjects remember, the strategies used to
organize ongoing experience, distortion in perception and
memory, encoding of events, are all, in part, determined
by the context, (mood, drug state) present at the time
information is being processed, or remembered. These mood
state dependent reflections of access to archival memory
can be quantified and are reproducible in similar mood
state conditions. This type of research is not only of
intrinsic interest by should provide us with an important
research approach to the study of how affective states
such as depression or anxiety mediate and modulate
different types of higher mental functions.

REFERENCES

1.   Bower, G.H. (1981). Mood and memory. Am Psychol
     31:129-48.
2.   Bower, G.H., Mayer, J.D. (1985). Failure to
     replicate mood-dependentretrieval. Bull Psychon Soc
     23:39-42.
3.   Eich J.E. & Birnbaum, I.M. (1982). Repetition,
     cuing, and state-dependent memory. Mem & Cog, 10,
     103-114.
4.   Eich, J.E. (1980). The cue-dependent nature of
     state-dependent retrieval. Memory & Cognition, #.
     157-173.
5.   Eich, J.E., Weingartner, H., Stillman R.C., &
     Gillian, J.C. (1975). State-dependent accessibility
     of retrieval cues in the retention of a categorized
     list. J Verb Learn Verb Behav, 14, 408-417.
6.   Fogarty, S.L., Hemsley, D.R. (1983). Depression and
     the accessibility of memories. British Journal of
     Psychiatry. 142:232-237.
7.   Laird, J.D., Wagener, J.J., Halal, M., Szegda, M.
     (1982). Remembering what you feel: Effects of
     emotion on memory. J Pers Soc Psychol, 42:646-57.

8.   Natale, M., Hantas, M. (1982). Effect of temporary mood states on selective memory about the self. J Pers Soc Psychol 42:927-34.

9.   Overton, D.A. (1978). Major theories of state dependent learning. Drug Discrimination and State Dependent Learning, pp 283-318. Eds: B.T. Ho, D.W. Richards & D.L. Chute. New York: Academic Press.

10. Overton, D.A. (1984). State dependent learning and drug discriminations. Handbook of Psychopharmacology, Vol. 18. Eds: L.L. Iverson, S.D. Iversen & S.H. Snyder. New York: Plenum Press.

11. Post, R.M. (1986). Effortful and automatic cognitive processes in depression. Arch Gen Psychiatry, p43, 265.267

12. Siegel, J.M., Johnson, J.H., Sarason, I.G. (1979). Mood states and the reporting of life changes. Journal of Psychosomatic Research, 23:103-108.

13. Snyder, M., White, P. (1982). Moods and memories: Elation, depressionand the remembering of the events of one's life. Journal of Personality, 50:142-167.

14. Tariot, P.N. and Weingartner, H. (1986). A psychobiologic analysis of cognitive failures. Arch Gen Psychiatry, 43:1183-1188.

15. Teasdale, J.D., Fogarty, S. (1979). Differential effects of induced mood on retrieval of pleasant and unpleasant events from episodic memory. J Abnorm Psychol, 88:248-257.

16. Teasdale, J.D. (1983a) Affect and accessibility. Philosophical Transactions of the Royal Society of London, Series B. 302:403-412.

17. Teasdale, J.D., Taylor, R. (1981). Induced mood and accessibility of memories: An effect of mood state or of induction procedure? British Journal of Clinical Psychology, 20:39-48.

18. Teasdale, J.D. (1983). Negative thinking in depression: cause, effect, or reciprocal relationship? Adv Behav Res Ther, 3-25.

19. Weingartner, H., Adefris, W., Eich, J.E. & Murphy, D.L. (1976). Encoding-imagery specificity in alcohol state-dependent learning. J Exp Psychol: Human Learn Mem, 63-67.

20. Weingartner, H., Murphy, D.L. & Stillman, R.C. (1978). Mood state dependent learning. Stimulus Properties of Drugs: Ten Years of Progress, pp. 445-453. Eds: F.C. Colpaert & J.A. Rosecrans. Amsterdam: Elsevier/North Holland Biomedical Press.

21. Weingartner, H. (1978). Human state-dependent learning. In: Ho, B.T., Richards, D.W., Chute, D.C., eds. Drug discrimination and state dependent learning. New York: Academic Press.
22. Weingartner, H. & Silberman, E. (1984). Cognitive changes in depression in (Eds.) R. Poast and J. Bollenger, Neurobiology of Mood Disorders. Baltimore: Williams and Wilkins.
23. Zuroff, D.C. (1980). Distortions of memory in depressed, formerly depressed, and never depressed college students. Psychological Reports, 46:415-425.

Molecular Biology of Stress, pages 285–294

THE EFFECTS OF STRESS AND DESIPRAMINE UPON ACTIVITY AS A MODEL OF DEPRESSION [1]

Paul H. Desan[2], Lee H. Silbert[3], Whitney W. Woodmansee[3], and Steven F. Maier[3]

[2]Department of Neurology, Stanford University School of Medicine, Stanford, CA, 94305, and [3]Department of Psychology, University of Colorado, Boulder, CO, 80309

ABSTRACT Rats were maintained in running wheel cages for the measurement of total daily activity. Following repeated sessions of certain stressors but not others animals showed decreases in activity persisting for weeks. Animals treated chronically with an appropriate dose of the tricyclic antidepressant desipramine returned to normal or supranormal levels of activity. These results are discussed as a possible model of human depression.

INTRODUCTION

An accurate model of depression would be of obvious usefulness, both in the pragmatic goal of developing modes of diagnosis and treatment as well as in the theoretical goal of understanding the underlying neural physiology of depression. A wide variety of syndromes have been investigated as models of depression and antidepressant action, and this field has been lucidly reviewed by Willner (1). Ideally an animal model of a human disease should resemble its human counterpart as closely as possible in etiology, symptomatology, therapy and pathophysiology (2). Of course, it will not be possible to duplicate exactly a particular illness in a different species. Indeed, a disease in one species may simply have no fundamental equivalent in another.

---

[1] Supported by NSF Grant BNS 85-07451 and RSDA MH 00314.

Some models may be very useful with little resemblance to the illness as it is seen in the clinic. The ability of antidepressant drugs, both tricyclic agents and monoamine oxidase inhibitors, to reverse the effects of reserpine and related agents was the basis for the first model of antidepressant action (3) and a series of related assays since. Since reserpine induces depression in at least some humans, this model has a superficial validity, although the acute stupor, hypothermia or ptosis actually quantitated in the assay is not a close analog of what is commonly considered depression. Such models have been responsible for the discovery of most of the current generation of antidepressant drugs. The danger of such assays is that since they do not reflect the integrated synaptic system mediating depression they may miss certain antidepressant agents and falsely detect others. Indeed, in practice the assay tends to identify adrenergic stimulant antidepressants but not to identify atypical antidepressants like mianserin (4). Nor are such models useful in studying the specific neural wiring underlying the syndrome of depression.

Since stress is widely held to be an important etiological factor in one form of depression in man, "reactive depression," much effort has been expended towards study of the behavioral effects of stress in animals in an attempt to construct more obviously valid models of depression (as well as other stress-related illnesses). For example, antidepressants are known to counteract the learning deficits induced by inescapable shock in the "learned helplessness" model (5,6), as well as the decreasing latency to cessation of struggle seen in rats exposed to repeated sessions of swim stress in the "behavioral despair" model (7). While not all agents have been tested, such models do appear to identify the antidepressant activity of at least some of the atypical agents. While such models do simulate forms of "behavioral inhibition" which have an appealing similarity with aspects of depressive behavior in man, these models do not duplicate the long-lasting persistence of human clinical depression.

In fact, as we have reviewed elsewhere (8), there are few examples of long-term behavioral changes induced by stress in adult laboratory animals. For example, the escape learning deficits of "learned helplessness" generally last less than 72 hours when escape testing is conducted in a situation very different from the original stress (9), although under some conditions they may be somewhat more prolonged (10). Longer effects have been found when behavioral testing was administered in an identical or similar environment to that in which inescapable shock was originally experienced (11). Such changes may reflect associative or conditioned changes, and their permanence is therefore not surprising. Chronic stress might be expected to produce more enduring deficits, but instead often produces an adaptation to stress and less final effect (12).

In this communication we describe some aspects of a potential model of depression in the rat. First, we show that spontaneous wheel running activity is depressed for many weeks in rats following exposure to chronic but not acute stress by inescapable electric shock, demonstrating a true, non-associative long-term behavioral effect of stress in the adult rat. Second, we suggest that certain other forms of stressor, such as cold swim, which might be thought an equally severe stressor in other contexts, do not produce long-term effects even upon similarly repeated exposure. Third, we find that chronic but not acute treatment with the tricyclic antidepressant drug desipramine reverses this activity depression, while having no effect in normal animals.

METHODS

Portions of the experiments described here have been published (8), and a detailed methodology is available there. Male Sprague-Dawley rats were maintained in running wheel activity cages on a 12:12 light:dark cycle, with food and water available throughout the experiment. After a stable baseline of activity was obtained, rats were removed from the activity cages and exposed to stressors, one session per day, for 1 - 4 days as noted below. The electric shock stress consisted of 100 X 5 sec 1.6 mA tailshocks while restrained in Plexiglas tubes over an approximately 2 hour period. Restraint stress animals were merely placed in the apparatus an equal period. Swim stress conisted of a 3.5 min swim in water at 2 C. Following stressor delivery animals were returned to the activity cages and their total daily activity monitored for the duration of the experiment. Desipramine (Merrell Dow) was administered in drinking water at the concentrations noted in Experiment 3.

RESULTS

Experiment 1

In the first experiment we observed the effect of one, two and four sessions of inescapable electric shock upon subsequent wheel running activity. Groups of 8 animals were stressed at the same time on 1, 2 or 4 days, and their total daily activity for the following 42 days compared with that of rats exposed only to sessions of restraint in the shock apparatus or with that of rats which were not disturbed at all.

The results are shown in Figure 1. The activity of individual rats varies widely, and so each animal's activity was expressed as a percentage change from its activity during a pre-stress baseline period. Mean activity scores for blocks of three days after stress are plotted. All treated groups show some reduction of activity in the first two such time periods. However, the groups exposed to 2 and 4 shock sessions show a substantial decrease in spontaneous activity which persisted for the duration of the seven-week experiment. The decrement in activity was approximately 40% and 60% in the group means for the two

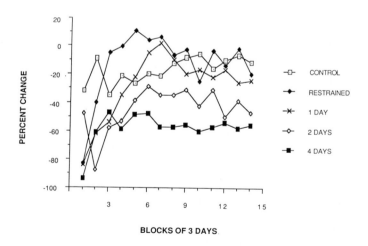

FIGURE 1. Mean daily activity from baseline following 1, 2 or 4 inescapable shock sessions, or 4 restraint sessions. From reference (8).

groups, respectively. Examination of the individual data
indicates that these groups contain a mixture of animals
showing only short-term effects of stress and animals
showing long-term effects of varying duration. Animals
exposed to restraint stress only returned to control levels
of activity by the third measurement interval. Control
animals showed a relatively constant level of activity; a
small temporary decline in their activity is perhaps
attributable to quieter conditions prevailing while the
activity of the other groups are massively depressed. A
more detailed statistical analysis of this experiment is
available in (8).

The weight and daily water intake of the animals were
quantitated following stress, and are also illustrated in
(8). Weight of rats exposed to 4 stress sessions was
depressed by approximately 10% shortly following stress but
returned to control levels by 8 days post stress. Water
intake was also transiently depressed but returned to
control levels by 12 days post stress.

Experiment 2.

The second experiment examined the activity of animals
exposed to 1 and 3 sessions of inescapable shock in
comparison to animals exposed to 1 and 3 sessions of cold
swim stress, a severe stressor in other systems.

The results are presented in Figure 2. As before,
several repeated sessions of inescapable shock, but not one
session, produce a lasting deficit in activity levels.
Neither 1 nor 3 sessions of cold swim stress produced an
analogous long-lasting decrease in activity, although both
treatments, as well as one session of inescapable shock,
did produce a short-term decrease.

Experiment 3.

In the final experiment a long-lasting activity
deficit was induced in four groups of rats by three
sessions of inescapable shock as described in the previous
two experiments. Three groups received 5, 10 and 20 mg/dl
desipramine in their drinking water beginning 3 days after
the last shock session, while the fourth group received no
treatment. A final group was left undisturbed in the
activity apparatus and served as a control group. After 30

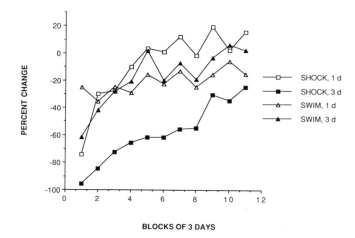

Figure 2. Mean daily activity following 1 or 3
sessions of inescapable shock, or 1 or 3 days of
swim stress, compared to control group activity.

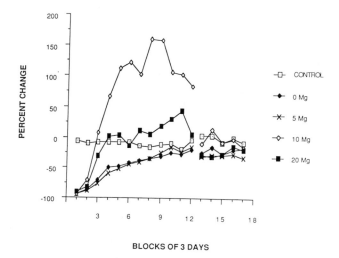

Figure 3. Mean daily activity following stress
combined with 0, 5, 10 or 20 mg/dl concentrations of
desipramine in drinking water. From (8).

days of drug treatment, the control and 0 mg groups began receiving 10 mg/dl desipramine, and the groups which had been receiving desipramine were given no drug. The experiment continued an additional 15 days.

The results are summarized in Figure 3. As before, multiple shock sessions induced a long-term decrease in activity. Animals receiving no drug required approximately 27 days to return to control levels of activity. Animals given 5 mg/dl desipramine in drinking water showed an identical recovery. However, animals given 10 mg/dl desipramine returned to and exceeded control levels of activity. The group mean exceeded control levels because several animals showed a dramatic increase in activity several fold their baseline levels, lasting about as long as the period of depressed activity lasted in untreated or undertreated animals. Examination of the individual day data indicates that a slight effect of desipramine was visible in the first 24 hours after the start of treatment, but approximately 7 days were required for a maximal effect. Animals given 20 mg/dl showed a much smaller effect. From the measured water intake it was estimated that the 5, 10 and 20 mg/dl groups received 4.0-5.0, 8.0-9.0 and 13.0-14.0 mg/kg drug per day.

In the second phase of the experiment, administration of the effective dose of desipramine failed to influence the activity of control, unstressed rats and of rats who had recovered normal activity levels post stress without receiving desipramine.

DISCUSSION

Thus, we demonstrate here a long-term, non-associative behavioral change in adult rat following stressful experience. The behavioral change noted here, a decrease in spontaneous activity in the rat's home cage, cannot be thought to be conditioned: the persistent activity deficits occurred in an environment that had few if any cues in common with the environment in which the animals were stressed. If any cues in common did exist, the animals were exposed to them as "safe" cues long before stress. Finally, any postulated association should have extinguished well before 7 weeks of exposure without stress.

The decrement in activity is seen in the majority of individual rats only after multiple sessions of inescapable

shock, at least at the parameters employed here. Another
form of stress, cold swim stress, does not produce the
effect even after 3 repetitions; it is possible that an
effect would follow a larger number of stress sessions.
This result emphasizes that not all severe stressors should
be assumed to produce states resembling depression. In
various experimental runs we have observed activity
depression ranging from 4 to greater than 7 weeks. The
influence of strain, age, rearing conditions and so forth
on the persistence of the phenomenon are under
investigation.

The effects of desipramine observed in this study
resemble those noted in clinical application. First,
desipramine has little effect on activity in normal rats,
even in chronic doses. Similarly, tricyclic antidepressants
appear to have little impact in humans with normal affect.
Second, desipramine has a potent stimulatory effect in rats
who are hypoactive following stress. In fact, several rats
in this study appear to have developed a hyperactivity
several fold times that of control, normal rats. This
excess stimulatory effect of desipramine dissipated at
about the same time as the depressed activity of untreated,
stressed animals returned to control levels. It is possible
that this overstimulatory effect is related to the switch
into mania occasionally noted in the clinical use of
tricyclic antidepressants (13). Third, maximal effects of
desipramine were observed only after about 7 days of
treatment, just as antidepressants are clinically effective
only upon chronic administration. Finally, we noted a
strongly curvilinear dose-response relationship, with the
maximum effect at the intermediate dose employed. This dose
represented approximately 8.0-9.0 mg/kg, a dose somewhat
higher than that typically employed clinically (300 mg in a
75 kg patient represents 4 mg/kg). In future experiments we
hope to measure the actual plasma concentration of drug,
which would be a more relevant comparison. A curvilinear
relationship of plasma level and clinical effect has been
reported in man for desipramine (14).

These features of the action of desipramine suggest
two cautions for research on such agents in rats. First,
the present results suggest that the stimulatory actions of
desipramine may appear only in appropriately stressed rats.
It is possible that studies in which biochemical effects of
antidepressants are evaluated in normal rats may be
misleading. Second, the antidepressant effect of this drug
may depend strongly upon dose, and studies using doses of

10 mg/kg or higher may not be using an effective dose for
antidepressant effects.

The phenomenon of long-term changes in activity level
described here shares certain resemblances with reactive
depression seen in man in etiology, symptomatology and
therapy. It is seen only after stress of sufficient
severity or chronicity. The diminished output of energy-
requiring, volitional activity in stressed rats resembles
the psychomotor retardation viewed as a core symptom in
many forms of human depression. Indeed, activity level has
been used to distinguish manic, depressed and euthymic
states in human patients (13). The period of diminished
activity in rats appears to last for weeks, and thus begins
to approach the timescale of months as in usual human
depression. Of course, the stressful experience employed
here is much more acute and delimited than that assumed to
induce human depression. Lastly, the activity deficit is
reversed by desipramine, which is not generally found to
have stimulant properties in normal man or animal.

Additional research will be required to determine
whether the syndrome described here is fundamentally
related to depression seen in humans. We are presently
investigating whether alterations of endocrine mechanisms
and circadian rhythms seen in human depression occur in
these animals, and whether other drugs which have an
antidepressant effect in humans have a like effect in this
model. It should be added that real differences may exist
between syndromes in man and rat. For example, differences
in peripheral drug metabolism, receptor selectivity,
neuroanatomical wiring or the like may cause differences in
the antidepressant potency of various drugs. Since most
work on the biochemical pharmacology of antidepressant
agents is done in rats, verification of antidepressant
activity in rat would be of considerable use.

If the syndrome described here does prove to have
resemble human depression, it may be of use as a model of
the human illness. Since it is a long-term effect, it may
be possible to study the neurochemical mechanisms of
depression independent of the many acute effects of stress,
and to assay the effects of antidepressant properties of
drugs in a realistic behavioral model with realistic
kinetics. Ultimately, we hope the model will be useful not
only in identifying neural changes fundamental to the
depressed state but also how such changes are reversed in
time and behavioral recovery effected.

BIBLIOGRAPHY

1. Willner P (1984). The validity of animal models oF depression. Psychopharm 83:1.
2. McKinney WT, Bunney, WE (1969). Animal model of depression: Review of evidence and implications for research. Arch Gen Psychiat 21:240.
3. Costa E, Grattini S, Valzelli L (1960). Interactions between reserpine, chlorpromazine and imipramine. Experientia 16:461.
4. Van Riezen H (1972). Different central effects of the 5-HT antagonists mianserin and cyproheptadine. Arch Int Pharmacodyn Ther 198:256.
5. Maier SF, Seligman, MEP (1976). Learned helplessness: Theory and evidence. J Exp Psychol (Gen) 1:3.
6. Sherman AD, Sacquitane JL, Petty F (1982). Specificity of the learned helplessness model of depression. Pharmacol Biochem Behav 16:449.
7. Porsolt, RD (1981). Behavioral despair. In Enna SJ, Malick JB, Richelson E (eds): "Antidepressants: Neurochemical, behavioral and clinical perspectives." New York: Raven Press, p 121.
8. Desan PH, Silbert L, Maier SF (1988). Long-term effects of inescapable stress on daily running activity and antagonism by desipramine. Pharmacol Biochem Behav 30:21.
9. Maier SF, Coon DJ, McDaniel MA, Jackson RL (1979). The time course of learned helplessness, inactivity and nocioceptive deficits in rats. Learning and Motivation 10:467.
10. Glaser HI, Weiss JM (1976). Long-term and transitory interference effects. JExpPsychol:Anim Behav Proc 2:191.
11. Henn FA, Johnson JO, Edwards E, Anderson D (1985). Melancholia in rodents: Neurobiology and pharmacology. Psycopharm Bull 21:443.
12. Weiss JM, Goodman PA, Losito BG, Corrigan S, Charry JM, Bailey WH (1981). Behavioral depression by an uncontrollable stressor: Relationship to norepinephrine, dopamine and serotonin levels in various regions of rat brain. Br Res Rev 3:167.
13. Wehr TA, Wirz-Justice FK, Goodwin FK, Duncan W, Gillin JC (1979). Phase advance of the circadian sleep-wake cycle as an antidepressant. Sci 206:710.
14. Freidel RO, Veith RC, Bloom V, Bielski RJ (1979). Desipramine plasma levels and clinical response in depressed outpatients. Commun Psychopharmacol 3:81.

Molecular Biology of Stress, pages 295–305

INFLUENCE OF PSYCHOSOCIAL STRESS ON MOUSE MAMMARY TUMOR GROWTH[1]

Joanne T. Emerman and Joanne Weinberg

Department of Anatomy, Faculty of Medicine
The University of British Columbia
Vancouver, B.C., V6T 1W5, Canada

ABSTRACT   An   animal   model,   utilizing   the transplantable androgen-responsive Shionogi mouse mammary carcinoma (SC115), was developed to examine the effects of psychosocial stressors on tumor growth. The data indicated marked and replicable effects of social housing condition and exposure to novel environments on tumor growth rate. Being reared   individually   housed   and   remaining individually housed (II) or being reared in a social group and then singly housed (GI) following tumor cell injection markedly increased tumor growth compared to that in mice remaining in their sibling rearing groups (GG), if animals were also exposed to acute daily novelty stress. In contrast, being reared individually and then moved to a large social group (IG) markedly reduced tumor growth, both in the presence and absence of acute daily novelty stress. Under the conditions of this study there was no direct evidence for the involvement   of   the   pituitary-adrenal   or pituitary-gonadal systems in mediating the effects of stressors on SC115 tumor growth. However, changes in the immune system were influenced both by housing condition and by the presence of tumors.

---

[1] This work was supported by a grant from the University of British Columbia Research Development Fund. It has been submitted in expanded format for publication.

INTRODUCTION

Epidemiological and experimental evidence (1,2,3) suggest that stress and ability to cope with stress may play a role in disease processes, including neoplasia. We have utilized the transplantable androgen-responsive Shionogi mouse mammary carcinoma (SC115) to examine the effects of psychosocial stressors on tumor growth rate. This tumor originated spontaneously in a female mouse of the DD/S strain. Following 19 generations of transplantation, an androgen-responsive subline arose that grew faster in males than in females. This subline is similar to some human breast cancers in its sensitivity to different classes of steroid hormones, including androgens (4,5,6), estrogens (7), and glucocorticoids (8), for growth. These same hormones are modulated by psychosocial stressors (9,10). Furthermore, growth of the SC115 tumor may be modulated by activity of the host immune system (8,11), which is also altered by stress (10). The experiments described demonstrate that this animal-tumor system can be used as a model to examine the effects of psychosocial stressors on breast cancer growth.

EXPERIMENT 1

Previous studies (12,13) have shown that the social stress of a change in housing condition is critical in increasing tumor growth rate. The first experiment was designed to investigate if 3 conditions of change in social housing group will alter the growth rate of the SC115 tumor in male mice. Interactive effects of change in housing condition and acute daily novelty stress were also examined. In addition to measurements of tumor weight, plasma corticosterone levels were determined. It is known that stressors activate the hypothalamo-pituitary-adrenal axis (14,15), and that SC115 tumor growth is stimulated by glucocorticoids either by direct action on these tumor cells or indirectly by suppression of the immune system (8,11).

METHODS

Tumor model. The SC115 tumor subline used in the present study is classified as Class I (4).
Animal model. Following weaning, mice were housed

individually or in sibling groups of 3 and at 2-4 months of age were injected s.c. in the interscapular region with a single cell suspension of 2×10^6 SC115 tumor cells in 0.1 ml vehicle (6). Four groups were formed immediately following injection: 1) IG – males raised singly housed were placed in non-sibling groups of 5; 2) IP – males raised singly housed were rehoused with a female; 3) GI – males raised in sibling groups of 3 were separated and housed singly; 4) GG – males raised in sibling groups of 3 remained in their groups. Half the animals in each condition were subjected to the acute daily stressor of exposure (15 min/day, 5 days/week) to a novel environment, a treatment known to reliably raise corticosterone levels (14) and to be slow to habituate (15).

Mice were palpated 2 times/week and tumor weights were calculated from caliper measurements (6). At 23-24 days after tumor cell injection, animals were weighed, decapitated and trunk blood collected for assay (16). Animals that had been subjected to novelty stress received their last exposure 15 min prior to decapitation. Those that had not been subjected to novelty stress were decapitated immediately upon removal from the home cage.

RESULTS

Tumor growth. In the absence of acute novelty stress, tumor growth in GI animals was similar to that of GG controls, while growth rate was reduced in both IG and IP animals, $p < 0.05$ (Fig. 1). With acute daily novelty stress, tumor growth rate was increased in GI animals and decreased in IG animals compared to all other groups, $p < 0.05$. Frequent bouts of fighting and extensive wounding were observed in IG compared to GG and IP animals, both in the presence and absence of daily novelty stress.

Endocrine measures. There were no significant differences among groups in adrenal weights or in adrenal weight/body weight ratios. In addition, housing condition did not differentially affect basal corticosterone levels or the corticoid increase that occurred following exposure to novel environments.

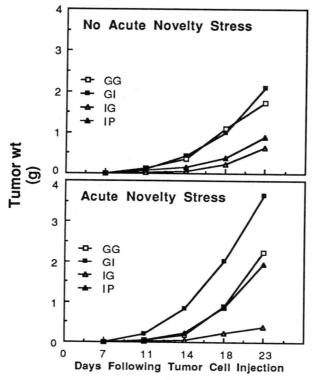

Figure 1.   Tumor growth in mice in the 4 housing groups.

EXPERIMENT 2

The data from Experiment 1 demonstrated that although growth rate of the SC115 tumor was significantly affected both by housing condition and by acute daily novelty stress, a change in housing condition did not necessarily alter the growth rate of this tumor. A second experiment was therefore undertaken to investigate if group vs individual housing as well as being moved from one housing condition to another affected SC115 tumor growth rate. Measures of endocrine function included testis and seminal vesicle weights and plasma levels of testosterone and dihydrotestosterone (17). These hormones stimulate SC115 tumor growth (5,6) and are known to be altered by stress (9). Two aspects of immune function, antibody production (18) and T lymphocyte proliferation (19), were also examined. In addition, animals in each housing condition were injected either with tumor cells in vehicle or with vehicle alone. The vehicle-injected condition was included because the effects of stressors on the immune system have been shown to differ in tumor-bearing and non-tumor-bearing animals, and the presence of a tumor itself can affect immune function (20). Spleen weights were also recorded.

METHODS

Animal Model. Male mice were reared singly housed or in sibling groups of 3 and at 2-4 months of age were injected either with tumor cells in vehicle or with vehicle alone. GI, GG and IG groups were formed, as in Experiment 1. The IP group was replaced with a group of animals reared individually housed and remaining individually housed (II) to control for the effects of isolation without a change in housing condition. All animals were subjected to acute daily novelty stress. At 19-21 days after tumor cell/vehicle injection, animals were removed from their home cages and decapitated immediately.

RESULTS

Tumor growth. Tumor growth was increased in GI, $p < 0.01$, and II, $p < 0.05$, animals and decreased in IG animals, $p < 0.01$ compared to GG controls (Fig. 2).

Endocrine measures. There were no group differences in plasma testosterone and dihydro-testosterone or in testis and seminal vesicle weights.

Immune measures. Analysis of secondary antibody response revealed that overall, response of IG animals was increased compared to that of GI animals, $p < 0.05$. Antibody response was generally suppressed in all animals injected with tumor cells (Table 1).

Analysis of splenic T lymphocyte proliferation in the absence of Con A showed no differences in activity among animals from the 4 housing groups, whether or not they were injected with tumor cells. With Con A, differential effects of housing condition were observed in animals injected with vehicle; GG controls showed greater lymphocyte proliferation than IG animals,

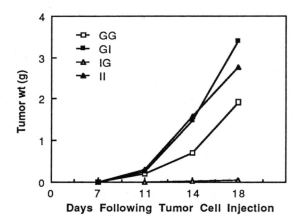

Figure 2.   Tumor growth in mice in the 4 housing groups.

TABLE 1
SECONDARY ANTIBODY RESPONSE IN MICE IN THE 4 HOUSING GROUPS.

Group*	Vehicle	Tumor[b]
GG	1.11 ± 0.02[a]	0.91 ± 0.08
GI	0.92 ± 0.12	0.95 ± 0.07
IG[c]	1.18 ± 0.03	1.02 ± 0.05
II	1.02 ± 0.05	0.98 ± 0.05

* n = 4-9
[a] Absorption at 400 nm, Mean ± S.E.M.
[b] Tumor < Vehicle, $p < 0.05$.
[c] Summed across Vehicle/Tumor condition, IG > GI, $p < 0.05$.

TABLE 2
SPLEEN WEIGHTS (g) IN MICE IN THE 4 HOUSING GROUPS.

Group*	Vehicle	Tumor[b]
GG	0.15 ± 0.01[a]	0.37 ± 0.07
GI	0.14 ± 0.01	0.28 ± 0.03
IG	0.25 ± 0.02	0.31 ± 0.03
II	0.12 ± 0.01	0.35 ± 0.04

* n per group = 4-7
[a] Mean ± S.E.M.
[b] Tumor > Vehicle, $p < 0.05$
No significant differences among housing groups.

p < 0.05. A differential effect of housing condition
was not observed in animals injected with tumor cells
but there was reduced proliferative activity in all
tumor-bearing animals compared to vehicle-injected
controls.

Vehicle-injected IG animals had somewhat enlarged
spleens; these were the animals that developed the
smallest tumors following tumor cell injection
(Table 2). Interestingly, animals injected with tumor
cells had markedly enlarged spleens compared to animals
injected with vehicle alone. However, there was no
differential effect of housing group in tumor-bearing
animals.

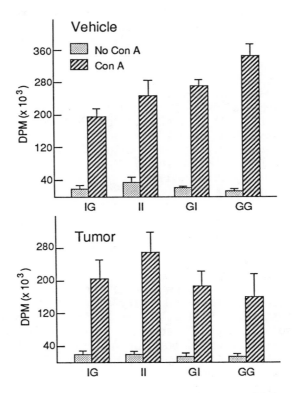

Figure 3. Splenic T lymphocyte proliferation in
mice in the 4 housing groups.

DISCUSSION

The data from these experiments clearly indicate dramatic and replicable effects of social housing condition and exposure to novel environments on tumor growth. Being reared individually and remaining individually housed (II) or being reared in a social group and then singly housed (GI) following tumor cell injection markedly increased tumor growth compared to that in mice remaining in their sibling rearing groups (GG), if animals were also exposed to acute daily novelty stress. In contrast, being reared individually and then moved to a large social group (IG) following tumor cell injection markedly reduced tumor growth, both in the presence and absence of acute daily novelty stress.

A mediating factor in reducing tumor growth may be the frequent fighting observed in IG animals in our model. We (21) and others (12,22,23), have suggested that fighting may provide a behavioral response that reduces arousal and enables animals to cope with stress. Sklar & Anisman (12) found that tumor growth rate increased in animals changed from individual to group conditions only if fighting among group members did not occur. In addition to psychological mediation, fighting may directly affect physiological responses. Increased wounding that occurs in fighters may stimulate the immune and/or endocrine systems, which could play a role in reducing tumor growth in the IG group.

Conversely, the lack of opportunity for individually housed animals to fight may be a mediating factor in increasing tumor growth in our model. Individual housing may have increased the impact of acute daily novelty stress in both the II and GI groups, resulting in an increase in tumor growth rate compared to that in GG controls.

In this study, there was no direct evidence for the involvement of the pituitary-adrenal or pituitary-gonadal systems in mediating the effects of stressors on SC115 tumor growth. In contrast, changes in the immune system were influenced both by housing condition and by the presence of tumors. Housing condition had differential effects on immune measures in vehicle-injected animals. Spleen weights and antibody response were increased and Con A stimulated lymphocyte proliferation was decreased in IG mice. However, changes in immune response were eliminated in animals injected with tumor cells. These results, as well as the lack of differential hormonal responsiveness, may be due to the fact that measures were only taken at one time point, approximately 3 weeks following tumor cell or vehicle injection. There is evidence that changes in endocrine and immune variables may occur immediately after or within the first 2 weeks following injection and group formation (10,20,24,25). Experiments examining endocrine and immune parameters at earlier time points are currently in progress. Furthermore, additional endocrine and immune parameters known to affect tumor growth and more specifically, SC115 tumor growth, are being examined.

In conclusion, we have demonstrated dramatic and replicable effects of psychosocial stressors on tumor growth. This animal-tumor system is unique in that both increased and decreased rates of tumor growth are recorded. This model will allow us to correlate modulation of endocrine and immune function with differential tumor growth rates in response to psychosocial stress.

ACKNOWLEDGEMENTS

The authors would like to thank Sharon Bezio, Gretta D'Alquen, Darcy Wilkinson and Shannon Wilson for expert technical assistance. Rosemary Rowan, Gerry Rowse and Andrea Scarth participated in different aspects of these experiments. Thank you also to Judith Bysouth for preparation of the manuscript.

REFERENCES

1. Fox, BH (1981). Psychosocial factors and the immune system in human cancer. In Ader, R (ed): Psychoneuroimmunology. New York: Academic Press, pp 103-157.
2. Riley, V, Fitzmaurice, MA, Spackman, DH (1981). Psychoneuroimmunologic factors in neoplasia: studies in animals. In Ader, R (ed): Psychoneuro-immunology. New York: Academic Press, pp 31-102.
3. Sklar, LS, Anisman, H (1981). Stress and cancer. Psychol Bull 89:369-406.

4. Bruchovsky, N, Rennie, PS (1978). Classification of dependent and autonomous variants of Shionogi mammary carcinoma based on heterogeneous patterns of androgen binding. Cell 13:273-280.
5. King, RBJ, Yates, J (1980). The use of cultured mammary tumor cells to study effects of steroid hormones. In Richards, RJ, Rajan, KT (eds): Tissue Culture in Medical Research II. New York: Pergamon Press, pp 221-227.
6. Emerman, JT, Siemiatkowski, J (1984). Effects of endocrine regulation of growth of a mouse mammary tumor on its sensitivity to chemotherapy. Cancer Res 44:1327-1332.
7. Nohno, T, Omukai, Y, Watanabe, S, Saito, T, Senoo, T (1982). Effects of estrogens and antiestrogens on androgen-dependent growth of the Shionogi carcinoma 115: role of estrogen receptor. Cancer Lett 15:237-244.
8. Watanabe, S, Nohno, T, Omukai, Y, Saito, T, Senoo, T (1982). Stimulatory effects of dexamethasone and indomethacin on growth of androgen-dependent Shionogi carcinoma 115 in the mouse. Cancer Lett 16:261-266.
9. Andrews, RV (1977). Influence of the adrenal gland on gonadal function. In Thomas, JA, Singhal, RL (eds): Advances in Sex Hormone Research Vol 3: Mechanisms affecting Gonadal Hormone Action. Baltimore: University Park Press, pp 197-215.
10. Riley, V (1981). Psychoendocrine influences on immunocompetence and neoplasia. Science 212:1100-1109.
11. Nohno, T, Watanabe, S, Saito, T (1986). Evaluation of effect of host immunity on growth of androgen-dependent Shionogi carcinoma 115 in the mouse. Cancer Lett 33:125-130.
12. Sklar, LS, Anisman, H (1980). Social stress influences tumor growth. Psychosom Med 42:347-365.
13. Steplewski, Z, Goldman, PR, Vogel, WH (1987). Effect of housing stress on the formation and development of tumors in rats. Cancer Lett 34:257-261.
14. Friedman, SB, Ader, R (1967). Adrenocortical response to novelty and noxious stimulation. Neuroendocrinology 2:209-212.

15. Pfister, HP, King, MG (1976). Adaptation of the glucocorticoid response to novelty. Physiol Behav 17:43–46.
16. Weinberg, J, Bezio, S (1987). Alcohol-induced changes in pituitary-adrenal activity during pregnancy. Alcoholism: Clin Exp Res 11:274–280.
17. Abraham, GE (ed) (1977). Handbook of Radio-immunoassay. New York: Marcel Dekker, pp 565–591.
18. Kelly, GS, Levy, JG, Sikora, L (1979). The use of the enzyme-linked immunosorbent assay (ELISA) for the detection and quantification of specific antibody from cell cultures. Immunology 37:45–52.
19. Bradley, LM (1980). Cell proliferation. In Mishell, BB, Shiigi, SM (eds): Selected Methods in Immunology. San Francisco: WH Freeman, pp 153–161.
20. Steplewski, Z, Vogel, WH, Ehya, H, Poropatich, C, McDonald Smith, J (1985). Effects of restraint stress on inoculated tumor growth and immune response in rats. Cancer Res 45:5128–5133.
21. Weinberg, J, Erskine, M, Levine, S (1980). Shock-induced fighting attenuates the effects of prior shock experience in rats. Physiol Behav 25:9–16.
22. Weiss, JM, Pohorecky, LA, Salman, S, Gruenthal, M (1976). Attenuation of gastric lesions by psychological aspects of aggression in rats. J Comp Physiol Psychol 90:252–259.
23. Stolk, JM, Conner, RL, Levine, S, Barchas, JD (1974). Differential effects of shock and fighting on the neurochemical response to a common footshock stimulus. J Pharmacol Exp Therap 190:193–209.
24. Coe, CL, Rosenberg, LT, Levine, S (in press). Immunological consequences of psychological disturbance and maternal loss in infancy. In Rovee-Collier, C Lipsitt, LP (eds): Advances in Infancy Research. Norwood: ABLEX Publication Corp.
25. Greenberg, AH, Dyck, AH, Sandler, LS (1984). Opponent processes, neurohormones, and natural resistance. In Fox, BH, Newberry, BH (eds): Impact of Psychoendocrine Systems in Cancer and Immunity. New York: CJ Hogrefe, pp 225–257.

Molecular Biology of Stress, pages 307–317
© 1989 Alan R. Liss, Inc.

THE NEUROPHARMACOLOGY OF NEONATAL RAT'S SEPARATION
VOCALIZATIONS

PRISCILLA KEHOE

DEPARTMENT OF PSYCHOLOGY
TRINITY COLLEGE
HARTFORD, CT. 06106

Abstract   Neonatal rats call ultrasonically in response to
maternal and sibling separation. The neuropharmacology of
such emotional behavior is complex with apparent multiple
neurochemical controls. Opiates and opiate antagonists
modulate rat pup's vocalizations during isolation; morphine
decreases the calling while naltrexone increases them and
at the same time reverses isolation-induced analgesia.
Neonatal calling and analgesia are both influenced by
opioids implying that separation vocalizations are
decreased over time in isolated pups by an endogenous
opioid peptide release. Moreover, cocaine significantly
reduces ultrasonic calling in isolated pups even though
they are hyperactive. In contrast to the quieting effects
of opiates and cocaine, clonidine, an alpha-$_2$ noradrenergic
agonist, produces a dose-dependent and age-dependent
increase in calling and hyperactivity. Furthermore, this
noradrenergic stimulation of ultrasounds was found in the
nest situation as well as in isolation, suggesting a
noradrenergic influence on calling initiation.

Introduction

Infant mammals separated from parents and siblings
evoke a measurable calling response which is ultrasonic in
the case of rodents. Neonatal rats under a variety of
social and thermal conditions vocalize ultrasonically in
the range of 30-50 hz which is beyond the range of human
hearing (1,2). Such emotional behavior is a potential
stimulus for maternal retrieval (3). The neuropharmacology
of these ultrasounds is complex and may offer a model of
infant affectional learning and social attachment

formation. In the case of infant rodents the presence of a female, albeit anesthetized, or the huddling of siblings quiets pups' vocalizations (4). Learned affectional relationships are of great significance to the infant's survival and perhaps for adult motivated behaviors, such as reproductive behavior in males depending on postnatal olfactory-maternal experience (5).

After investigating the crying of neonatal chicks it was concluded that the opiate system had the most powerful specific effect on distress vocalizations (6). Moreover, opiates and opiate antagonists were found to modulate emitted cries in young guinea pigs (7) as well as adult squirrel monkeys (8). Additionally, clonidine, a noradrenergic agonist, caused a decrease in calls in chicks (6) which was reversed by the noradrenergic antagonist yohimbine (9). Similar effects were seen on the isolation calls of adult squirrel monkeys (10).

Since the opioid and catecholamine systems are importantly implicated in the neurochemical control of crying (6) it is possible that these systems might influence the general stress response seen during maternal separation. Past studies examining separation anxiety demonstrate the effectiveness of imipramine in quelling distress in puppies (11), separation induced social disorder and vocalizations in rhesus monkeys (12, 13) and separation anxiety in children (14). It has been suggested that the imipramine is working through a feedback inhibition mechanism of the alpha-$_2$ noradrenergic receptor. Ultrasonic vocalizations of isolated neonatal rats can be demonstrated soon after birth but is most intense from postnatal days 5 through 12 (2). After eye opening there is a rapid decrease in the number of calls and finally disappears completely by day 19 (15). The pharmacological modulation of isolation vocalizations in rat pups may actually act upon the same neural systems by which natural stimuli produce calling behavior. By employing the naturalistic response of separation vocalizations of neonatal rats a variety of drugs which affect specific neural systems can be tested for their modulatory effects. In addition to pharmacological effects, environmental stimuli can be utilized in terms of initiating and quelling the rat pup's calling response.

To further explore the neuropharmacology of separation vocalizations in neonatal rats, the albino rat pup was isolated for a short time (minutes) under thermal nest conditions and monitored for ultrasounds (15,16,17,18,).

Because an ambient temperature less than nest conditions (32°-34° c) can in itself be stressful to the pup and perhaps increase calling behavior, a paradigm using an environmental chamber simulating nest conditions was used in all of the following studies. The pup is isolated in a cup with clean but familiar bedding for a period of 5 to 10 minutes during which time any ultrasonic vocalizations are monitored through a qmc bat detector and recorded. All activities such as grooming, circling, wall climbing, head toss, etc. Are also monitored and recorded.

OPIOIDS AND ISOLATION DISTRESS

A behaviorally positive opioid system appears to exist in neonatal rats as young as 5 days of age (17,19,20). Recent studies in which a novel stimulus, odor or taste, was paired with morphine administration peripherally or centrally resulted in the acquisition of a conditioned preference. These associations were not acquired if naltrexone, an opioid antagonist, was administered prior to the morphine. It appears then that opiates in neonates seem to produce a positive reward state resulting in preference behavior (17,19,20). As in adult rats, endogenous opioid systems also appear to be involved in mediating pain and stress in neonates. Individual isolation, a seemingly social stress, produced an analgesia that was blocked by pretreatment with an opioid antagonist (16,17,21,24).

To further understand the role of the endogenous opioid system in the neonate during stress, it was necessary to establish a relationship between separation vocalizations, response to nociception, and opioids in isolated infant rats (16,17). Prior to isolation the 10-day-old pup was pretreated with no injection, saline, naltrexone (0.5Mg/kg), or morphine (0.5Mg/kg) ip. Immediately after the isolation period during which time the vocalizations are monitored the pup is tested for paw withdrawal from a heated plate.

Isolation from the dam and siblings resulted in increased latency to heat withdrawal relative to non-isolated controls (figure 1). Naltrexone administration caused shortened paw-lift latencies and greatly increased the number of ultrasounds relative to those isolated pups given saline or no injection; morphine greatly increased paw-lift latencies and decreased the number of calls. Analgesia and neonatal vocalizations are both seemingly influenced by opioids, suggesting the level of ultrasounds in isolated pups is modulated by a release of endogenous opioids.

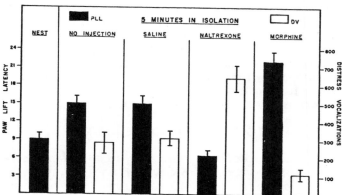

Fig 1. Black bars represent mean paw-lift latency to a hot 48° plate. White bars represent mean number of ultrasonic vocalization during 5 min. isolation.

Proximity to the anesthetized female caused heat withdrawal responses closely resembling those of the nonisolated sibling (figure 2). Pups that remained isolated exhibited elevated latencies while pups placed on a female showed a reduction in time to withdraw from heat after only one minute. Thus, an inactive female rat is a sufficient

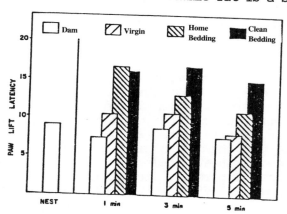

Fig 2. Mean paw-lift latency of pups taken from the nest or isolated for 5 min and then placed in clean bedding, home-bedding or anesthetized virgin or dam.

stimulus to reduce the endogenous opioid activity
seemingly initiated by the stress of isolation.
The vocalizations emitted during isolation were effectively
reduced when the pup was placed in close proximity to a
warm anesthetized female, dam or virgin (figure 3). The
maternal odor alone, did cause the pups to decrease
responding over a 5 minute period but did not seem as
salient as the female herself. Pups treated with
naltrexone prior to isolation also significantly reduced
their calling behavior when placed next to the female
(unpublished results). In short, the opioid influence on
separation vocalizations seem to be situation specific.

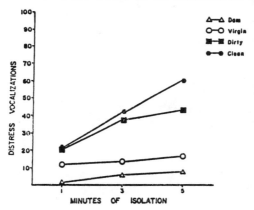

Fig 3. Ultrasonic vocalizations during the 1-, 3-, or 5-min
period in clean bedding, home-bedding, anesthetized female.

CATECHOLAMINES AND ISOLATION VOCALIZATIONS

The noradrenergic system has been implicated in
separation vocalizations in chicks and adult monkeys
because of clonidine's effective quelling of separation
calling (6,8,10). Pharmacologically-induced behavioral
changes have been demonstrated ontogentically in the
noradrenergic system in the rat. Clonidine, an alpha-2
noradrenergic receptor agonist, produces dose-dependent
hyperactivity in the rat pup during the first 14 days
postnatally (23,24,25,26,27). Between 15 and 20 days of
age, a chnage in these clonidine effects are seen, with a
shift from hyperactivity to hypoactivity, an effect delayed
in malnourished rats (23). The ontogeny of noradrenergic
effects on isolation-induced calling in rat pups from day

10 to day 18 also were evaluated (15).

A profound developmental change in separation vocalizations occurs between 10 and 18 days of age (figure 4). Ten-day-old pups pretreated with saline cry almost 200 times in a 5 minute isolation period in a heated environment. This level drops significantly after eye opening on day 14 to 100 calls in 15-day-old pups, 25 calls in 17-day-old and 10 calls in 18-day-old pups.

5 MINUTE ISOLATION-INDUCED VOCALIZATIONS

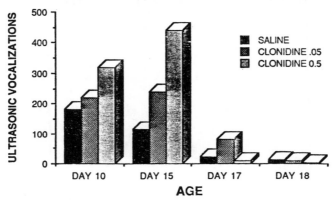

Fig 4. Ultrasounds of pups during 5 min isolation after pretreatment with saline or clonidine .05 or 0.5 mg/kg.

The calling response after clonidine administration presents an interesting ontological profile with an interesting change occurring between days 15 and 17. (Figure 4) on day 10 clonidine (0.5Mg/kg) produced a significant increase in separation vocalizations during the first 5 minutes of isolation. Furthermore, pups at 10, 15, and 17 days of age after clonidine injections continued to vocalize in the nest even with dam retrieval and licking (unpublished results). The pup at 15 days of age was significantly effected the first 5 minutes by either dose of clonidine in that 0.05Mg/kg clonidine caused more than two-fold and 0.5Mg/kg caused a four-fold increase in separation calling. By day 17 there is a disociative response to clonidine dependent on the dose. The lower dose of clonidine (0.05Mg/kg) caused a significant rise in calling level whereas the higher dose (0.5Mg/kg) causes a decrease in the already low level of ultrasounds. On day 17 the pups begin to show an adult response to the clonidine (.5Mg/kg) whereby their vocalizing is reduced as is their activity levels. By day 18 this change seems to be complete although at this point their spontaneous isolation-induced vocalizing is almost absent.

After 5 minutes of isolation the above pups were injected with a second drug either yohimbine (0.1Mg/kg), an alpha-2 noradrenergic receptor antagonist, or saline ip and monitored for ultrasounds 20 more minutes. Yohimbine, which has been shown to reverse the activity levels induced by clonidine administration does reverse the calling behavior as well (figure 5). After being isolated for 20 minutes 10 day-old control pups are relatively quiet and vocalize very little. The pups that received clonidine at either dose demonstrated a dose-dependent and significant increase in vocalizing throughout the entire isolation period except for the first 5 min. Yohimbine led to a reversal of the increased vocalizing caused by the clonidine and, in fact, blocked the communicative call of the isolated rat pup if given prior to isolation.

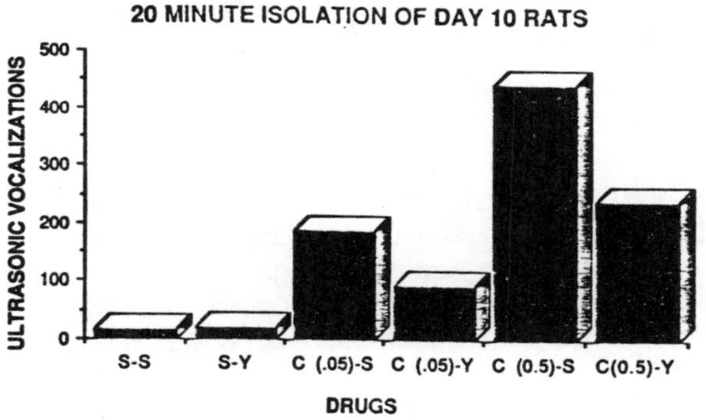

20 MINUTE ISOLATION OF DAY 10 RATS

Fig 5. Ultrasounds of 10-day old pups during the 20-25 min. of isolation after saline-saline, saline-yohimbine (0.1mg/kg), clonidine (.05)-saline, clonidine (.05)-yohimbine, clonidine (0.5)-saline, clonidine (.5) yohimbine

Cocaine, a potent dopamine-uptake blocker, has been shown to support appetitive conditioning in 5 day-old rat pups (18). Pairing cocaine with a novel odor produced a dose-dependent preference for the odor some 5 days later. Cocaine at doses from 2.5 To 20 mg/kg caused a marked decrease in isolation vocalizations in day 10 pups (figure 6). Although the opiates like the stimulant cocaine can reduce rat pup's calls, cocaine produces hyperactivity in the neonate, including repeated circling. To control for cocaine's activity effects on separation vocalizations, control pups received caffeine prior to isolation. Caffeine administration had no effects on calling behavior although activity levels were significantly greater than saline administered pups.

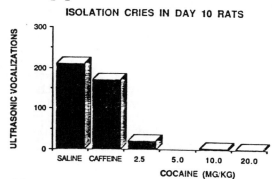

Fig 6. Ultrasounds of 10-day old pups during 5 min isolation after saline, caffeine (10mg/kg), or cocaine 2.5-20mg/kg Ip

SUMMARY

The opioid system seems to be directly and specifically involved with ultrasounds induced by separation from the dam and siblings. Pups administered naltrexone did not vocalize in the nest or when placed with siblings, but vocalized at extremely high levels when isolated, suggesting an important role for the endogenous opioid system during neonatal stress. Conversely, clonidine, a noradrenergic agonist, induced ultrasonic vocalizations in both isolated and non-isolated rat pups. Yohimbine reversed this calling behavior suggesting an alpha noradrenergic receptor involvement. Furthermore, some psychoneurobiological event seems to occur on approximately day 16 which changes the effects of clonidine administration, interacting with changes in natural behavioral patterns, such as separation vocalizations. Cocaine, a dopamine-uptake blocker, significantly reduces ultrasounds, and like morphine, promotes positive associative learning. Whether the drug must have reward properties to quell isolation cries remains to be tested since yohimbine reduced calling in the day 10 pups as well as the anxiolytic agent, diazepam (33).

REFERENCES

1. Allin, J. T., and Banks, E. M.,(1972). Functional aspects of ultrasound production by infant albino rats (Rattus norvegicus). Ani Beh 20:175.
2. Noirot, E. (1972). Ultrasounds and maternal behavior in small rodents. Dev Psychobi 5:371.
3. Smotherman, W.P., Bell, R.W., Starzec, J., Elias, J., and Zachman, T.A.(1974). Maternal responses to infant vocalizations and olfactory cues in rats and mice. Beh Bio 12:55.
4. Kehoe, P., and Blass, E.M. (1986). Opioid-mediation of separation distress in 10-day-old rats: Reversal of stress with maternal stimuli. Dev Psychobi 19:385.
5. Fillion, T., and Blass, E.M. (1986) Infantile experience with suckling odors determines adult sexual behavior in male rats. Science 231:729.
6. Panksepp, J., Meeker, R., and Bean, D.H. (1980). The neurochemical control of crying. Pharma Biochem Beh 12:437.
7. Herman, B.H., and Panksepp, J. (1978). Effects of morphine and naloxone on separation distress and attachment: Evidence for opiate mediation of social effect. Pharma Biochem Beh 9:213.
8. Harris, J.C., and Newman, J.D. (1986). Synergistic effects of alpha$_2$ adrenergic and opiate receptor blockade on vocalizations in adult squirrel monkeys. Soc for Neurosc Ab 12:1133.
9. Rossi III, J., Sahley, T.L. and Panksepp, J. (1983). The role of brain norepinephrine in clonidine suppression of isolation-induced distress in the domestic chick. Psychopharm 79:338-342.
10. Harris, J.C. & Newman, J.D. (1987). Mediation of separation distress by alpha$_2$-adrenergic mechanisms in a non-human primate. Brain Res 410:353-356.
11. Scott, J.P. (1974). Effects of psychotrophic drugs in separation distress in dogs, "Proc IX Cong Neuropsychopharma (Paris)," Excerpta Medica Int Congr Series No. 359: Amsterdam, pp. 735-745.

12. Suomi, S.J., Seaman, S.F., Lewis, J.K., DeLizio, R.D. and McKinney, W.T. (1978). Effects of imipramine treatment on separation-induced social disorders in rhesus monkeys. Arch Gen Psychiatr 35:321-325.

13. Suomi, S.J., Kraemer, G.W., Baysinger, C.M. and DeLizio, R.D. (1981). Inherited and experiential differences in anxious behavior displayed by rhesus monkeys. In D.F. Klein and J. Rabkini (Eds.), "Anxiety: New Research and Changing Concepts," Raven, New York, pp. 179-199.

14. Gittelman-Klein, R. and Klein, D.F. (1971). Controlled imipramine treatment of school phobia. Arch Gen Psychiatr 25:204-207.

15. Kehoe, P. & Harris, J.C. Ontogeny of noradrenergic effects on ultrasonic vocalizations in rat pups. Beh Neurosc, in press.

16. Kehoe, P., and Blass, E.M. (1986). Opioid-mediation of separation distress in 10-day-old rats: Reversal of stress with maternal stimuli. Dev Psychobi 19:385.

17. Kehoe, P., and Blass, E. M. (1986). Central nervous system mediation of positive and negative reinforcement in neonatal albino rats. Dev Bra Res 27:69.

18. Kehoe, P., Shaw, L. & Sakurai, S. (1987). Cocaine quiets the isolates cries and promotes associations in rat pups. Soc for Neurosc Abs 13.

19. Kehoe, P., & Blass, E.M. Conditioned opioid release in ten-day-old rats. Beh Neurosc, in press.

20. Kehoe, P., and Blass, E.M. (1986). Behaviorally functional opioid systems in infant rats: I. Evidence for olfactory and gustatory classical conditioning. Beh Neurosc 100:359.

21. Kehoe, P., and Blass, E.M. (1986). Behaviorally functional opioid system in infant rats: II. Evidence for pharmacological, physiological and psychological mediation of pain and stress. Beh Neuros 100:624.

22. Belluzzi, J.D., and Stein, L. (1977). Enkephalin may mediate euphoria and drive reduction reward. Nature 266:556.

23. Hunter Jr., G.A., and Reid, L.D. (1983). Assaying addiction liability of opioids. Life Sciences 33:393.

24. Spear, L.P., Enters, E.K., Aswad, M.A., and Louzan, M. (1985). Drug and environmentally-induced manipulations of the opiate and serotonergic alter nociception in neonatal rat pups. Beh and Neu Bio 44:1.

25. Goodlett, C.R., Valentino, M.L., Resnick, O., and Morgane, P.J. (1985). Altered development of responsiveness to clonidine in severely malnourished rats. Pharma Biochem Beh 23:567.

26. Nomura, Y., Oki, K., Segawa, T. (1980). Pharmacological characterization of central alpha-adrenoceptors which mediate clonidine-induced locomotor hypoactivity in the developing rat. Nau Schmied Arch Pharma 311:41.

27. Nomura, Y., and Segawa, T. (1979). The effects of alpha-adrenoceptor antagonists and metamide on clonidine-induced locomotor stimulation in the infant rat. Bri J of Pharma 66:531.

28. Reinstein, D.K., and Isaacson, R.L. (1977). Clonidine sensitivity in the developing rat. Brain Res 135:378.

29. Spear, L.P., and Brick, J. (1979). Cocaine-induced behavior in the developing rat. Beh and Neu Bio 26:401.

30. Moore, K.E. (1977). Amphetamines: Biochemical and behavioral actions in animals. In L.L. Iversen, S.D. Iversen and S.H. Snyder (eds.) "Handbook of Psychopharmacology, Volume II, Stimulants." New York: Plenum Press.

31. Barr, G.A., and Lithgow, T. (1986). Pharmaco-ontogeny of reward: Enhancement of self-stimulation by d-amphetamine and cocaine in 3- and 10-day-old rats. Dev Brain Res 24:193-202.

32. Pedersen, P.E., Williams, C.L., and Blass, E.M. (1982). Activation and odor conditioning of suckling behavior in 3-day-old albino rats. J of Exp Psych: Animal Beh Pro 8:329.

33. Insel, T.R., Hill, J.L. & Mayor, R.B. (1986). Rat pup ultrasonic isolation calls: Possible mediation by the benzodiazepine receptor complex. Pharm Biochem & Beh 24:1263.

Index